D1000444

A BIRD WATCHER IN KENYA

A BIRD WATCHER IN KENYA

by

Vernon D. van Someren

M.B.E., PH.D., A.R.P.S.

OLIVER AND BOYD

EDINBURGH: TWEEDDALE COURT

LONDON: 39A WELBECK STREET, W.1

FIRST PUBLISHED . . . 1958

PRINTED IN GREAT BRITAIN
FOR OLIVER AND BOYD LTD.
BY ROBERT CUNNINGHAM AND SONS LTD., ALVA

To my Father
the late R. A. L. van SOMEREN, M.D., D.P.H.
in remembrance of many
birding days together

PREFACE

KENYA HAS BEEN CALLED the land of contrasts, and so indeed it is. The contrast of sparkling sunshine and deepest shadow: of waterless thorn bush desert and fertile green valley; of muddy tropical rivers and crystal ice-fed streams; of highland mist and tropical downpour; languorous warmth and biting chill; coconut palms and primroses; of six-storey buildings and blackest witchcraft; all these still make up the Kenya of today. It is indeed a land of black and white, but to me it will always be the land of the dancing whydah, and all those other birds – beautiful, bizarre or just ordinary – whose ways I have been able to watch from the intimacy of a hide.

It is always curious to reflect back on the beginnings of one's hobbies. Years ago, when in my boyhood days in Scotland, I remember once going out for a walk with a schoolboy friend of mine. As is the way of boys at that age, he carried an air rifle, and with the unthinking carelessness of youth he shot with it a little blue tit we had been watching in a tree. It fell to the ground mortally wounded, a rumpled ball of feathers. As he picked it up, its beady little eye held, it seemed to me at that impressionable age, such a look of agony and accusation as it glazed in death that I have never been able to forget.

Like so many of such childhood incidents, it created in me a deep and lasting impression, and a feeling of repugnance at such wilful taking of life that remains with me still. From that day to this, I have never lifted a gun against another living bird, and I hope I never shall. Yet the pursuit and outwitting of a creature in the wild remains one of the strongest primitive instincts of mankind, and for my own part I have found a lasting satisfaction of that drive in the photographing of birds. The thrill of outwitting a wild bird, of watching it going about its business from a hide a few feet away, and unconscious of being observed, remains as fresh today as it did in those days long ago when I started as a schoolboy on the sport. For essentially it is a sport, and a superb one too – because in the end the trophy is yours, and the quarry unharmed. What could be better?

A great many unkind things have been said about bird photographers in the past; about the desertions they cause, the needless anxiety to birds, and so on. Nearly all such criticisms are unfounded, and are certainly not true of the many bird photographers whom I know, all of whom are most scrupulously careful in their work – and indeed have to be, if they wish to make a success of it.

There is often, too, a slur implied that bird photographers are rarely good ornithologists, and are interested only in obtaining good pictures; and critics draw a peculiar distinction between those they term photographic ornithologists, and ornithological photographers. The distinction, if any exists, is absurd, since good bird photographers are inevitably good ornithologists too, and indeed must be so if they are successfully to adapt their chosen medium to the ways of a bird; the reverse is seldom true!

Even as a biologist myself, I have never seen why the competent photographer of birds should be taken to task for not producing learned papers on what he has seen at the nest, any more than why the thousands of amateur ornithologists who derive great pleasure from merely watching birds, should be expected so to do.

Over the course of years, a number of scientific papers on East African birds have indeed been published, dealing with systematics or biology. Most of these have appeared in the austere pages of scientific journals not usually read by the public, and thus have been directed to a particular audience. There have been very few accounts of bird watching in East Africa written with a wider appeal, such as appear so frequently for the birds of Great Britain. This book therefore is presented in the hope of filling such a gap.

Watching birds for pleasure is an essentially human kind of activity, and birds have a sentimental appeal far transcending their value as objects of scientific study. Hence these pages, though scientifically correct in content, are nevertheless reminiscent in tone, and will I hope, be regarded as supplementary to the colder scientific accounts of Kenya birds published elsewhere. They are gleanings from my notebooks kept over a period of seventeen years abroad, and I have tried to infuse into them something of the excitements and disappointments which are as much the lot of a bird watcher in a 'far country', as they are at home. The bird life of such tropical regions is rich beyond compare, and for those readers who may know something already of Kenya birds, there may perhaps be some surprising omissions of birds more familiar than those which have been mentioned. I make no apology for these, since I have dealt only with some of the birds which I have had opportunities to watch and photograph myself – and these have not yet included all the commoner birds by a long way! Nor in these pages have I made any particular reference to what others may already have recorded about the birds described; this is a purely personal tale, and those who have synthetic minds may derive some pleasure from fitting in my own notes with those made by other watchers elsewhere.

From a general point of view, the birds of eastern Africa offer an almost unlimited field for study at the nest, or elsewhere, and for photographic opportunities. In the British Isles, there is scarcely a single species still who has not faced a camera lens at some time or another; and some of the rarer or more unusual birds are almost compelled to say 'next please!' to the waiting queue of photographers. In Africa, on the other hand, there are many hundreds of kinds of birds awaiting the time and patience of a competent photographer to portray them for the first time ever at the nest, and the rewards are rich indeed.

For the technically minded, I have added a chapter on my own technique of bird photography. In some ways this is rather unique, for I am one of the very few bird photographers who use a 35 mm. camera exclusively, and various adaptations have had to be made in the method of use, and the general application of bird methods to East African conditions.

Leading British natural history photographers are almost unanimous in condemning the 35 mm. miniature for any serious work, and almost all extol the virtues of the field camera in quarter-plate format for this type of work. This condemnation varies from the sarcastic to the dogmatic, but having used both types of camera, I would not agree, and I feel that a good deal of this criticism stems from either inadequate trial or downright misuse of the miniature technique. I remain unconvinced by optical arguments against the 35 mm. size, for I have used my Contax with complete satisfaction to myself and independent exhibition judges on birds from wrens to eagles, and on subjects from diatoms to landscapes. I have seen, I admit, some perfectly horrible examples published of miniature natural history work, over-enlarged and grainy, which bring nothing but discredit to this smaller format; but many larger negatives would be equally unpleasant if enlarged to the same dimensions, and their faults are concealed by their relatively smaller print size.

Miniature technique demands a more complete mastery of methods and materials than any other, and a detached and ruthless sense of self-criticism; otherwise nothing but disappointment can follow. I am as critical as anybody of definition and fine detail, and I hope the illustrations in this book will show what can be done with a 35 mm. camera used with care. They may also dispel some of the unreasonable criticism of this method, but I would also emphasise that good results can only be expected in this line of work from expensive high precision miniatures, with finest quality interchangeable lenses; the cheaper 35 mm. cameras now flooding the market are incapable of reaching the high standard required for zoological photography.

This book therefore is just the warmer recollections of many happy hours spent alone with birds, and if it can bring to others even some idea of the pleasure which can be gained from so doing, I shall be content; and it may perhaps too, bring some pleasure to find at least one book nowadays which has no connection with the grim realities of Mau Mau, or the tedious, turgid politics of black, brown and white in this land of sunshine.

The patient guidance of my publishers at all stages has been much appreciated, while Mr W. P. Langridge has proved no

TECHNICAL NOTE

Except where otherwise indicated, all the photographs in this book have been taken in normal daylight without a filter, on Agfa Isopan F, Ilford F.P. 3, Ilford Pan X, or Adox KB 14 film. They have all been taken with a Contax camera, usually with the 13·5 cm. F 4 Sonnar lens, at apertures of F 8 or F 11, at shutter speeds of 1/25 or 1/50 sec., and developed in Meritol-Metol, Meritol-caustic, DK 20, Microdol, Promicrol or Neofyn Blau. All are enlargements of practically the whole negative frame on Kodak paper. My own particular preferences in technique are indicated in more detail in the last chapter of this book.

CONTENTS

PHOTOGRAPHS

CHAPTER 1

IN THE SHADOW OF MOUNT KENYA

It is nearly half-way across the world from the Scottish hills, where I now live, to the Highlands of Kenya, where I used to work. Formerly a journey which took several weeks by steamer across five seas, the distance is now annihilated in twenty-four hours or less by aircraft as a regular daily routine. You can watch a sunbird in a Nairobi garden one morning and be watching a blue tit in an English suburban orchard the next; Kenya seems now just at the bottom of the garden, where the fairies used to live when we were very young, but the birds of Kenya have no longer the remote quality which characterised those lovely mythical creatures of our childhood.

Across the six thousand mile span of the earth's surface from Scotland to Kenya, the birds change in kind, but not in character, and the fascination of bird watching is the same wherever you are. Some of the happiest times of my life have been spent alone with birds, and they have taken me to some of the loveliest places on earth. Halcyon days spent with the grouse, dotterel and ptarmigan of the high tops of the Cairngorms gave way to days with the flamingoes, plovers and eagles of the equatorial lakes, plains and forests of Kenya. And now I am back where I first started, with keenness still undiminished, but alas – with as little time as I ever had before to spend with birds!

I have been luckier than most people, for I was brought up in a family with a traditional interest in all wild things, and one whose associations with Scotland on the one hand and the tropics on the other have been intimate and long. I have never been convinced of the old story about schoolboy days being the happiest of one's life, and even now, with the richer experiences of life at home and abroad, I would maintain still that no time of my life can compare with those glorious, carefree days as a university student when, on the threshold of my career, the whole world was my oyster. For this alone would I envy my children in the years to come. It was in those days when my early schoolboy interest in birds first deepened and quickened into the lifelong passion it has now become; and it was then, under the influence of my biological training in the university, that I first realised that such a hobby could become an engrossing pursuit of knowledge for its own sake, and an exciting intellectual pastime as well. My interest in photography and the watching of birds combined, under the influence of a childhood incident I have mentioned elsewhere, to form a sport which has satisfied me above all others; although time and circumstances have now changed and the preoccupation of a career and family cares have become paramount, I know now that I have found one pleasure that will never pall wherever I may happen to be.

Since my earlier days with the birds of my native Scotland, I have travelled a great deal, both during the War and in the first part of my career as a Colonial Officer. For the past seventeen years I have spent the greater part of my time abroad, mainly in Kenya – that part of our Colonial Empire, as I still like to think of it, being an old-fashioned, or should I say unfashionable, imperialist, which is now undergoing some unhappy experimentalism in changed governmental procedure, and whose future still seems so uncertain. But reflections on this are not the purpose of this book, and my only concern is to recall some of the pleasant moments I have spent watching birds there, and perhaps to show something of the similarity which exists wherever one may be. I doubt if anybody else in that country has spent as many hours as I have watching birds from a hide in so many different places, though there are now a goodly number of bird watchers whom I am happy to count as friends there. The intense interest which has been growing in recent years since the World War in Great Britain in watching birds is fast spreading to such tropical regions too, and now I know of a great many people who are finding in it an absorbing and pleasant pastime in that land of sunshine. My father first took his love of birds to Uganda some fifty years ago, in those 'good old days' when twentieth-century civilisation had scarcely touched the African, and the three 'Rs' had not yet exerted their present malignant effect; so that my path in following his early lead has been easier than for most.

Though this book is mainly about East African birds, such is the nature of a bird's world and character, that a great many of the more general observations I have written on the behaviour of such African birds could equally well apply to birds of the Scottish hills or English fields and woods. Comparisons will be obvious to those familiar with only our British birds, and exceptions where they occur serve only to emphasise the greater similarities of the way of a bird at its nest.

Such is the structure and geography of Kenya that a great deal of my time there has been spent living at an altitude some two thousand feet higher than that of Ben Nevis or Ben Macdhui, the two highest hills of the British Isles. For part of that time, my wife and I lived where we could look on snows more eternal than those which lie on the shoulders of Cairngorm or Sgoran Dubh, or the shores of Choire an Lochain.

From the front verandah of our house near Nyeri, we could look through the gap I had cut in the trees across a hummocky sea of tree-tops coloured with infinite shades of green, and dusted here and there with the delicate pink of Cape chestnut flowers in the months after the rains. This forest canopy merged in the far distance with ravine-scarred tussocky moorlands above the twelve thousand foot mark, and over these towered the snow-capped twin peaks of Kenya – cold, clear and remote. We never grew tired of this stupendous view, for the mountain itself makes this part of Kenya, and its moods are infinitely changing. Though the peaks have been named after famous Masai persons – the tribe which once overlorded this part of Kenya while the Kikuyu cowered in the forests – the god of the ill-starred Kikuyu themselves is believed to live in the uppermost parts of Kerinyagga, as it is known to that tribe.

In the clear hot weather of January to March, when the mornings dawned crisp and cold with a sprinkling of hoar frost on the ground, the mountain's slight veil of tenuous mist drew away early, and the peaks of Batian and Nelion, with the Gate of the Mists between, stood sharply out against the sunlight flooding behind. On really clear days, we could even see, without glasses, the Gendarme who guards the Gate of the Mists above the Diamond Glacier, and the whole vast west face of Batian which falls steeply away to the hummock of Arthur's Seat – so nostalgically Scots in outline! Point John too would be clear, as a miniature model of the main peaks, standing out in front of Nelion and masking the foot of the saddle of the wide Lewis Glacier which falls from the minor peak of Lenana to the east. In the brilliant sunshine of those early months of the year, the black rocks contrast starkly with the white of the snow and ice which straddle the Equator in this high land of the tropical belt.

Sometimes, if in a kindly mood, the old mountain would stay clear all day long till the last rays of the westering sun laid a deep rosy flush on the snowfields; but on most days the trailing wisp of cloud from the peaks would thicken to a billowing plume, as if the old volcano was still active, and the mist would roll down the moors as I have so often watched it do on the Scottish hills, blotting out the rocky crests with a white impenetrable veil. Perhaps it would clear again for the briefest of glimpses in the short tropical twilight, and then each ridge and rocky valley would stand sharply shadowed in the slanting rays as the sun sank behind the Aberdares; but in this hot dry season in particular, the mysterious god who lives up in the snows is a shy deity, and conjures up from the melting snow and ice a veil to cover his face from the gaze of man below.

Later on in the year when the monsoon swung from north to south, we would wake in the mornings to see the peak mantled in snow, the white skirts often spreading right down to the lowest moorland slopes, with that lovely crystal sparkle which only fresh fallen snow can give. We knew then that two days later the welcome rain would fall, for the appearance of snow so low on the slopes is an almost infallible barometer in this part of the world. Then, as the rains supervened, black stormy clouds covered the peaks as the mountain god grumbled and vented his wrath in thunder, lightning and torrential rain; but as his fury spent with the weakening of the monsoon in June, a grey impenetrable veil again drew flatly across the slopes, and the misty dull wreaths of July and August covered the land, to lift again two months later. Sometimes in the dry season the

Reichenow's weaver male at nest, Kabete 1946

PLATE 2

Golden-breasted bunting, removing excreta sac from nest, Kiganjo 1952 (Electronic flash)

red glow of moorland fires would pulsate in the sky, leaving a wide blackened scar on the slopes as they died; and in those brief tantalising glimpses as the storm clouds cleared for a moment in the rain, we could see the fresh green of young moorland grass spreading across the blackened waste, and in the clear rain-washed air the peaks seemed startlingly near.

In the days before the dark evil of Mau Mau so foully desecrated this land of its own devilish birth, you could walk up to the snows of Kenya – not indeed as a stroll, but as an organised party with proper equipment for the several days required. For the journey was all of two full days to the snowline at fourteen thousand feet, and the bitter frosts every night of the year and the cold thin air at such heights had to be taken into account. The last three thousand feet up the peaks is a matter for only the most expert of rock climbers used to rope work on precipitous ledges, and there are few who have attained the highest of the two peaks, Batian – amongst them some of later Himalayan fame and tragedy. A few years ago, my work as a Colonial Fishery Officer took me up to that snowline, on a comfortable organised trip, to survey the high waters of those mountain valleys.

On the first day, we climbed steadily up through the green gloom of the bamboos, the yodelling of the African porters making a continuous background of noise to the great stillness of the deep wet forest. Occasional crashes in the distance, and one much nearer at hand, spoke of big game on the move – the grey shadowy bulk of great elephant who normally slip through the thick tangle with scarcely a sound, and for whom the yodelling was intended as a warning that we wanted the narrow twisting track to ourselves on this day. On the steep muddy path, the mules slipped and staggered as their saddle loads swung their weight backwards and forwards, and they, at least, were I am sure glad when we made our first camp under a huge podocarpus tree at about eleven thousand feet and they were free to roll in the cool sweet grass.

Next day, with the thin air catching at our lungs, a short steep struggle brought us up to the thin belt of giant heath which fringes the upper forest edge, and beyond this the open moorland stretched upwards to the foot of the peaks. Breasting the final ridge, we dropped down a slow incline to the shallow, wide Teleki Valley, where the young Naro Moru river tinkled and sparkled from pool to pool like a Highland burn. The sight in front was immense; we looked on a strange grey-green world of giant lobelias and huge tree groundsels dotted about in the grass, with here and there a flaming red spike of the mountain gladiolus thrusting up through the coarse tufted grass, and patches of papery grey showed where the everlastings defied the snow and bitter night frosts. At the head of the valley, the peaks towered above, silent and massive, their flanks scarred with black ice, and the sparkle of new-fallen snow.

Headquarters camp was at the base of the peaks, where a little cluster of brown tents was our home for the next week, and to this day I can still smell the queer acrid smoke of the groundsel branches we burnt for cooking and warmth. At these great heights, the silence hung heavy and brooding, and I could understand the primitive Africans' fear and reverence in the cathedral-like stillness near the peaks. One almost spoke in a whisper; and every night black frost would grip the whole valley, forming thin sheets of ice on every pool which melted only long after the welcome sun had risen late over Lenana's saddle each day. Far below us, the main cloud belt lay spread over the plains, and I experienced that curious unreal sort of feeling I have often felt when flying above the clouds, and a strange sort of urge to step out and see if I could really walk on them. Here, at fourteen thousand feet, the air was sufficiently rarefied to make walking a matter of slow deliberation, and sleep for the first few nights a time of restless tossing and turning till we acclimatised ourselves. We were glad indeed of the thick sheepskin mattresses and close-zipping Eskimo bags. During the day I found myself doing some curious muddled thinking over the quite simple calculations I had to make in connection with some chemical analyses of the water I was carrying out, but this not uncommon phase passed quite soon, and only on one day did I feel somewhat queer with that strange mountain sickness which so often afflicts the climber at such heights; and after a time the opposite feeling of exhilaration set in – the companion feeling to *l'ivresse du grand profondeur* so graphically described by Cousteau as occurring to divers far under the waves, but without the subtle danger of the latter.

Each day we went off on a different line, collecting samples of water from the various tarns, townetting the still waters and picking and probing on their stony shores for the various aquatic creatures we were anxious to study; for even at these great heights, the waters are not sterile, and many curious beetles, worms and other aquatic beasties came our way. As we walked and climbed from valley to valley, the sharp buttressed peaks and fields of eternal snow were staggeringly huge, and seemed far from the Equator on which, in fact, we stood. Birds were disappointingly few, and indeed only two of the high-level birds were at all frequently seen. The iridescent green Johnston's sunbird was, however, surprisingly common, and we often saw them sitting on the squat lobelia tops, to which they are almost solely confined. I often watched a pair working the tall thick spikes from bottom to top, probing each tubular flower with a long tongue to pick up the small spiders, insects and the drops of nectar at the bottom of each.

It was August, which is the main nesting season for these high-altitude birds. Though we found several new sunbird nests, there were disappointingly none with eggs or chicks. Most of the nests were curiously located near ground level in tufts of the coarse mountain grass, unlike the nests of the bush-haunting sunbirds of the highlands below us, though we did find just one or two nests in the withered leaf crowns of groundsel trees. Though they seemed so tame, I found I could never get near enough to a bird on its characteristic lobelia perch to get a good picture. This particular sunbird is a most interesting species, for each of the great mountain massifs which rise from the East African plains has it own peculiar race, which has developed in the age-old isolation afforded by the great height of Kilimanjaro, Kenya and the fabulous Ruwenzori Mountains of the Moon in Uganda.

Confiding tameness too was the main feature of the other common little bird which lives at these undisturbed heights. This was the hill chat, which has the unjustifiable trivial Latin name of *sordida*; though it is a dun little creature, it is far from sordid, and has the endearing ways of the English robin. One pair near the camp showed a great liking for the pats of butter on our camp table, and I wondered – perhaps not so idly after all – if they did not suffer from a physiological craving for fats to keep out the cold.

The mountain voles, too, showed a ridiculous tameness, and the tufted grass was tunnelled in all directions with their runs. They were everywhere abundant, a fact which made me wonder at the strange absence of predatory birds at the time of our visit. They seemed easy prey for the taking, and I expected to see numerous buzzards, kestrels and owls quartering the crags and moorland slopes, but it was never so when we were there, even though the migrant kestrels and harriers were now passing through Kenya from their European summer haunts.

After a long slog over to Lake Hohnel, and a scrambling visit to Teleki Tarn, a place which has a most curious poached-egg appearance due to the ring of flocculent green algae round its edge, our last visit was to the saddle of Two-tarn Col, and the little lakes there near the Mountain Club Hut. This is perhaps one of the most impressive places round the Kenya peaks, and as I stood by the hut and gazed up at the stupendous west face of Batian towering above me, I recalled that only once before had I had the same impression of awe-inspiring, overpowering height, and that had been while standing near the foot of the smooth man-made face of the Aswan Dam on the Nile; an impression which had been intensified there by the sense of irresistible power conveyed by the surging sluice outlets at the base of the dam.

When our survey was done, we turned at last from the dazzling whiteness of the snows, and as we wended our way down the valley and into the forest again, the air became sweeter and heavier, and our footsteps seemed to grow lighter and lighter. There was no longer any need for the intense physical and mental concentration required at the heights above, and a grand sense of well-being and relaxation was the reward of our endeavours. As I sat on our own verandah again the next evening, and looked up at the clear distant peaks above the trees, I felt a quiet satisfaction that I had been there at last, and that I knew now what lay in that distant view.

The forest around our house, on this south-western side of Mount Kenya, was quite different from the dripping rain forests of the eastern slopes which catch the rainfall first in each monsoon. There, the undergrowth is thick, luscious and tangled, with broad-leaved dombeya trees and huge podo and muna thrusting their way into the upper air and covering all beneath with a wet, heavy shade. Thick green mats of moss softly blanket the trunks, which are spiky and stiff with a wild profusion of ferns and sweet-scented orchids. Here, in the rain-shadow slopes, the forests are dry and brittle, the undergrowth sparse and the foliage drooping. Only feathery crotons, muhugus and the soft pink-flowered Cape chestnuts form the uppermost canopy, and the forest floor is everywhere dappled with patches of sun.

Like all forests, this type requires a bird watching technique of its own; walking around is quite useless, for one seldom sees forest birds that way. But choose a quiet open glade and sit quite still, and the birds will come round you themselves. During the heat of the day, the forests are still, and the silence broken only by the dry rustle of small creatures in the dead leaves carpeting the ground; for in the dry dusty air of these parts, the leaves never rot down to form the rich humus of beechwoods and oakwoods at home. At such a time, the birds too are quiet, and only the metallic clinking of the tinker barbets, and the chuckle of forest bulbuls coupled with the monotonous three-note call of the robin chat proclaim their presence. But in the crisp early morning hours, or in the cool of the evening, many birds break into song for a short while, particularly when the rains first break, and this is the time to go out for a wait and watch session.

There is a curious little bird which is sometimes seen creeping about in the thick undergrowth, whose repeated clicking note is the nearest natural noise to a typewriter I have ever heard. For reasons beyond my ken, this is burdened with the name of the Abyssinian grey-backed glass-eye, a quite extraordinary title which is neither descriptive nor even a literal translation of its rather pleasant Latin name. I always think that the great Sir Frederick Jackson and William Sclater must have had a lot of fun concocting the English names for African birds in their monumental three-volume work, and most of them are reminiscent of a certain ribald party game we used to play in our youth. The habits of this bird resemble a wren most markedly, and it often flicks its greenish-yellow wings as it clicks about in the bush; I watched them often, for we had a pair near our home and year after year I failed to find their nest in spite of close watching. Some years before, on Karen Estate near Nairobi, I had actually found one, a small domed nest sewn over with leaves and near the ground and had tried to picture the birds but had been almost defeated. They were almost the shyest birds I had ever tried, with one exception I shall describe later, and the dull patchy light on the forest floor was almost impossible photographically, for I had no flash outfit in those days. This pair fed their chicks on large black caterpillars and big white moths and showed a curious phenomenon I have often noted in birds before, that of transferring their alarm to the nest site alone, which they were scared to visit, although perching frequently and boldly on the brushwood hide within a few inches of the camera lens and my face.

A bird too of these deep forests is the brilliantly coloured trogon, with its rosy belly and brilliant green upperparts; yet it is strangely inconspicuous in the contrasting light and shade of the trees. It is oddly like a parrot in some ways, though quite unrelated, but its deep booming *coo-coo* note resembles a pigeon's call, though slower in tone. I have often watched them sitting on a branch cooing away, sitting almost upright and with their throat feathers puffing out and tail moving backwards and forwards with each note; and then quite silently they fly away to another branch nearby.

Only once before had I found their nest, about thirty feet up in a hole in a dead tree in the Karen woods, and an impossible place photographically. One year at Nyeri therefore I was delighted to find the nest of a pair in an old split tree trunk only a hundred yards from the house, and not more than five feet off the ground. There were two well-fledged chicks at the bottom of the hole, which was lined only with chips of wood. When I erected a hide nearby, I found the pair surprisingly tame, and they visited the chicks frequently, bringing fat caterpillars or moths each time. I could watch them flying silently from tree to tree as they approached the nest, till they finally pitched on top of the stump, and here the birds would sit for a full minute or more, eyeing me quietly with their large crimson eyes before diving into the hole.

As happened so often with my forest birds, the pictures I took were appallingly bad, and the tremendous contrast of light and shade by the nest was greater than the film could cope with. Sunlight dappling the leaves and trunks of trees may be aesthetically beautiful, but is ruinous for bird photography in the tropics, and deep shade is equally disastrous. The only way successfully to cope with such conditions is by flash work, and when I had purchased a suitable outfit I was therefore very pleased when at the same time the following year I looked into the same hole and the bird slipped silently off the two pure white rounded eggs lying on the chips at the bottom. Nothing, I felt, could stop me this time from getting a unique set of observations and photographs. How wrong I was.

The eggs had seemed fairly fresh, so I left the area severely alone for about a week before I walked over again to see what was happening, fairly late one evening, which is always the best time to look at a nest. On approaching the stump, we saw it was covered all the way up with a black crawling mass – the dreaded 'siafu' or soldier ants of which we had more than our fair share in that part of the world. In considerable alarm and at the cost of some ferocious bites, I looked in the hole and saw what I had feared; the bird had escaped, but the eggs were covered with the vicious black ants. Running back to the house, we fetched a tin of Gamatox powder and literally plastered the tree white, and liberally dosed the eggs and nest as well. We were too late. Three days later the eggs were stone cold, lying on a bed of dead and dying ants, and the birds had deserted. They never came back.

These 'siafu' or 'safari' ants are one of the most ferocious pests in Kenya. Once they start on the march, flanked by their big-headed soldiers, practically nothing will turn them aside. Anything living in their path is covered in seconds and bitten to death, and I have known them wipe out a whole aviary of living birds, since the poor creatures could not keep on the wing the whole time; a more dreadful death it is hard to imagine. They have their uses, too, however, for they are a powerful controlling factor, stopping the spread of the insidiously destructive white ants or termites, whose nests and trails they raid, and if they can be persuaded to enter a house or kitchen infested with cockroaches – as so many in Kenya are – they will clean it in a night, and no cockroaches will be found there for months afterwards. Their long columns on the march are often a sign that the rains are near, probably because of the increasing humidity of the air which enables them to move more freely in the open, and for that reason they often too move at night time when the air is damp. We have had many midnight encounters with 'siafu' invading the house, and have often blessed the protection of a mosquito net when the beds lay in their line of march. Their insistence on keeping going was once turned to useful account amusingly by a friend of mine who one night was disturbed by them entering his window; they dropped onto a long mat below, and by judiciously guiding them round, he persuaded the trail to keep going all round the edges of the mat till they formed a circle. When this was going nicely, it was an easy matter to lift the whole mat and deposit the circus in one piece outside the house again.

They are, however, completely suicidal in their intent to keep going and will form living bridges across small channels of water which lie in their path, those individuals forming the chain bridge sooner or later being drowned by the weight of numbers passing over them. Trout know this well, and I have often found rainbow trout stomachs crammed with ants fallen from such a bridge. Often too, if a lighted cigarette end falls in their path, the nearest ants will smother it with their bodies immediately, losing their lives in the process. The Japanese 'Kamakaze' suicide pilots did no better than these humble ants. Kenya is one country of the world where a sudden loss of modesty and a mad strip-tease act in mixed company is quite permissible and understood if 'siafu' are about; for the heads of the ants will still keep biting after the bodies have been pulled off, and their attack may be quite insidious, but incredibly painful. I am always very careful when siting my hide at a bird's nest.

It is curious what brilliant colouration these birds of the forests may show. The grunting turaco of the eastern Kenya forests, for example, shows the most gorgeous crimson on

PLATE 3

Coly brooding, Karen 1940

PLATE 4

Streaky serin feeding chicks by regurgitation, Kiganjo 1953 (Electronic flash)

its wings in flight. They were common enough in our area, though I never found their nests there. After the rains, when the wild figs and the olives swelled on the trees, we always had a visit from our 'bomber squadron' – those clumsy black and white, grotesquely casqued silver-cheeked hornbills who follow the ripening fruit around, and who excite such curious interest in the zoo aviaries at home. Great, ungainly creatures, they glided in formation from tree to tree, and the forest resounded with their raucous braying as they shambled about the topmost branches raining twigs and ripe fruit to the ground with their clumsy movements. From our house, we could look down on the tree-tops, and these great birds and the graceful leaping of the white-caped colobus monkeys are some of our most precious memories of that once peaceful spot.

On the open grassy plains fringing the forest, we often used to see a party of their quaint, ungainly relatives, the ground hornbill, whose queer booming notes are weird when first heard at night. Their beautiful long curved eyelashes would be the envy of a mannequin, but not their weird and waddling walk. Only once did they come into the forest proper, when we had been evacuated in later days. Some particularly vicious mortar fire directed at a Mau Mau gang in the area where they usually fed, drove them to seek the shelter of the enclosed ground by our houses, and here unfortunately they landed first near one of the houses whose windows were near ground level. Their reflections in the window panes drove them quite mad, and they smashed the glass to smithereens; later the few remaining panes of glass were smeared with mud, and the damage ceased, for they stayed nearby for several days.

Looking back on those years, I seem to have been singularly unsuccessful in dealing with the true forest birds, and I have few worthwhile pictures to show for all the hours I spent watching among the trees. I found a great many nests, it is true, but many of these were on high inaccessible outer branches and during the years we were there we had several with a very poor rainfall which led to sporadic breeding only. I suppose this accounts for the lack of results.

In and around the more open parts of the garden, however, where the shrubs and flowers attracted birds, I was much more successful. The crushed maize we placed on the verandah bird table each day was attractive to many of the smaller birds, the weavers, finches and the like. Ripe fruit and seed of all sorts are appreciated by most Kenya birds as bird table bait, and the coconut, fat and nuts which does so well in the winter at home is useless in Africa. Our most faithful attendants were a pair of Reichenow's weavers whom we christened Pa and Ma. As cake-stealers from the tea table they were unsurpassed, but we forgave them this, for each year they brought their latest brood to be introduced to us and to learn the art of stealing cake, and butter too, when we were not looking. We got to know them and their families well, and both must have been at least seven years old when we last saw them. Although bold beyond compare, and quite unscrupulous where chocolate cake was concerned, they never played the game with their nests, and year after year they built in the most impossible situations where I could never place a hide and get to know their home life better.

I never really worried about this because some years before I had had some very pleasant afternoons with some very distant relations of theirs at Kabete, near Nairobi, also Reichenow weavers. I remember this pair well, because they built their somewhat untidy ball of a nest in one of those impossible, but so aptly named, wait-a-bit thorns, which formed part of the boundary hedge between two fields. This particular plant is armed with the most viciously recurved pairs of thorns all the way down each stem, and as it is long and straggly, the mess one gets into trying to get past it has to be experienced to be believed. This pair of course nested on the end of a branch right in the middle of it, and many were the exasperating minutes I spent unhooking myself from its clutches when examining the nest. The male, like most weavers, had a sizzling little song and a sharp alarm call of *spek-spek*. In one spell of two hours watching, they fed their chicks sixteen times, entirely on insect grubs and caterpillars. In spite of their seed-eating beak, they are, like the English house sparrow, entirely insectivorous when it comes to feeding the chicks. Like the golden weavers described elsewhere in these pages, they would not perch on branches anywhere near the nest, but flew straight to the entrance, and hanging upside down, there fed their very silent chicks through the doorway in a most deliberate fashion. (Plate 1).

Two of our tamest verandah visitors were a pair of golden-breasted buntings. They spent a great deal of their time scurrying about like little mice beneath our feet, humbly picking up the crumbs knocked off by the squabbling weavers above; they rarely flew up to the table themselves. For two seasons they appeared with a single chick, but I was quite unable to find where they nested in spite of careful search. The next year, however, I caught one of them in the act of pulling out some hair from the back doormat, and following his flight soon located the nest being built on a thin branch of a golden wattle tree between the kitchen and the 'wee hoose' – which, as usual in this land of primitive sanitation, was outside. From then on, our acquaintance became much more intimate, and in due course the two scribbled bunting eggs were laid in the astonishingly flimsy cup of hairs and rootlets. The birds sat close, and when the chicks were hatched they objected not at all to my erecting the hide on a platform some five feet away. They were most conscientious parents, and fairly stuffed their offspring with great fat caterpillars at frequent intervals. (Plate 2). The cock, however, had to spend a great deal of his time chasing inquisitive Pa and Ma away, who this year had chosen to nest right at the top of the same tree, and who for some reason found the buntings' goings-on below most intriguing.

As with so many photographs I have taken in Kenya, the results disappointed me because of the terrific play of light and shade dappling through the leaves, so in the year following I was again delighted to catch them in the act of building, this time in a much more suitable straggly bush at the end of the garden. Later I spent many happy hours studying their behaviour at the nest here.

These odd pollarded trees scattered about the grounds were a favourite nesting place of a good many different birds. The long-tailed colies or mousebirds used them a lot for their bulky, untidy cups of nests, in which they reared innumerable chicks to the detriment of our fruit, vegetables and flowers. For they are indeed one of the most destructive garden pests there are in

Kenya, and nothing in the British Isles can compare with them; much to my wife's disgust, I could never bring myself to rob their nests, and in due course the masses would descend on the tomatoes, pea-seedlings and everything else and rip them to shreds. For sheer depravity of taste, they are hard to beat, and even unopened flower buds are fair game. The descent of a pack of colies always reminds me of a shower of meteors, with their long tails trailing behind them, and the damage they do is perhaps more selective, but equally complete. They are well named mousebirds, for the curious way they creep and crawl about the branches is most rodent-like, while my wife finds their bare pink feet rather revolting. Absolutely nothing that is luscious and growing is safe from them; seedlings, ripe fruit of all sorts and flower buds are all grist to their insatiable mills. We never once had a decent flowering of the avenue of many lovely pink and white bauhinia trees we planted along the road. The birds would eat the heart out of each bud just before it opened, and then strip the leaf buds too until in time the trees gave up the unequal struggle and stood stark and bare as if they had been blasted by lightning. On the serious side too, they can be the cause of severe economic losses to fruit growers, as one settler friend of ours nearby who grew grapes commercially knew to his cost. With the advent of the Mau Mau emergency in Kenya and the subsequent high loss of firearms to terrorist murders and thieving, he had to withdraw his African shooters who controlled the colies in his vineyards, and suffered severe destruction of his crops by the birds in consequence.

On the whole, however, shooting seems of little avail in the ordinary garden, and there is really only one effective form of control, apart from the uncertainty of poison, and that is to trap them. The most useful trap consists of a large portable wire netting cage of half-inch mesh, about six feet by four feet by four feet. On all four sides, near the top, there is a long non-return funnel made of wire netting, sticking into the cage, and at the end of this you hang a ripe, red, squashy tomato on a hook. The colies cannot resist this luscious bait, and fairly queue up to get in, and show an uncanny persistance in trying to find the way in, finally entering the funnel quite readily. But once in, they lose their heads and seem unable to find the way out again, and they seem to have but a tenuous hold on life in spite of their persistent deviltry, and very often all are dead the following morning.

One friend of ours who had thus trapped some birds successfully for the first time found himself in a quandary as to how best to kill them inside the trap. So he hit on the bright idea of introducing his large tabby cat into the cage, who then made short work of the job. On subsequent days he was enormously puzzled to find that no further birds entered the trap, in spite of the large flocks still round about; but the puzzle was solved when he went out very early one morning and found his fat tabby cat sitting on top of the cage, licking his chops in anticipation of the meal which he fondly hoped would soon enter below him!

Perhaps because so many hands have been raised against them, these colies are one of the most difficult birds of all to photograph at the nest. Their shyness is quite uncanny, in spite of all the precautions taken, and they are suspicious to a degree of anything strange near their nest. Like the behaviour of the bateleur eagle so ably described by my friend Leslie Brown, one feels that one is in the presence of a bird whose intelligence in the exact sense is far above that which the modern school of ornithological behaviourists will agree to any bird possessing.

I have tried them repeatedly with all the usual tricks of the trade and had to confess myself beaten. Either they can easily count up to three, or can distinguish black and white, or else possess some peculiar sense, like wild duck, which tells them at once that the hide is occupied, for they will spend literally hours sitting in the bush just behind the nest without once coming on to it. I have indeed, by patience almost beyond endurance, succeeded in getting a few portraits of a sitting bird (Plate 3) (pictures which therefore I prize enormously), but I have never yet seen them behave normally at the nest or been able to watch them feed their chicks, and I do not know how this is done. I suspect it must be by regurgitation, probably a contributary cause of the long waits I have had. The chicks are most extraordinarily reptilian creatures, with a bare yellow face, hooked beak and prominent eyes, and quite a long tail stump; they seem to spend most of their time in the nest yawning and crawling about like small pterodactyls.

As I have frequently mentioned later in this book, those birds which feed their chicks by regurgitation can be amongst the most trying of all to photograph owing to the long wait between visits which is necessary. The common little streaky serin of Kenya gardens is no exception. Their nests were common in our garden, but at each I tried with chicks I had the same long dreary wait while the parents prepared the chicks' next meal in their stomach. At the nest, this oozes from their bill as a thick white milky fluid, brought up after the most ghastly retching efforts. (Plate 4). In the case of the serins, the parents thrust the whole of their own thick bills into the chicks' gaping mouth, but this is not always so with other birds.

Then, too, the red-eyed dove, perhaps the commonest of all the doves which live in Kenya gardens, feeds its chicks on 'pigeons' milk', like all pigeons do, and takes a long time to do so at the nest. These red-eyed, or ring-necked doves as they are sometimes called, are apparently quite oblivious to all the seasons' changes and will court and nest the whole year through. The pouting, bullying, cooing cock chases the hen unmercifully every month of the year and has many sharp tiffs with cracking wings and bluster at all intruding cocks. Typical pigeons' nests, their frail platforms are built in the branches with little attempt at weaving them into a solid whole; they are built in all sorts of places and at almost any height from the ground. Two oval white eggs are the usual clutch, and incubation and rearing of the chicks is a prolonged business; the fat young squabs are favourite prey of the forest raptors and few ever survived in our garden. The black forest sparrow hawks regularly quartered our grounds, and pigeon pie was their favourite dish.

These doves are really rather dull birds to photograph at the nest. They take a long time to return and when they do, if the squab is small, will just sit for hours beside it, or on top of it, before producing a meal. When the chick is larger and feathering well, the parents spend many hours away from the nest and leave the chick to its own devices; this is probably one reason why the casualty rate is so high for the chick is defenceless and apparently voiceless too.

It was two or three years before I managed to find the nest of another pair of birds which frequented our garden a great deal – the puffback shrikes. Season after season, I used to watch the cock chasing the hen through the trees with his piercing whistle, and rump all puffed out white, like a powder puff, in their courtship pursuit. Then one day they would be quiet, and I knew that nesting had started, but all my searching for their nest was in vain until one day in May 1953 I spotted a small nest fairly high up in a sapling Cape chestnut tree. Climbing gingerly up, I had at last the pleasure of looking into their nest, a neat deep cup of grasses and lichen right at the end of the outermost thinnest twigs. The sitting hen did not leave until I was quite close to her. A few days later the two eggs hatched, so I trundled my movable platform nearby and erected the hide on it. Even with this I found the nest was still rather too high, so tying a stout cord to the branch, I pulled it down to the right level and pegged the cord firmly into the ground.

Just as I had completed all these preparations, orders came to evacuate our home because of Mau Mau activity in the area, and I gave up all hope of getting to know the birds better; but in the course of our future wanderings from house to house, I managed to get back for just one day, and spent the morning with the birds; seldom have I been rewarded more richly. The birds were delightfully bold, and came to the nest frequently with food for the chicks; these were still fairly small, and the hen brooded them a lot, perched high in the nest. The cock often came while the hen was sitting, and either passed the food he had brought over to her, leaning down from a twig above, or else she moved off and allowed him to feed the young himself. For two whole hours I sat in the hide entranced, watching these two small black and white birds. Like all shrikes, they have a most alert bearing, and at close quarters their eye is a striking and brilliant crimson colour.

The solicitude of this particular cock in feeding the chicks called to mind another pair I had once watched building sometime before near Nairobi. This pair were putting the final touches of lichen and cobweb to their nest, and were truly indigenous creatures of Africa; for the hen did all the work, flying incessantly to and fro with building material, while the cock merely followed her around encouraging her with merry whistles to work harder – a truly African and unequal division of labour! The sexes are easy to distinguish as the hen has a white streak on her face. (Plate 5B). This particular pair I had later watched from a hide at close quarters as well for a short while. I remember it was a very hot sunny morning, and the *Rhus* tree in which they had built their nest was a highway for ants, on one of their numerous trails. They had clearly invaded the nest, though they were fortunately not the ferocious 'siafu' type, and the hen, who was brooding small chicks, had a most uncomfortable time, twisting, turning and poking in the nest the whole while and panting in the heat with wide open bill. During the time I watched, she left only once to fetch food – a large whitish cricket – which curiously enough she swallowed herself before sitting on the chicks without even offering it to them. I felt sorry for the poor creatures, but there was little I could do to help. It is a curious thing how often the indigenous birds of Africa seem to suffer from heat, and yet will often nest in places exposed to the full sun at midday when other shade is still readily available nearby.

Two other small black and white birds were frequently seen on the forest fringes. One, a restless little pair of chin-spot flycatchers, led me a dance year after year trying to track their nest, but never once did I succeed. I had actually found their nest elsewhere in Kenya, and the very small lichen cup on the upperside of a branch is a masterpiece of camouflage. Its presence can often only be revealed by the behaviour of the birds themselves, but as any bird watcher knows, it is quite extraordinary how secretive the commonest bird can become at that all important time of nesting.

The other black and white bird was the white-bellied tit, which little resembles its British cousins in either looks or behaviour; but unlike the chin-spots, these showed us their nest one day while strolling round the garden. This was in a split tree trunk, about ten feet up, but the nest itself was so far down,

PLATE 5A. Red-rumped swallow leaving nest, Kiganjo 1950 (Electronic flash)

PLATE 5B. Puff-back shrike, female at nest, Kiganjo 1953 (Electronic flash)

PLATE 5A

PLATE 5B

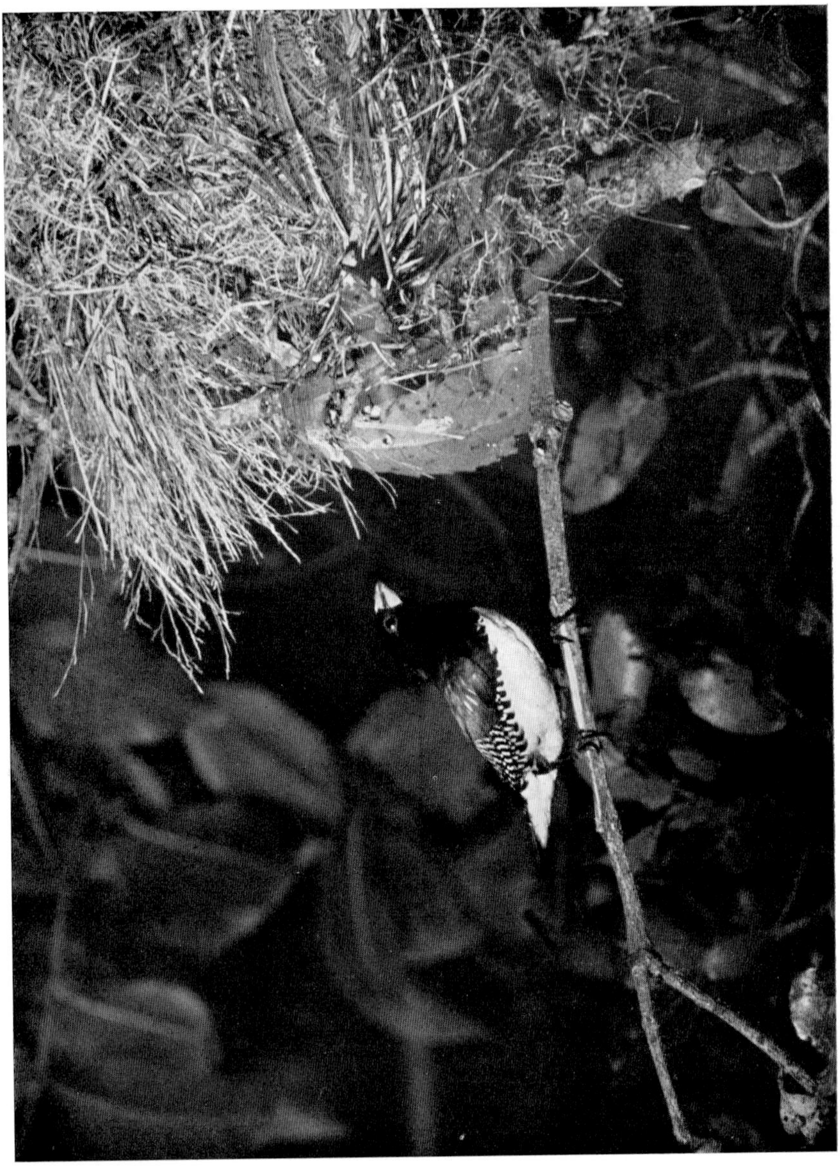

Bronze mannikin at nest, Kiganjo 1953 (Electronic flash)

I could not see what was in it. From their behaviour however, they clearly had chicks, and from a very rickety pile of old boxes nearby on which I erected the hide, I was able to get a few pictures of the birds. These were not as good as I could have wished, but the position was not ideal, and I could not really steady the tripod on the unsafe erection I had made; the slope of the hillside was too steep to move it elsewhere. The following year the bottom fell out of the split and the birds moved elsewhere. Although I have mentioned above their lack of resemblance to the British tits, yet there is at the same time a strong family likeness in their call-notes and song; so much so, that when hearing it I have sometimes looked up sharply to see what a great tit was doing in Africa!

Every year we used to look forward to seeing from our verandah at breakfast time, in the season just after the rains, the curious undulating flight across the lawn of a pair of scimitar bills – birds not unlike small choughs – who reared their chicks in a series of old woodpecker holes in a twisted tree near the forest edge. Normally, these are birds of the more open bushveld, and it was somewhat curious to find them in such relatively thick forest; but this pair remained with us for at least four years and for all I know are still there yet. Their daily flight across the lawn was the first indication we usually had that they were nesting again. They had a most regular route, collecting insects in a restless tit-like manner in the topmost branches of a tree at the end of the lawn, often hanging upside down to do so. With a beakful all ready, they then cut across the open lawn and undulated up to the top of their nesting tree; this was a rather remarkable old half-dead tree with no less than three old woodpecker holes in a line along an upper branch, and a deep split in the trunk where this branch had its base.

The birds used all three holes and the split in turn, but I was never able to climb high enough to see into their nest. By steps nailed on to the trunk I could get as far as the fork which was about ten feet from the nearest nesting hole, and by cradling myself in the fork and keeping still, I often watched the birds clinging on to the branch and poking their long curved bills into the hole as they fed their chicks. From my uncomfortable saddle, the background was all sky as I could get no higher, so of course all the pictures I took were doomed to failure from the start, and I gave up trying. The general colour of the birds is in any case black, so the results were mere silhouettes and neither artistic nor useful; no bird photograph silhouetted against a sky ever is, even with flight pictures – the result must show detail in the plumage to be satisfactory.

Verreaux's starling is another tree-hole nester, and in Kenya a somewhat mysterious bird, for it comes and goes in a most puzzling fashion. It is in fact a wanderer from the south, but birds can certainly be found in Kenya in most months of the year, and as Jackson records, it will also nest in Kenya when the fancy takes it.

Its pure white underparts contrast strongly with the rich metallic violet or purple of the back in the male; this back colour varies according to the light in which it is seen, but it is often a real royal purple. For this reason we thought it most appropriate that it should be the first bird to nest in an old tree left standing just by the verandah of the Royal Forest Lodge when this was built a few hundred yards from our house on the banks of the Sagana River. This Lodge was Kenya's wedding present to the Queen and the Duke, and was occupied by them for only a few days in early 1952 on that visit which was cut so tragically short while still there. She came to us as a Royal Princess and left a few days later as Queen; but I doubt if she even saw this gorgeous pair of birds wearing their royal colour too, for they nested by her house some two months before her arrival. Gorgeous and regally coloured are truly the words for the male, and to catch sight of it invariably causes an exclamation of surprise by those who have never seen it before; and this royal pair who frequented the Lodge nearly stopped all work for a few days when they first started building their nest in a hole. The male is mainly the active partner, and his more dowdy, spotted mate takes little part in bringing the simple grass lining to the hole.

We were desperately short of suitable dead trees or holes in our own garden, so we never had the luck to attract more than casual visits from birds migrating through; but I once had the chance to watch a nesting pair a few miles away, who had most accommodatingly nested in a split tree trunk so low that it could be commanded by a rough brushwood hide built on the ground nearby. I found their behaviour typically that of a starling – though they do not descend to the clowning buffoonery of the frequenters of our British chimney pots which we know so well.

I was also interested to see however that, unlike so many bright-plumaged cocks who have dowdy wives, this cock took his full share in feeding the chicks, and visited the hole as frequently as the hen. Even at close quarters, I could never make out what food it was they brought; it just looked large and black and squashy, and I can only presume it was of insect origin. I suspect the birds had discovered a private store of cockroaches, which they mangled before bringing to the chicks.

These lovely iridescent colours are common in birds of these sunny lands, and another such gorgeous bird was seasonal in our garden – the emerald cuckoo, a bird of the same lazily parasitic habits as its more sombre British cousin. Two years ago, at the break of the April rains, I had watched a pair of these flirting and courting in the trees at the foot of the lawn, the male with his loud *teeu-tu-tui* call chasing the hen through the branches and showing off to full advantage his metallic green wings and golden belly as he flicked from branch to branch.

A month or so later, I saw the result of this courtship play, for I watched an obvious chick of theirs – with the same beautiful metallic green back, but a plain whitish barred belly – being a perfect nuisance to its foster parents, a pair of harassed looking yellow-vented bulbuls who followed their queer looking offspring from tree to tree as it called incessantly for food; but like the outrageously demanding European cuckoo chick, it could never be satisfied.

Curiously enough, on the same day, I had found another bulbul's nest built in a very open fork of a big yellow moonflower bush in the flower beds, which contained one egg. Two days later it had two, and I somewhat idly noted that the second egg was not quite alike, being a little larger and paler; but as bulbul eggs of the same clutch often differ in size and colour, I thought no more about it. Just over a fortnight later,

I looked at the nest again, and it now contained only one newly hatched chick, perhaps a day or two old. While wondering what had happened to the other egg, the penny suddenly dropped and I remembered the cuckoos. Searching below the nest, I soon found the original bulbul's egg, fortunately still whole; and to test the possibility placed it back in the nest again and watched to see what would happen.

Surely enough, after a few minutes the little naked chick started wriggling and heaving as he felt the hard eggshell against the sensitive skin of his back. Waggling his ugly bulbous head from side to side, he pushed and strained with his feeble little legs till he had got the egg in the small of his back. Shoving and pushing with his feet braced against the bottom of the nest, and his wing stumps held out to hold the egg on his back, he slowly backed up the side of the nest until he reached the edge; and with a final heave the egg went overboard again. There could be no doubt about it – this pair of bulbuls had a cuckoo in the nest as well, and were in for a harassing time. I had never at any time seen more than the one pair of cuckoos in the garden, so that, interestingly enough, their egg laying could be prolonged to about a month.

That afternoon, I tried the chick again with the egg as I wanted some pictures; and though he took longer this time, the performance was repeated all over again. But two days later, although already bigger and stronger, he refused to tip the egg out again, and left it beside him in the nest. Since the bulbul clutch is normally two, I presume the cuckoo parents had removed the second real bulbul's egg when they substituted theirs – a performance I would have given anything to have seen.

The diagnosis of a cuckoo in the nest was completely confirmed a week later, when the sprouting wing quills split to reveal the tell-tale golden-green feathering, and if birds ever do such things, no doubt Father had some pretty nasty remarks to make to Mother bulbul on the subject! The changeling grew at an amazing rate, his foster parents stuffing him every few minutes with caterpillars, and becoming most agitated whenever I examined the nest. Apart from a very short session one day, I deliberately left serious photography till later, as I wanted to get (for Africa) a unique series of the young cuckoo being fed by his foster parents at a size when he would be distinctly recognisable as a cuckoo in the print.

It was not to be so. The nest had worried me from the start, as it was so exposed to the full sun, and I had already tried to tie some of the big leaves over it for shade; but these soon withered, and the chick became more and more restless as the sun beat down on it day after day. It was so big that the bulbuls soon refused to brood it, and one day the inevitable happened. The chick fell out of the nest in its struggles, and as it moved feebly on the ground below the nest, the ants found it before I did. All I could see on my next visit to the nest was the chick, now quite dead, with its skeleton picked clean and only a dull gold gleam from the untouched feathers; the foster parents called distractedly in the tree nearby for a whole day, and then forgot the whole thing.

Although the other golden cuckoos of Africa – Klaas's and the didric – visited us from time to time, I never found their eggs in any other nest, nor did the emeralds parasitise any more nests which I found there.

Speke's weavers started a small colony in the eucalyptus trees behind our house and their cheerful sizzling noise welcomed each day, though their nests were quite ungetatable from the photographic point of view. On the verandah bird table, which they soon found, they were quarrelling noisy bullies, and the males could certainly have done with a proper course of nest building and architecture; their nests were always falling down, much to the delight of my small son who soon had them strewn all over the house. But they made clean messes, relative to some of the other bits of garden which he introduced from time to time indoors.

While the Speke's may be haphazard as householders, the cheerful little bronze mannikin finches who fed in the mule pasture nearby are perhaps some of the most fastidious nest builders in Africa. Their domed nest with its long porch entrance is indeed rather untidy, but they are most pernickety about the material they use, since this is always the green growing tips of the so-called asparagus fern (which is really a lily) which rambles all over the tree trunks in such forest. Furthermore, they will choose only the fine kind, and the coarser species they leave entirely alone; the living tips are always nipped off the plant by the bird, who will often fly a long way into the forest to get just what is wanted.

With one nest which I watched being built, some sort of minor soviet system seemed to be in force, since no less than three birds were building the nest together in comradely style. Two of them were doing the fetching and carrying of asparagus tips, the third was sitting inside and doing the arranging. In our garden, they usually built in the centre of a thick ant-infested bush, never an easy place to get at, and their minute little white eggs, perhaps five or six to a nest, are lovely delicate little things, and are brooded most closely.

One year, a pair nested in a more reasonable position on the outer side of a low tree, and when the chicks had hatched I was able to erect my hide on a platform nearby, confidently expecting to get a good series of the birds near the nest. I was rudely disappointed. They proved to be one of the most difficult birds I had ever tried, and literally hours of waiting resulted in exactly two pictures when the cock paid one brief visit to the nest. (Plate 6). Whether the excessive shyness is typical of the species I do not know, for I have not tried another, but certainly these small finches as a tribe can be most trying; I have bitter memories of many fruitless hours spent waiting at the nests of others of their ilk, such as the cordon-bleu, plum finch and waxbill. It is most curious that these little birds should be so friendly and confiding in their flocks at the bird table or in the garden, and yet as shy as a greenshank at their nests.

No country home in Kenya is complete without its pair of swallows nesting in the eaves, and two species in particular become most tame – the wire-tailed and the red-rumped swallow. According to the charming old wives' tale, the nesting of a swallow in the eaves usually means a household later to be blessed with the laughter of little children, but none of our children, alas, have ever been foretold by this happy omen. We had indeed a good many visits from both kinds, twisting in and out of the verandah day after day, but no bird ever built. Looking back on it now, I suspect that the architecture of our home-built house was not really suitable; our verandah was really much too small, and the roofing beams did not offer the good foundations necessary. Our neighbours, however, in the house just behind us, duly had their fortune told by a pair of red-rumped swallows which occupied a corner of their large verandah roof, and lo! in due time a baby girl appeared.

The seasons at our place were astonishingly erratic, however, even for Kenya, and many times the swallows were deluded by the poor quality of the local mud which resulted from the insufficient rain. The red-rumped swallow builds a most elaborate nest in the form of a large hemisphere adherent to the roof, with a long entrance tunnel at one side. Like all swallows' nests, this is laboriously made of mud pellets fetched one at a time and stuck with great care to each other. This particular pair of birds tried very hard, but at first could not get the mud nearly sticky enough and the nest fell down repeatedly. But they were determined that their hosts should have a baby and tried again and again. The final result was an astonishing patchwork of different coloured muds, as they tried each roadside pool in turn, but the feather lining was finally added at last, and two broods reared for good measure.

They are, of course, impossible subjects to photograph by any means except high-speed electronic flash. Their nesting place is always dark, and they enter the entrance tunnel full tilt on the wing without a pause. Unlike our home swallow with its open cup, once inside the nest they cannot be seen. When the chicks are fed, they drop like a plummet from the entrance hole (Plate 5A), and are swiftly away to hawk in the open for the next beakful of rations. A somewhat hopeless proposition altogether. Ordinary flash bulbs are too slow, and using hand-operated electronic flash I wasted some dozens of negatives without getting anything really good except pictures of odd bits of tail or wing tips.

The wire-tailed swallow – so like our familiar English bird to look at – is however a much easier subject, for like the European species it builds a half-cup nest, open at the top, and one can see what is going on. They never nested on our property, but a pair on the front verandah of a charming house some miles away were very tame. They required no hide at all, and fed their chicks repeatedly in front of the bare camera and myself seated nearby, not even taking the slightest notice of the sudden flash as I recorded them. (Plate 7).

The focal point of our little forest settlement was of course the river, since it was, too, the main reason why we were there at all. It rippled and tumbled and sparkled its way from pool to pool, and in the clear brown depths swam lazy trout whom we watched from the bridge as they nuzzled and fed on the gravelly bed. I knew the river and its inhabitants so well that in the brief twilight I could tell exactly where to look for the plop and the ring of a rising trout in each pool; and marvelled thereby at the inefficiency of the anglers who flogged the public waters downstream of the bridge for the number they repeatedly missed. Upstream of the bridge was my closed research area, and here I knew almost every trout by name.

In early April, when the Old Mountain drew a veil over his head and gathered his black skirts around his waist, and the lightning split the darkness on the high moors, then our river – so placid and peaceful throughout the still hot days before – became a roaring red demon. With the growling noise of distant thunder, the rainfall on the moors swept down as a tidal crest, and the turgid swirling flood spread over all the flowers on its banks, bringing with it the dark dank smell of rotting leaves and trees from the miles of forest above. Sailing down like prehistoric monsters on the hissing, sucking waters would come great fallen giants of forest trees which battered and smashed against the stout timbers of the bridge as the water leapt down the fall. This was our anxious time for the rearing ponds below and my research trap above, for millions of twigs, dead leaves and other trash piled up on the screens, stifling the flow, and a twenty-four hour flood control watch had to be kept.

Then too, as the ripening trout felt the surge of clean cold water from the moors, they ran the falls like great salmon running the caulds at home, and we knew that our busy spawning season would soon start.

Even as these first floods of the year urged the trout upstream to spawn, so too did they herald the rains and the onset of nesting for all those birds for whom the river banks were home. The charming, graceful mountain wagtails always stayed with us where the river passed under the bridge. In the low clear water of the dry season, they stepped their way daintily over

Wire-tailed swallow feeding chicks, Kiganjo 1950 (Electronic flash)

Cinnamon-chested bee-eater at nest hole with butterfly for chick. Kiambu

the gravel beds and the smooth water-worn rocks of the fall, just getting their feet wet as they picked at the water's edge for gnat larvae, and the darting olive nymphs, and wagging their tails with a low sweet trill. They had a regular beat of a few hundred yards above and below the fall, and on each side other pairs patrolled their private stretches too. They always seem lively and happy, and were we given a choice of our next re-incarnation, I think I would choose to be a mountain wagtail. I would then be able to spend all my days in the pleasantest of all surroundings, by the running water's edge, in the loveliest spots of this land of sunshine; and one would be thrice blessed too, for they remain most faithfully paired, and a wagtail without a mate is rare indeed.

Year after year this pair nested with us there, but how seldom did their labours bear fruit. The old timbers under the bridge were almost lined with their nests, in which one after another the rats took toll of their eggs, for the birds would never learn to build their nests out of reach of the sure-footed rats. One year they seemed to do a little better, and built and laid their eggs in a nest in a bush overhanging the stream, but here too they were doomed, for they made the rare and most unusual mistake of building too low down; the next flood plucked and swept away the nest from under them. The next year, however, they at last chose one of the few rat-proof places on the bridge where two timbers crossed and here at last two grey little chicks with stumpy wagging tails were left in peace to learn the later art of stepping stones.

I was able to fix a hide on the wet slippery rocks near this nest, and found the birds almost ideal subjects for my newly acquired electronic flash outfit; for they had a regular route across the falls below to the nest, and as they jumped from stone to stone, I was able to gauge the exact moment at which they would make the last short flight up to the nest. They were a busy and devoted couple, and used to feed the chicks well on into twilight darkness as I sat and watched them. I have very often stopped fishing for an hour or more to watch pairs of these birds on the Kenya trout streams, and the music of the creamy foaming water as it lipped the fall, and the peace of green surroundings near this hide make this one of the pleasantest memories of all my bird-watching days. I owe a lot to those charming white and pearl-grey birds for many tranquil moments in my life.

These mountain wagtails have a cousin, the African pied wagtail, which is very similar to our British bird, though it is more domestic than the trout stream birds. Like most gardens in Kenya, we had a pair of the pieds, who usually used the thatched roofs of outbuildings for nesting; but one pair was fond of water too, and latterly took to nesting by the ponds. Several times they built on the sloping grassy banks of these, the nest being tucked well under a tuft of the thick green Kikuyu grass. Once too they built in a tuft of fern growing between the plank revetments of a ditch, and this was one of the most picturesque nests I have ever found. As I watched them from a hide, I found them equally confiding, as were their river-loving cousins. Just like the mountain wagtail, they too had a regular route to the nest, and I could watch them coming all the way along the bank till they took the final short flight up to the nest. But, photographers beware! all the wagtails just never stop living up to their names, and the wag is much faster than you think. Many of my pictures have been spoilt by a blur where the tail ought to be.

The little dusky flycatchers were very much at home near the river too, and in fact collected a great deal of their food from near the water's edge as the spinners and the stoneflies emerged from their nymphal shucks below the water and dried their wings on emergent stones. They too nested in bushes overhanging the pools, and I often found their small round cups; but rarely in a position where I could do anything about it, except once when I was able to pull the thin branch on which a pair had built and peg it down near enough to a hide on the bank. They are no trouble at the nest, and will pose perfectly in the typical flycatcher manner with head on one side.

Near this one flycatcher's nest, but on the opposite side of the river, a pair of olive sunbirds built their nest in 1952, the usual small hanging gourd of a nest with a porch entrance at one side. It was in a good place to watch the birds from a hide, being near the bank, and I kept a careful eye on it each day. It was just at the time when their chicks were due to hatch, that the Queen, then Princess Elizabeth, and Prince Philip came to stay at Forest Lodge for the first time, and we were given a great deal to do to provide first class fishing for them on our river which ran past the Lodge. Several rustic bridges were built across the stream, and the banks were cleared to make the going easy. One day as I went down to look at the work in progress, I found to my horror that the clearing gang, with the enormous enthusiasm the Africans display when they come to hacking down trees, had chopped down all the bush in which this sunbird's nest was built, leaving only the one long thin branch on which the nest was hung, which now stood out on its own conspicuously for all to see.

To my surprise, however, the birds were not the least concerned, and I subsequently collected a good series of pictures of them both, my hide no doubt being noted with the supreme interest which our Royalty shows in all around, though an object of some disquiet to the Security Officers! Unlike the other African sunbirds, there is little marked difference in plumage between the sexes and the dun-coloured cock takes his full share in feeding chicks. As there were no longer any nearby branches on which to perch, the cock would hover in the air in front of the nest just like a humming bird, until the hen at the nest had fed the chicks and he could take his turn; but owing to technical hitches with the high-speed flash outfit, I could never get this interesting shot.

During the six pleasant years we spent in the shadow of Mount Kenya here, we had only two in which the rains – which mean so much to nesting birds in Kenya – could be called at all normal. The so-called 'long rains' due from March to early May failed with peculiar regularity, and seldom lasted more than a week or so at most, adding but a few inches to swell the yearly total.

By contrast, the 'short' rains in November and December usually did us well, and were often longer than the 'long'. We could always tell when the short rains had really started with us by the behaviour of the small colony of cinnamon-chested bee-eaters who lived down near the bridge. During most of the year, they sat in twos on the high tree-tops overlooking the river, and their wonderful aerial acrobatics were a never-failing source of fascination as they dived and twisted through the air, their beaks closing with an audible snap as they caught their insect prey on the wing. The pairs used to sit side by side on a prominent branch until one saw a good sized insect flying by; diving down, it followed the wildly flying insect through the air, catching it on the wing and sailing up to its perch again with a beakful of frantically waving legs and wings. Then it was either swallowed whole or beaten against the branch before being tossed back. The birds then perched again with quickly moving tail, and head constantly turning from side to side as they weighed their chances of catching this or that as it flew below them. If a butterfly was the victim, the wings were neatly sheared off and fluttered to the ground as the succulent body was swallowed whole.

About October, when the reeling bubbling calls of the migrant blue bee-eaters from the north had passed on further south, the first few showers of the 'grass rains' caused wild excitement in the colony, and the birds tumbled off the trees to fly in dizzy circles against the steep earth banks which lined the road. Their peculiar high-pitched reeling call and 'chissick' cries greeted each day afresh, and soon the birds were tunnelling hard, enlarging the numerous old holes which already pitted the red earth, and starting others afresh; a restless activity spread over the whole small colony as the breeding fever urged them on. Each day would see fresh holes dug, some only a few inches in, others a foot or two until a hard impenetrable root would cause them to abandon it and try elsewhere. Each new-dug hole showed two deep grooves on the entrance ledge where the feet of the birds had scrabbled in and out, and little conical mounds of red dust accumulated in a pile below. Though industrious, they are not persistent diggers, and only a minute or two in the hole suffices before the owner flies out again to resume his aerial wheeling round the bank. They are supremely birds of the air, and like the martins, swallows and swifts are more constantly on the wing than perched.

Then came a day when the colony was quiet, and within a few days more I knew to take a torch and do my rounds of peering in the holes. Those with cobwebs across the door – the birds' 'To Let' sign – I did not trouble to examine, but in per-

Fiscal shrike, male at nest, Karen 1941

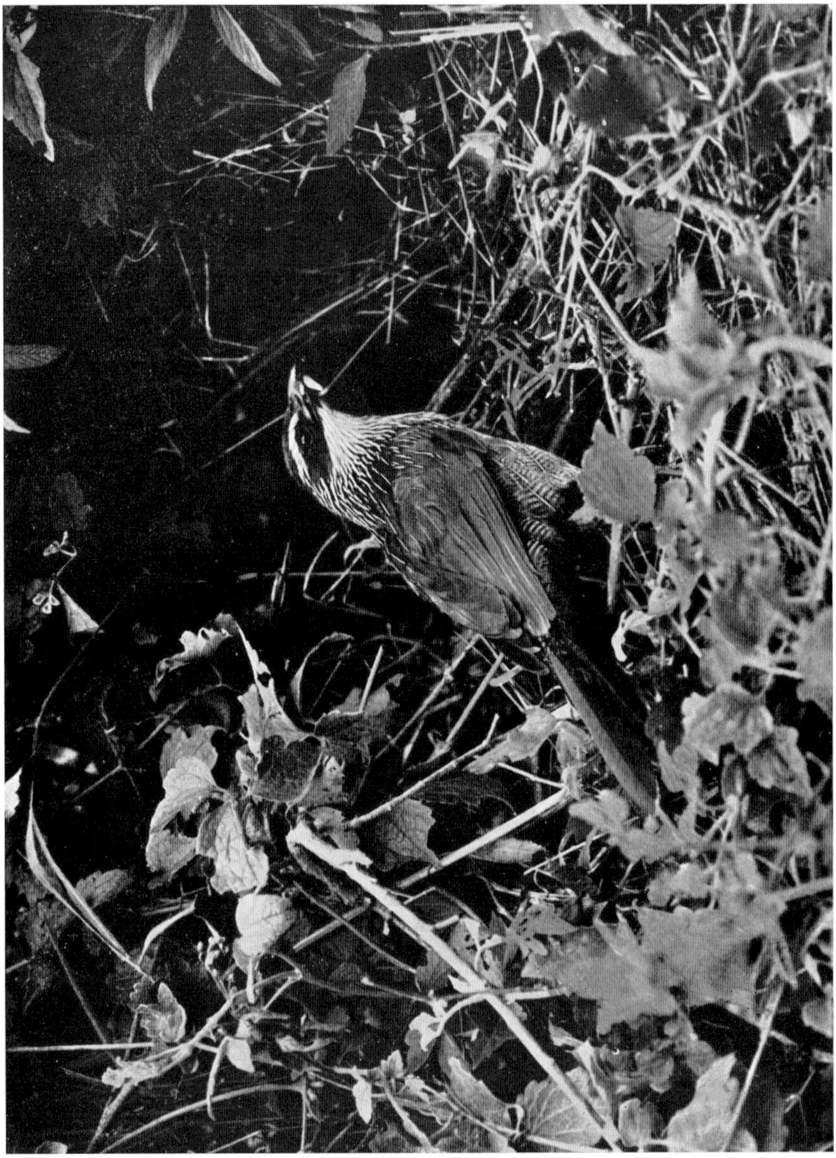

White-browed coucal at nest Karen 1949

haps a half-dozen more, the beam of the torch would shine on a beady eye and a long curved bill peering round the far corner of the slightly angled hole. (Plate 8).

Associated with the bee-eaters were a few pairs of the jet-black saw-wing swallows, a bird whose mastery of the air surpasses that of the bee-eaters themselves. They clearly had some sort of understanding with the latter and often took over one of the abandoned holes so conveniently dug for them; I do not think they themselves ever drove a bee-eater from its hole.

The swallow-occupied holes were quite distinctive, because the light of the torch would show at the end a deep soft cup made of 'old man's beard' – a grey and shrivelled looking lichen which hangs down in tangled skeins from the upper branches of the trees and which the birds undoubtedly pick off on the wing. They use this nest-building material quite exclusively, and as far as I know will not breed, unless a supply of it is to hand. Often the identity of the occupant of a hole was proclaimed by a small piece of this grey lichen caught up on a rootlet at the entrance.

They, even more than the bee-eaters, have a habit of wheeling past their nesting hole time after time before finally diving straight in. I spent many pleasant hours watching the bee-eaters going in and out of their holes when feeding chicks, and though they, too, tend to dive straight in, a twig sticking out from the bank below the hole is always very welcome, and a pair will often sit closely side by side on such a perch either before or after feeding their chicks. Like wagtails, their tails are in constant motion back and forth, and it is not easy to get just the perfect picture. The quick-flying black saw-wings are, however, a very different proposition. They will never settle by the nest if they can help it, and always dive straight into the hole when they have made sufficient circuits past it. I have described in the last chapter of this book the ruse I finally adopted to take their picture, and it has worked quite well, ensuring that brief cling to the entrance ledge that gives a fleeting chance.

One pair of these latter birds laid claim for years to an old bee-eaters' hole in an earth bank elsewhere in the garden, and reared at least two broods in it every year. Their chicks, when on the wing, circled and manoeuvred for weeks after leaving the nest in company of their parents. Like many other kinds of birds, these bee-eaters and saw-wings are very restricted in their selection of breeding areas; in their case it is quite essential to have such earth banks in which to tunnel, and they will stick to the same breeding bank year after year. Although I have not infrequently found them breeding almost at ground level where a small earth slope, perhaps only a few inches high, borders a path, they nevertheless prefer a higher bank, and a colony will establish itself in any judiciously cut earth bank in a garden. The bee-eaters are some of the most brilliantly plumaged birds to be found in Kenya, and are an attraction wherever they can be induced to stay, and a never-failing source of pleasure and wonder at their mastery of the air.

Even as I write, our little forest clearing with its cluster of wooden houses still lies deserted; the forests round about are full of far grimmer things than birds; but I know too that at least the bee-eaters will not have left the place, and they will still be circling round the tree-tops by the river as we knew them – it seems so long ago – and the twin peaks of Kenya will still be towering over the trees.

CHAPTER 2

THE WAY OF A SHRIKE

NOWADAYS IN Kenya, it is, alas, necessary to take far sterner measures to keep the old flag flying than to dress for dinner in the jungle; but it is still a truism to say of the Englishman that wherever he settles he makes a garden. If two or three settle together they of course start a club and make a golf-course too.

Man seems destined to change the face of the earth wherever he goes, and as there is settlement, so the old order changes. Even for those such as the African, to whom a garden of flowers is a useless and unnecessary thing, the ground must be cleaned and tilled to plant his maize and his bananas, and in this part of Africa his goats complete the cycle of vegetation change and soil erosion.

There are many very lovely gardens in East Africa, and when the rainfall is less uncertain or water plentiful there are rioting banks of colour of tropical and temperate flowers, for here in the cold nights and cool days over six thousand feet, in the abundant sunshine, one can grow a great many of the temperate flowers of England, though the even lengths of daylight throughout the year and the absence of a frosty winter check restrict the flowering of all the many lovely spring bulbs so characteristic of the old country.

Man too alters the face of the land as he lays out macadamised streets, builds skyscrapers, and spreads his shops and offices all over the plains like the Nairobi of today. In Kenya, all such vast alterations of the countryside have taken place in under sixty years, but in spite of the rapidity of change, a great many of the native birds have taken kindly to man's handiwork, unlike the bigger creatures of the wild, and find in cities and gardens conditions which suit them well. They are happier perhaps in those gardens which have planned wisely to leave even a little of the native wild within their formal bounds.

Even the most casual visitor to an East African garden anywhere in the suburbs, or on an up-country farm, cannot fail to notice one of the commonest of Kenya birds, the fiscal shrike, jackie or butcher bird. (Plate 9). Given a lawn, or open space of grass, with a few convenient trees and shrubs nearby, the fiscal asks no more, and with its conspicuous black and white plumage and long tail it is as common in the civilised parts of Kenya as the robin is in England. Indeed, in many ways, it is *the* domestic bird of Kenya, and its striking individualism is parallel to that of the homely redbreast, while its behaviour is of the same classic type so well described by Lack in his *Life of the Robin.*

For some time, in the earlier part of the last World War, I became a member of the notorious N.N.N. Brigade – those elegant gaberdine soldiers who were Never North of Nairobi; to pass that somewhat dismal time, I paid a good deal of attention to the habits and ways of the fiscal, which I had frequent opportunity to watch as I passed to and fro from where I fought the war from an office desk. A perusal of the various ornithological journals published in the years following the war shows very clearly how birds and bird watching helped to pass the time so tediously spent by prisoners-of-war all over the world. Birds are no respectors of barbed wire, and their glorious freedom to come and go provided a harmless form of escapist thought, and much useful work on bird behaviour was done by those who lacked this freedom in the various P.O.W. areas. It was therefore interesting to see how the self-same fiscal shrike appealed in the same way to the more bird-minded Italians interned in Kenya as a useful and interesting subject of study to pass the time. For example, Doctor Augusto Toschi, who was taken in Addis Ababa when it fell to British troops, was interned for a time in Kenya, and later allowed to work at his own profession at the Coryndon Museum in Nairobi. He became a 'fiscal fan', and the results of his studies as an internee in Kenya of this bird were embodied in a paper which he published in an Italian scientific journal in 1950. His fascinating study of this bird was complementary to the notes I had myself collected earlier in the war, and now we know perhaps a great deal more about the fiscal shrike than about many other Kenya birds. I wonder indeed how many people who have watched this bird in their garden realise quite how intriguing its behaviour really is?

It is common knowledge that a pair of fiscal shrikes – perhaps the same pair – will occupy the same small area of garden year after year; they are always there whenever you care to look. Further, over a large area of ground the total number of these shrikes appears to be remarkably constant. As I travelled to and fro from Nairobi along the Ngong road in those anxious days, I made a point of counting all the birds I saw on the journey both morning and afternoon; for they are easy birds to count, since they are so conspicuously marked and usually perch in a high part of their territory – even from a moving car they can be readily ticked off one by one.

It would be wearisome indeed to describe here the results of this census in detail, and I will do no more than summarise the main results, which show how remarkably stable the fiscal population of an area can be. In those days (but not now with post-war development which has since taken place) the stretch of road from Karen Estate, where I lived, to the Royal Nairobi Golf Club – a distance of some six miles – could be divided into three distinct types of habitat; a portion running through a eucalyptus plantation, a portion running alongside open plains to Dagoretti Corner, and a built-up area through the residential suburbs of the town. Running alongside the road in all these areas were telephone wires which formed the favourite perch of the shrikes. During a period of some nine months, I made three hundred and six counts along the road morning and afternoon. When worked out, the figures showed a remarkable stability in number of shrikes. Firstly, it was evident that more shrikes frequented the gardens and built-up area along the road (some eight pairs of birds), than the plains area (four pairs), and both had more than the woodland area (one pair only), although all three areas were roughly equivalent in length. These findings are much in accord with what one can note from any pair of shrikes; there are two features which are essential in its territory; one a fair amount of open ground on which to catch its prey, and the other a fair number of reasonably high perches on which to sit, both for territorial display, and from which to watch out for prey. The woodland area lacked the first, and the plains area while having plenty of open short grass ground, lacked the second requisite of sufficient perching places. Gardens, with their lawns and shrubs, provide both in ample measure.

Although such regular counting from a car gives no idea of what size of territory each pair of shrikes requires, it was nevertheless remarkable how much vacant ground there seemed to be. Pairs would frequently be counted on the same perches day after day, with a wide stretch of lawn and gardens between them and the next adjacent pair, but probably closer watching of each pair would have shown that this was not really so.

Like the red-eyed dove I have described in a previous chapter, the fiscal shrike appears to take little notice of the seasons as regards nesting, and as the birds remain paired throughout the year, so the nests may be found in every month; but superimposed on this apparently haphazard nesting, there is still the rhythm of the rains shown by most other African birds, and a larger number of fledging chicks were counted in the rains of March-April and November-December than at other times. The daily counts showed that in the following months of May-June and January-March, the total number of birds nearly doubled themselves, as young birds on the wing joined their parents on the perches. Sometime later than this, these brown juvenile birds must be driven out of the parents' territory to settle themselves elsewhere; but this phase of the birds' life cycle is still a mystery to be solved, for the totals rarely increase.

Shrikes do not like rain or mist, as in such conditions they cannot see their prey which is probably in hiding anyway. Thus on bad-weather days, the daily counts were a good deal lower. Then too, it was curious to notice how the afternoon counts, made at about 4.30 p.m., were always lower than the 8 a.m. counts. This puzzled me a lot, until I had watched individual pairs elsewhere all throughout the day for several days on end; and then the explanation was obvious. The birds in their territory showed a marked and regular change of behaviour through the day, and in the mornings as the sun climbs vertically in the sky they perch high to watch for food; but as the day wears on and the sun sinks in the western sky, the birds choose perches lower in the territory, until from about 5 p.m. onwards till sunset at 6.30 p.m. they spend a great deal of the remaining daylight on the ground. I suppose that the altering incidence of light dictates this diurnal movement, and thus in the afternoon counts the birds were perching too low to be seen readily from a moving car.

Another curious thing that was evident from the daily counts was that apparently a man-made tar-macadam road acts as an efficient territorial boundary between pairs of birds on opposite sides of the road. In all the many times I travelled on this road, I practically never saw a fiscal flying across the road. The reason is again I think quite natural, since insect prey moving on the surface of a busy road must be negligible in quantity, and the birds have no cause to regard the road as a food-collecting area; for with these shrikes, unlike the whydahs described later on in this book, the territory is a well-defined food supply area as well as being the display and breeding ground.

All these sorts of observations led me to consider what a fiscal shrike does with itself all day long; and indeed it is remarkable how little we know of what any individual bird does do throughout the daylight hours. To find this out, requires prolonged, patient and often very boring hours of watching, and this (being then a bachelor) I set out to do in all my leisure hours, particularly when I could get a whole day off and could watch a selected pair from dawn to dusk. Statistical analysis of results is almost *de rigeur* amongst modern ornithologists, and no doubt I should manipulate the number of hours spent watching and the number of seconds I recorded the birds doing anything to produce a significant result; but the answer is simple enough without recourse to mathematics. The bird spends most of its time simply doing nothing, or occasionally feeding itself. Other actions of course occur from time to time as I shall show later. Although I have stated that most of the time the bird seems to do nothing, it would be more correct perhaps to describe this prolonged sitting on perches in more active terms, for it does in fact spend most of this apparently idle time in watching for food, and changing from perch to perch to do so. The shrike method of feeding is quite characteristic; it will perch for minutes on end looking at the ground, occasionally switching its tail, and as soon as it sees something move, it will pounce down and pick it up, usually flying back with the prey in its beak to the same perch, or another nearby, to eat it at leisure.

Grasshoppers are probably favourite prey, but lizards, butterflies, bugs and the larger insects of all sorts are taken. Warning colouration of the latter seems to matter little. Prey is often held against the perch by one foot; with grasshoppers the spiny legs are broken off in the beak, and butterfly wings are torn off and thrown away with a shake of the head. Usually only the succulent abdomen is eaten. Lizards are either bitten hard behind the head to kill them (a painful sort of bite as I know too well!) or thrashed to death against the perch, and then held in one foot and torn to pieces. Feeding occurs throughout all the daylight hours, as one would expect naturally enough from the nature of the food taken, since insects are active most of the time, except in rain or mist.

It is all-important that the prey should move. A shrike will ignore completely a motionless insect, but one slight movement catching the keen eyesight of the bird, and down it will come. If this fact is borne in mind, they are easy birds to trap and ring. After the war, when I was stationed at Kabete, near Nairobi, Alex, Bill and I started a large scale study of individually rung shrikes, and to catch them we used a large spring trap on a board, worked on the same principle as an ordinary mouse trap except that as the trap was sprung the hoop of wire brought over a loose bag of net in which the bird was caught. The trap was set near favourite perches, on the ground, and the trigger baited with a live grasshopper on a pin. As soon as the grasshopper waved its legs, the birds would drop down to investigate, but if it was still, the shrikes ignored it altogether. Taking the birds out of the net was a tricky game, for the shrike can nip painfully hard, but once held upside down in one hand they became quiet, and could easily be ringed. By this means we colour-ringed several dozen birds in this area, and obtained very useful results in following their subsequent life history.

Most colour rings are easy to see at a glance with glasses from a distance, though the more dull colours are of little use.

While most of the fiscal's food is taken off the ground, they will also hawk in the air just like a flycatcher if a swarm of insects passes near, but this is not usual. From all observations I have made, the Kenya fiscal is not nearly so rapacious as its related races are reported to be elsewhere on this continent. Though they will in Kenya very occasionally take young birds in the nest, and sometimes other small birds too if they can catch them, accounts of this shrike in South Africa brand it as a real butcher bird, taking canaries and other kinds of birds very frequently.

There is a related bird in England, the red-backed shrike, whose provisioning habits are almost traditional, and which makes regular larders of its prey. So too, occasional Kenya fiscals will stock a larder in their territories, using either the common jasmine bush, or the convenient barbs on a barbed wire fence. I once counted the contents of one such larder for several weeks on end. All the usual types of food were pinned, but it was curious that little if any of it was ever eaten again by the birds, who merely left the various small lizards and insects to dry and shrivel in the sun. All told, this larder habit seems a very wasteful and purposeless sort of behaviour, and it is probably a form of behaviour known as substitute activity, a not uncommon thing in birds, which show mainly a one-way reaction to most situations; when the main drive in response to a situation is thwarted in some way it finds an outlet in some form of displacement or substitute activity which is quite purposeless except to relieve inner tension. Not all fiscals in Kenya pin their excess food, and the larder habit is indeed rather rare. Another common action, which is however but rarely seen, is the casting up of pellets of indigestible insect remains such as beetle wing cases and bones of lizards, as is the habit of other birds such as owls. These pellets are quite large and hard, and require a considerable effort to bring up and though I suppose all shrikes do so at least once a day I have watched the performance on very few occasions only in spite of the many hundred hours I have spent with the birds.

Watching a pair of fiscals closely for several days on end, one begins to realise how very rigidly they keep to their own territorial bounds, some imaginary lines enclosing an area of about half an acre. Both cock and hen know the limits well and rare indeed are the occasions when they will go outside these. The boundaries are not a rigid line but are elastic and depend on the presence of neighbouring pairs, though it is puzzling sometimes how a bird will delimit its chosen area, in spite of the fact it may have no reason to do so in the absence of other shrikes in its neighbourhood. Where pairs are adjacent however, there is often a no-man's-land between which ownership may change from time to time. But the territory is not compressible below a certain limit, and unlike the affairs of man, appeasement and the cession of all rights is just not possible; reaction to a real intruder is swift and effective. It is usual in most territorial studies of birds to plot such areas by noting the limits at which aggression to neighbouring birds occurs, but with the boundary-minded fiscals there is a much easier way to plot the limits; you just chase them judiciously round and round in their territory till all the perches have been recorded, and then everything from twenty to thirty feet radius round each perch is part of their chosen home. They will seldom if ever fly outside this perimeter, and territory mapping is an easy game.

Fiscals in Kenya have only two main calls; one a long wavering whistle which appears to be related to the time of breeding, and the other the common grating call, which is used as a warning to intruders, an alarm, or a definite threat when accompanied by a switching tail and half-spread wings. But it is interesting to note that the geographical races of this bird in the various parts of Africa show variations on these two. Thus in southern Africa for example, the fiscal is said to imitate the calls of other birds, and in West Africa they have a short form of real song. As is the case with so many other widespread species, the minute but constant differences in plumage or size which constitute a race, are often accompanied by 'live' differences in behaviour or voice. The clearest case of this in Kenya is perhaps with the common yellow-vented bulbul. The race in Uganda is known as the *quick-doctor-quick* bird, for such is its monotonous but very human call; on the Kenya coast, where a different race of the same species is found, this call is never heard, nor do the east Kenya Highland races use it. But as you go over the Rift and drop down the Mau westwards to Kisumu the race there not infrequently includes a call phrase reminiscent of the Uganda bird, though not in its clear and unmistakable Uganda form; but most of the time calls with the tuneless chuckle of the eastern birds. There is a most distinct gradation.

Just how and when fiscal shrikes first pair I do not know. It is not an easy thing to watch, this first meeting of a pair, and the reactions they show in first courtship. The difference in plumage between the races is very slight, the female having small chestnut patches on her flank which cannot be seen when the wings are closed. As with most birds, recognition of sex is probably by behaviour of the hen when she meets a cock. Since a pair may remain mated for several seasons, the first formation of a new pair is rarely seen, but the behaviour of mated pairs may give a clue, though it is modified by married custom. The final consummation of a union is elicited by a crouching attitude of the hen, inviting the cock to mount, and a submissive appearance; but the union is reinforced from time to time by the ritual pair-bond ceremony of the hen begging food from the cock in the attitude of a chick, and this is frequently seen.

I have mentioned above that most of the time in the territory is spent either doing nothing or feeding; but not all the time, for next to the feeding drive in intensity comes the need to protect the territory against invasions by birds of a kind. Acts of warning, threat and active aggression take up quite a lot of time of the male in particular. For the possession, and protection of, an area which they can call their own and in which they can rear their young without undue disturbance is the premium paid by individual pairs to effect a communal insurance for the survival of the species as a whole. Just as money must be earned to pay an insurance premium in the affairs of man, so does a bird pay its premium in effort and time.

In between feeding themselves therefore, the pair, and especially the cock, keep a sharp look out for intruders in their area who might be competitive and predatory in nature. In this respect, it is therefore interesting to watch the birds' reactions to other living things and more especially other living birds, and to this end I have watched many pairs of fiscals in their territories for hours on end.

It is obviously a waste of time for them to pay any attention to other kinds of birds who cannot possibly affect their lives, and thus we find that they ignore all the following common types with which they come in daily contact; they in turn are certainly unaware of the boundaries of the fiscal territory, though they are not unaware of the fiscals themselves, for to them it is a predator in turn. Reichenow's weavers, yellow-vented bulbuls, coly, grass warblers of three different species, streaky serins and bronzy sunbirds are all birds to whom the shrikes are completely indifferent, and indeed I have on occasion found all these various kinds nesting within the bounds of a fiscal territory. Similarly too, cars, cycles, casual Africans, cattle, sheep, goats and horses are all ignored.

I have however noted them to react sharply by warning calls or aggressive threats to the following intruders on their ground: black-shouldered kite, yellow-throated long claw, redwing lark, red-tailed buzzard, white-browed coucal, boubou shrike, red-eyed dove, Jackson's whydah and stonechat, while snakes, Europeans and dogs are all also objects of alarm. Now this is a curious sort of list; one can understand reaction to the raptorial kinds and obvious predators such as the coucal and the boubou shrike, but why do they object to the other kinds? I do not know, and perhaps the answer depends on the state of the shrike under observation, for while aggressive tendencies are very marked in the early nesting and incubation stages, it wanes when chicks are in the nest and food collecting for the extra mouths is paramount. I have never been able to understand the deep enmity which seems to exist between these shrikes and larks – particularly the yellow-throated longclaw, which is always chased most unmercifully by any fiscal I have ever watched.

The longclaw does not in the least resemble a shrike and its feeding habits are quite different; admittedly it has a mewing call which slightly resembles the whistle of the shrike, and it is a perching bird, but these hardly seem to justify the inevitable attacks made upon it. I often think, from watching many fiscals, that their nature is something of that of a bullying little schoolboy, and such larks always fly away in a most satisfactory sort of way when chased! Curiously enough however, the related pipits are not attacked, nor is the African pied wagtail, in spite of the latter having black and white plumage of roughly similar appearance, and a long tail too.

If however, a common enemy appears, like a snake, the warning call of the shrike is clearly understood by all other birds, just like the more familiar *spink-spink* of the chaffinch or the scolding of a blackbird at home, and all birds will sink their differences in a communal mobbing of the foe.

The establishment of territory by a pair is very efficient, and hence boundary squabbles between neighbouring pairs of shrikes are very rare; the mutual respect which exists is seldom transgressed. This respect is built up and perhaps exists for several years, for the same patch of ground by the same pair of birds, and there is therefore not the need for frequent adjustment of boundaries so often seen amongst those other birds which pair afresh each year and stake out a claim for the short nesting season only. Most fiscal shrikes establishing a territory for the first time however seem to be able to fit into a vacant space somewhere; but another fiscal need not necessarily be a fully adult bird to be chased away if trespassing on private ground, for I have watched the male of a nesting pair chase a young shrike away which was still in the barred brown plumage of its year.

It is interesting however to see what a shrike will do to any intruder of the same species on its ground, and to this end I have made innumerable experiments setting up stuffed adult and juvenile birds in various parts of an occupied territory, and also by using painted cards to see exactly what features of another shrike really annoy the owner.

While the results of such experiments are always amusing, and sometimes instructive, I am not greatly in favour of such techniques. The whole set up is really most unnatural, and not to be compared with watching two live birds in nature. In the first place of course, the stuffed bird does not fly into the territory; he is placed there deliberately by an observer who himself introduces an unnatural element, and his actions are almost invariably seen by the bird. Secondly, the stuffed bird does not react as a live bird would, and his very 'staying-put' makes any subsequent reactions unnatural. He does not threaten back or fly away, as a live intruder would, and if he is attacked physically, he still stays there! His very immobility must be strange to a bird like a shrike, whose whole life is patterned on reaction to movement all round him. Most birds believe very strongly in the old proverb that he who fights and runs away lives to fight another day; real bird fights are extraordinarily rare, and indeed wasteful of life, and even any sort of physical contact is very uncommon.

Bird fighting is usually symbolic, by sound and vision, and he who blusters most usually wins the day; there is surely a moral here for humans too, and I suppose economy in human lives has already been achieved by a similar means.

Such experiments too must be interpreted with care, since as I have mentioned before the aggressive drive is not maintained equally throughout the year, nor indeed even throughout the nesting cycle only. It waxes and wanes according to the internal state of the bird, nor is it the same over the whole area of territory, being evinced more strongly in some areas than in others at any one time; and lastly, repetition of such a stimulus soon causes waning in reaction of the bird being tested.

With these limitations in mind however, the pattern of behaviour is usually much the same. Sometimes the stuffed bird on its perch is ignored for a while, and often it seems as if some extra little stimulus is required such as the presence of its mate before the owner's threat and attack is pushed home. Then often too, the cock in ownership is clearly in two minds what to do, and this will be expressed as an anxiety reaction, or displacement activity such as 'false feeding', so well shown by plovers when anxious by their nests.

If however, the owning male takes active notice of the stuffed bird, he threatens first with a harsh grating call from his perch, quivering half-opened wings and switching his tail slowly from side to side. This clear warning to get out is usually understood by a live bird, which then flies away; the threatening behaviour of the cock being followed by pursuit and flight of the intruder to the borders of the territory. But our poor stuffed bird can do no such thing, and sits there motionless inviting attack. The pursuit-flight reaction to an intruder's escape therefore gives place to an actual physical attack instead, which is carried out by the owner cock either on the wing or actually standing on the dummy's back. The attack is a really vicious exhibition of striking at the nape of the neck – the most vital part; though other focal points of attack are the eyes and the base of the tail, which are severely pecked till the feathers fly. The stuffed bird cannot strike back, so the whole situation becomes a farce, and the cock soon desists. He may perhaps return to the attack a short while later, even if the dummy is by then hanging upside down, but it is interesting to note, as I have done in repeated trials, that the dummy whatever its actual position must be on a perch above ground level. A dummy on the ground means not a thing, and is completely ignored even by a most aggressive bird.

Sometimes a cock will posture before the stuffed bird, crouching before it with erected tail, or standing vertically before it, but such is rare. It is immaterial whether the dummy is a male or female; the chestnut flank patches of the latter are apparently meaningless without the behaviour reaction of a live bird which goes with them. Cocks are always more aggressive than hens, though I have one or two records of the latter showing aggressive action, but never to the point of physical attack. I have not been able to determine which part of a shrike annoys another shrike; its plumage does not appear to be reaction specific as in the case of the robin whose red breast, according to Lack, is the main source of grievance to another robin.

Experiments with cards painted in various ways to emphasise or minimise plumage pattern I found of little use, although they clearly interested the birds I tested, all of whom showed full aggression to a dummy. The only thing which seemed to produce a reaction was a stimulus of 'something like another shrike, sitting on a perch'. Very rarely, if the owner of the territory was in that fleeting mood, a stuffed bird would elicit a mating reaction – a mounting by the male, and a crouching solicitation by a hen. But such were most temporary, and in most respects abnormal to watch, once the live bird realised that the stuffed dummy would not play the game.

Now it is interesting to note that the artificially evoked reaction could only be elicited in a very small portion of the whole territorial area; stuffed birds placed near the boundaries would generally be ignored; but watch a live shrike come over the boundary anywhere, and he will be driven off. This spatial difference in intensity of reaction is, I am sure, due to the movements of a natural stimulus (a live intruder) as opposed to the stiff and unnatural immobility of a dummy. There was another curious result of these experiments also. While a stuffed shrike perched within a few feet of the nest would usually evoke some sort of threat or attack, yet if the same dummy was placed actually on the nest itself, its presence would be completely ignored by the pair at the nest, who would fly to the nest and feed the chicks normally as if the dummy was not there at all; but move it away from the nest again, and it was once more attacked.

As mentioned before, once a bird embarks on a certain line of action, it does not seem to be able to alter its course as it were, and either goes through with it to normal completion, or else shows some completely inappropriate false reaction on which it expends its pent-up drive if normal completion is thwarted. This is a well known fact of bird behaviour which has been studied in many different kinds. Birds too, usually react in the appropriate way to the various situation patterns confronting them in what seems to be a rather automatic fashion, and often senseless in nature to our way of thinking; thus eggs, or any round hard thing of similar size will cause them to go through the motions of brooding, if in a broody state. The gaping mouths of chicks, or an artificial mouth in the nest, will cause them to stuff these cavities with food. Pellets of excrement, or plasticine of the same size will cause the 'pick-up and carry away' reaction if placed at the side of the nest, and so on. There is seldom room in a bird's mind to do two things at once, and little intelligent thought as we know it. If confronted by two situations requiring action, one situation becomes dominant over the other, and this is clearly what happens when a stuffed bird is placed at the nest. Once at the nest, the shrike is confronted by two things requiring action; one is the chick's

Masai waxbill at nest, 'Cock's' nest above true nest, Kabete 1946

PLATE 12

gaping mouths requiring to be stuffed with food, the other the stuffed bird whose presence has annoyed elsewhere. In this case the chicks waggling their feeble heads is a powerful moving stimulus to one line of action, so they are fed and the other alternative is ignored. But away from the nest itself, the bird is not distracted by the presence of the chicks, and the attack reaction can go on uninhibited. The nest and its contents induce nest-behaviour only, and there is not room to worry about anything else in the bird's one-track mind.

Once the chicks have left the nest, the area round about ceases to be of such importance to the parents, and in places near the nest where previously a stuffed bird caused violent tumult, aggressive tendencies wane and die away. It is interesting to get even a glimpse of what the chick's mind-world is like, and though I cannot emulate the brilliant exposition of the herring gull's chick world given by Dr Tinbergen, yet a few observations of shrike chicks may be of value as we follow their growth.

For a few days after hatching, until their eyes first open, the chicks are rather helpless, automatic little creatures; but even in this naked bulbous-headed stage they can respond in two quite definite ways to two important stimuli. The quezzing warning call of the adult bird conveys its message clearly to the feeble-minded little chicks, and they respond instantly by crouching low in the nest from the day after birth as soon as they hear this note; this is clearly not learnt, but inborn. Secondly the begging for food, wagging their top-heavy little heads on their scrawny necks is an almost immediate reaction to a gentle touch on the branches at the side of the nest; it is the vibration to which they respond, since almost any bird or artificial *slight* movement of the twigs around will cause this begging. This is clearly a dangerous reaction, for such movement may be due to a predator, and here the utter dependence of the chick on the presence of its parents in the territory is emphasised, for they can give warning by call that such movement is not due to them, and the chicks' reaction switches instantaneously to a passive crouching, for even with sharp-eyed predators immobility pays; the predators respond to movement of their prey.

The adult at the nest responds to the row of gaping beaks by stuffing them with food it has brought, and this again is a very automatic response, which explains those instances sometimes recorded of adults of one kind of bird feeding the chicks of another, and so beautifully photographed by Richard Kearton long ago in the case of a missel thrush feeding a brood of robins in their nest nearby. The sight of gaping mouths and wagging heads, perhaps *en route* to its own nest, will cause a bird to fill the beaks, even though the chicks are not her own. It is a curious thing however, that in spite of this apparently automatic reaction, adult birds, not only shrikes, but other kinds too that I have watched, appear to be able to distinguish which chick was fed last. I have watched this point most carefully, and it appears to be nothing to do with more vigorous begging by the unfed chick, and I cannot explain how it is done. But one must be careful here, for this apparent selection of which chick to feed applies, I suspect, only to those birds whose eggs hatch almost simultaneously; in other words to those birds who do not commence brooding until the last egg is laid. In others, such as herons and most of the raptorial birds, the parent commences incubation from the laying of the first egg, with the result the eggs hatch asynchronously, and the chicks may be of widely varying sizes. This is especially noticeable in owls, and it has recently been suggested that such asynchronous hatching and differential growth of the chicks may in fact be a survival mechanism in such birds whose larger prey such as fish, frogs or rodents vary in abundance at nesting time due to climatic or biological conditions. In such cases, the chicks are fed 'first come, first served', the larger chicks getting the lion's share, and hence becoming more vigorous still, while the smaller chicks get what is left, if any, when their larger brothers and sisters are satisfied. If food is scarce, then the younger and weaker chicks die, and ensure by their death the more certain survival of the stronger; a ruthless, but efficient method. But a good deal more attention should be paid to this point in the two types of birds.

The shrike chicks will try to swallow almost anything that is placed within their gape, but with one pair of fiscals I watched, I noted a very remarkable thing. The grasshoppers and crickets which the parents brought often proved too large or too hard for the chicks to swallow at one go; having tried once, the parents removed it from the chick's beak, pinned it on a convenient thorn, and 'chewed' it hard before re-offering it to the chick. This was done, not once, but several times, and it causes one to wonder somewhat whether a bird's world is quite so automatic or instinctive as many behaviourists believe.

As with many other species of birds, notably the plovers and waders, the parent shrikes have a special tongue in which they speak to their chicks alone, and this has clearly a reassuring function which the chicks well understand. One day, with a particularly bold pair of birds, I several times removed the chicks from the nest and held them in my hand in full sight of the parent birds a foot or so away. As soon as I handled the chicks, the parents swore at me good and hard with their harsh grating call, and at close quarters their wide open pinky gape was somewhat startling in its sudden appearance. The insides of birds' mouths are often brightly coloured and used for just such warning and display effects as Armstrong has pointed out; ornamentation of chicks' mouths with coloured spots and tubercles is alleged to be a guide to the parent where to place the food, but may have a warning function too to predators reaching the nest unawares.

The chicks immediately responded by cowering in my hands, but at a later date when fully fledged, tried to escape. As soon as I replaced them in the nest however, the note of the parents changed to a softer, more sibilant tone as the birds looked at the chicks and not me, and the chicks on hearing this note sat quietly in the nest without cowering down.

Once their eyes open, and the quills begin to split, the world of the chick enlarges greatly, and eyesight begins to play an important part in its reactions to the world around. They begin to pay a good deal of attention to movement in particular, and flies buzzing round the nest are a great source of interest and perhaps even play. They follow the flight of an insect near the nest with close attention, and their efforts to catch it are often comical in the extreme, since their judgment of distance is still very poor. But it is all good training.

Then too, as they grow, their reactions change and instead

of waiting for the nest to quiver before begging food in the infantile automatic way, they use their new found vision to watch for the approach of the parent, and their pattern perception becomes much more acute, being clearly split into two components – the movement of the pattern, and the pattern itself. Thus the flight of the adult bird begins to possess food valence, and the chicks will respond by begging as soon as they see the parent shrike flying towards them perhaps some ten to twenty feet away; but – and this is the interesting point – they will show interest in, but not a begging response to, the flight of other kinds of birds at the same distance and in the same direction. The flight of a black and white shrike is conspicuous and presents a bold, typical pattern even to a human observer; how much more so to the acute perception of a chick with which it is early associated with a subsequent giving of food. But movement alone is not sufficient; it must be black and white movement.

This visual stimulus to food-begging does not, even at a late fledging date, entirely supersede the earlier interpretation of vibration near the nest. For in one nest which I watched, in which both chicks were well fledged, one left the nest one day and clambered on to the branches above. Every time it moved, and shook the nest, the chick remaining in the nest begged food from it, although its eyes were wide open and it could clearly see the source of the shake was not the black and white adult.

When however, the chicks have left the nest, and are well out in the territory, the flight of an adult to the ground possesses the highest food value for the chick, and squeaking and begging start the moment the adult takes off and continues even if the parent goes out of sight, until it returns. At the same time, though, now that the chicks themselves are mobile, the movement of the parent is now perhaps not quite so important as its appearance, and the chicks will start responding to a motionless black and white pattern on a perch, and will fly up and beg from a stuffed bird. Their hormones are still too juvenile and insufficient to elicit any form of aggression. On the whole however, it is clear that the pattern of 'shrike in movement' is much more potent than 'shrike on a perch', and they will cease begging from the stuffed dummy as soon as they see their real live parents flying, and transfer their attentions to them once more. I have noted that they will start begging from a dummy anywhere near them at thirteen days after leaving the nest.

Twenty days out of the nest, the chicks learn one stage more, and will begin to follow their parents to the ground for food, although they do not learn to catch prey for themselves for a few weeks more yet; but they obviously learn by example of the parents how it should be done, and this technique is taught and not instinctive.

It is a remarkable thing how soon the chicks start to preen themselves in the nest, as early as a week or so after hatching, and the toilet of the nest by both chicks and adults is scrupulous. The chicks defaecate immediately on being fed, and the parents often pull the excreta from the cloaca as soon as the chick lifts its behind. This sac is usually carried away and dropped, seldom being swallowed by the parent as is the case with some other passerine birds.

As soon as the chicks are big enough to co-ordinate their movements in the nest, they start lifting their stumpy behind over the edge of the nest and defaecating well outside as many raptorial chicks will do, but the excreta is enclosed in a mucus sac and not liquid as in the latter, hence there is little mess even if the sac is not immediately cleared away by the parent. The sight of this sac usually produces another almost automatic response on the part of the parent in picking it up, and I was amused one day to watch one parent shrike carry out one of those nonsensical reactions so often shown by birds. A chick had lifted its tail over the edge of the nest as usual, and the parent on the nest flew down and caught the sac in mid-air and carried it off. There was not the least chance it would have soiled the nest. There is possibly more to it than mere sanitation however, for white excreta are always conspicuous, and fouling of the nest surroundings draws attention to its presence, as it so often does with raptorial nests. The latter however are not always accessible, whereas a shrike's nest usually is, and the apparent sanitary precautions taken by the parents have a survival value also.

The chicks will start waving their stumpy tails soon after leaving the nest, but the area in which they move is often considerably less than the adults' territory, the boundaries of which seem to mean little to the brood. They leave the adult territory long before they have acquired adult plumage, but how and when it is done I do not know. This phase of their life cycle is still one unsolved mystery. I suspect post-nest mortality is high, and the brown plumaged chicks seem very scarce on the whole at the close of a nesting cycle.

There is still a great deal of most interesting work to be done on the behaviour of the chicks themselves, and to trace their reactive behaviour as it develops to the full adult pattern, and to discover the way in which a young bird begins to distinguish these features of its environment which mean so much to the adult bird. Some is instinctive, some is undoubtedly learnt, and Konrad Lorenz has already pioneered the way in this fascinating field.

A study of bird behaviour can never be complete, and day after day watching of a single kind of common garden bird alone will still produce surprises. I remember a curious incident which happened one day with a pair of fiscal shrikes whose nest I had been watching closely for several hours a day for several days on end. The normal clutch of eggs is two or three, rarely four. This nest had three; one chick had hatched and five days later it was clear that the two remaining eggs were addled and would never hatch, so I kept a very close eye on the bird. One morning, the behaviour of the hen seemed rather restless and abnormal in so far that on each visit she hopped round the nest for several minutes at a time, without attending to the chick, and occasionally poked at the remaining eggs as if somewhat puzzled and undecided. On one visit, after a time, the hen suddenly picked a dead brown leaf off a twig about six inches from the nest and flew off with it. This leaf was in no way obstructing the nest, and appeared the same as numerous others round about and equally available. But this purposeless action seemed to set the right train of reaction off in her mind, and after a short while she returned to the nest, raked around in the bottom, picked up one of the addled eggs in her beak and flew off with it. Meanwhile the cock returned and fed the chick, and in a few seconds the hen returned also and without hesitation, in a quite purposeful manner, raked again in the bottom of the nest, picked up the second egg and flew off with it too. What she did with them I could not see.

Now there are all sorts of curious implications in interpreting such behaviour, such as an appreciation of the fact that the eggs were now useless, or in the way; that there were two of them, since the second removal was most unhesitatingly made, and one could not deny that the second visit was for that very reason, and so on. Her earlier behaviour suggested a curious unsettled state of mind, and why the eggs should have been removed on this particular day, some five days after the chick had hatched, I cannot say. Often if eggs are all addled, a bird may go on brooding long after they are due to hatch till the urge wanes; but once an egg hatches, the living chick induces a different form of behaviour, and the eggs no longer exert their spell.

Removal of normally hatched egg shells is of course almost universal, probably both for sanitary and survival reasons, as with excreta sacs, and for twenty-four hours or so after hatching, sight of a broken egg shell causes an immediate pick-up reaction; but after that time it is ignored. So automatic is this reaction, that I once very unkindly caused a particularly tame ringed plover on the west coast of Scotland to think she must have hatched out at least ten chicks. Owing to a series of disasters due to sheep and unsure placing of her nest, she hatched only one egg remaining out of her normal clutch of four, and I was watching from a hide as it hatched. The empty egg shell was at once picked up and carried a short distance away, one half at a time. Wishing to get a good picture of this event, I replaced one half again near the chick and she repeated the performance; she did this about ten times, one after another; but the next day she ignored the empty shell again placed by the chick. It is one of those actions which is repeated at only a very brief phase of the nesting cycle.

Bird watching at the nest is full of such little incidents, and the interpretation of their meaning in modern terms is not easy always. One must steer a middle course between the purely mechanistic and purely animistic or perhaps even anthropocentric explanations. With the shrikes, as with all other birds, the cycle of life and its behaviour adaptations is complex; even with these I know as yet so little of their courting, nest building and future of the chicks, but with patient watching every now and then some little act clicks into its proper place and gives the clue to the whole behaviour sequence.

CHAPTER 3

THE WILDER GARDEN

I KNOW ONLY too well that I myself have always been too restless to follow out for long the study of one particular bird. Africa is always new and bewildering in its variety, and I envy those who have had the ability to detach themselves from the general whole and concentrate only on one particular aspect – perhaps a special group of birds or one special feature of behaviour such as song. I suppose I should have carried on for many years the studies I have described in the previous chapter and the subsequent one on the dancing whydah, but variety of occupation, time and place have always appealed far more to me, and I tend to skim the cream and leave the milk. A failing – yes, I admit it – but one that has given few pangs of conscience so far. In Africa there always seem to be other birds waiting to be watched, and in the garden where I stayed near Nairobi a good few years ago, there was an abundant surfeit of other birds to study. Being new to Kenya, I was bewildered at first at the vast variety and scarce knew where to start.

It was a very typical Kenya garden, part of it in the formal English tradition, but part was still left in a natural wild state, with a little bit of scrub, some open grass, and a lovely patch of untouched forest. This wilder garden always attracted both me and the birds, and so we met on common ground.

One of the most frequent residents of such a garden is the fiscal's cousin, the pied or boubou shrike; black and white too like its relation, its habits are however very different, and it prefers to creep about in the thicker bushes, picking its insect food as it goes, and not perch and watch. It is indeed not so often seen, but is frequently heard and is the author of the most amazing duetting calls so common in Kenya gardens. The male will call to his mate, and she will answer in such perfect time that it is often hard to believe it is not one bird alone. They have a wide range of notes, and I have filled pages of my note-books with phonetic interpretations; but in cold print these look soulless and indeed meaningless to those who have never heard them in the field. Some of the notes are most musical, others a peculiar grate or hissing squeak, and a wooden *tok-tok* note is often interspersed with these; but all of them have a curiously unbirdlike quality about them which is quite indescribable.

I have watched several pairs at the nest at one time or another and found them confiding birds, though they skulk about low down in the bushes a great deal, and a musical deep-toned *poop* nearby is often the first indication they are returning to the nest. Their young are fed mainly on soft caterpillars which are pulled off the leaves as the parent creeps about – a very different feeding habit to the fiscal. But they too, are most inveterate destroyers of eggs and chicks, and many a promising subject has been ruined for me by the attentions of these boubou shrikes.

The big and clumsy white-browed coucal too, is a menace to young birds in the nest, and is the author of another curious noise so often heard in Kenya, which resembles water pouring out of a gourd; hence its popular name of water bottle bird.

By many of the settlers in this Colony, this bird, together with the boubou shrike and the solitary red-chested cuckoo with its unmistakable three-note whistle, is one included under the collective name of rain-bird whose call heralds the onset of the always welcome rain. As far as I can judge, nearly every settler has his own especial sort of rain-bird, but by listening to the calls of all, I have always found them to be one or other of the three kinds mentioned above. Their calls are usually mating calls, and since all these breed whenever the rains commence, like all wild things they react almost instantaneously to the first few showers which start them off. Hence I think their supposed ability to supersede the Meteorological Department. They respond to the slightest sprinkle, which is not counted as rain anyway, but I am not at all sure that they will call constantly without this slight stimulus first, and encouragement later!

These coucals are commonly seen on roadsides in Kenya, particularly the blue-headed coucal – which of course has a jet-black head – which frequents the more marshy places; their heavy flopping flight and long black unwieldy tail are characteristic sights to the traveller on highland roads. They seem loth to take wing, and flop heavily into the nearest bush when disturbed, and there they skulk about in the thickest vegetation.

I have a special affection for these scoundrels, for the white-browed variety was the first bird I ever photographed in Kenya at the nest. A pair made their great untidy ball of grass nest in a thick bush at the bottom of the garden, and I soon had a hide nearby when the five white eggs hatched. Here too, I had one of my most unpleasant frights in this land of surprises, for the very first time I went to sit in the hide, I noticed in the nick of time that it was already occupied by a nasty looking four foot puff-adder – the first African snake I had seen, and for which 'loathsome' is the only really descriptive word. We despatched him with a shot-gun, for they are sluggish reptiles, and hence the more dangerous since they are so easily trodden on, and very venomous. The very next day, the same thing happened again, and there was his mate all coiled up just where I was going to put my feet in the hide. She was wiped out too, but in all my subsequent sessions in that hide I had a prickly tingling in my scalp at any rustle in the long grass all round.

At close quarters, the coucals are really rather handsome birds, with a striking large and luminous red eye. I was thrilled to the core when the big creature flopped back to the nest within ten minutes of my first settling in, with a small white tree-frog in its beak. (Plate 10). It waddled to the domed nest, poked its head in and fed the chicks. Then rain stopped play.

On subsequent visits both birds came to the nest at about twenty-minute intervals; the male arrived at the front of the nest, the female from behind. They did not go far for food, and brought only one item at a time, usually something quite enormous in the way of green or grey caterpillars, beetles or very big grasshoppers; whether these were ever apportioned between the chicks I could not see, and how a chick ever managed to swallow them I do not know. The chicks are jet-black skinned, astonishingly reptilian sort of creatures, with a prominent broad flaplike tongue, and they hissed like snakes while the adults have a deep grunt while at the nest.

The whole time I watched at the nest, they were well behaved and I never recorded them as bringing another bird as food, but another person who occupied the hide one day watched the hen bring a naked chick from some other nest, and once a lizard. When handled, the habits of the chicks leave a lot to be desired; they will void a nasty black liquid excrement all over one's hands, unlike the clean white pellets of smaller birds. How this domed ball of a nest is kept sanitary I do not know.

The bushes at the bottom of that garden were full that year of all sorts of birds nesting. The weather had been kind, and heavy rain all through March and April had started nesting off in full swing. Very close by the coucal's nest, there was a yellow flycatcher's nest, an untidy little cup in a low bush. They are dainty little birds with a short sweet song, but this pair was one of the few birds which have had me completely defeated; though I tried them several times they would not return to the nest, and the same species again defeated me several years later with a pair in another area; though not at all striking in appearance, they would be quite a photographer's prize, for there is something odd in their extreme shyness.

I nearly had to admit defeat that first year in Kenya too at the wings of a pair of Falkenstein's sunbirds who also nested in a bush nearby, their hanging porched nest only a few feet off the ground at the end of a long thin twig. The male objected strongly to the hide, and kicked up a fearful row the whole time I was in it, though after a time his more sober mate refused to be put off and quietly fed the chicks repeatedly. Although I tried all sorts of ways to get her to pose for just one instant, instead of sticking her head into the nest, she would look everywhere except at the hide, and the only thing which disturbed the even tenor of her ways was the arrival of a boubou shrike in the bush above; this set them both off in a chattering scolding rage. Later on, the cock thought better of his bad behaviour, and within a short time both birds were feeding the chicks at the incredible rate of twenty-four times an hour, and became so oblivious to the hide and myself that I could actually get out and move around without upsetting them in the least. This gradual winning of a wild bird's confidence holds an infinite charm for me, and I rarely start photographing them till they have reached this stage.

The little scrubby clusters of bushes one so often sees in the Kenya highlands are beloved of birds. There is one bush in particular, a thorny solanum whose yellow tomato-like fruits have recently become notorious as items of ritual used in the revolting Mau Mau oath-taking ceremonies; but it is a bush dearly beloved by that supreme architect amongst Kenya nest-builders, a bird which goes under the cumbersome name of the tawny-flanked longtail. But it is far better known by its more descriptive name of tailor bird, for it is indeed a tailor of distinction and the way it sews two or three of the solanum leaves together to cover its deep and cushiony nest is a work of art. I used to find a good many nests of this bird in this garden, and it is a lovely, lively little creature, related in its ways to the great African family of grass warblers. The nest resembles the downy, domed cup of the latter, and the leaves sewn on the outside are an artistic and yet most practical addition, since they make the nest itself most hard to see. I do not know how the stitching is actually done, and there is scope here for some original observations.

The first birds of this species to which I introduced my hide were shy, but I did not at that time have a proper canvas hide, which was in use elsewhere, and the rough shelter of brushwood and weed soon withered in the hot sun, and did little to conceal my essential movements. Shortly after I found another pair with three chicks about four days old, and after some sharp and noisy protests when I first settled in a hide nearby, sitting on top of it and scolding me with a sharp *chi-chi* note, they soon forgot me and returned to the duty of the day.

With all the many birds which I have watched at close quarters, I have rarely seen such an industrious and busy little pair as these, nor chicks which have been stuffed with food at such a rate – no less than twice every minute for the first half hour. The chicks had a tremendously varied diet of small green caterpillars, large brown ones, and huge beakfuls of small insects and lacewing flies, all of which were collected within a few feet of the nest itself. As a revelation of the wealth of African insect life in the rains it astonished me. At first each bird announced its arrival with a chattering note, but as the pace increased, they either had no time to call or were out of breath as one after another they silently and quickly fed the brood; in spite of the frequency, the visits of cock and hen coincided only once – as usual at a time when I was not ready.

I was interested to see however, that occasionally one bird would slacken the pace, and take time off to hang upside down on a stalk by the nest and poke at the outer lining from underneath. This is a common habit amongst these birds which nest low down, and I imagine must be to clear away possible marauding ants.

Like the longtail, the singing grass warbler also tailors its nest to a certain extent, and seems to use a silk from moth cocoons; but it is not so expert as the longtail, and not so partial to solanum bushes. It is common too, in many Nairobi gardens, and is conspicuous as it perches on the tops of bushes, flirting its tail and calling with a ringing *wee-tit* note. Like the longtail too, it is a confiding little creature at the nest, but like all such quick moving little birds, it is hard to get really good pictures of it. It is very restless and flicks its tail the whole time. I recall with amusement one very tame little pair I once watched who had tiny little new hatched chicks. The hen therefore spent a good deal of time brooding them, and in the small domed ball of a nest there is little room for a tail; so she folded it over her back and sat facing the entrance with her tail actually resting on her head. As I spoke to her in a low voice – as I often do with birds at the nest – each time she heard me she acknowledged the fact by raising her head feathers up and down, thus pushing her tail up and down, as if taking off a hat. The effect was extremely comical.

Writing of tails calls to mind another bird whose nest we were lucky to find down the drive, where natural forest trees had not been cleared; this was the black-collared forest warbler. Its tail is indeed a most extraordinary thing – not in appearance since it is quite a normal sort of long thin warbler tail – but in what the bird can make it do. It holds it well cocked up, but instead of wagging it up and down like an ordinary sort of bird, it wags it from side to side. The effect as the bird works its way through forest twigs, hanging upside down and poking here and there, is quite astonishing to watch.

What is more, as far as I have been able to make out it rarely if ever builds a nest of its own, but appropriates some other kind usually of the hanging gourd type like a sunbird's. This one we found was in an old sunbird's nest, built of grey and yellow lichen and fairly high up in a thin tree. Not an easy place to be sure, but we managed to rig some sort of hide in a tree nearby, although we were unable to get high enough to eliminate having the sky as a background. I was somewhat fearful of the safety of the chicks, since the old nest seemed to be in a most decrepit stage, with holes all round. This did not seem to worry the birds in the least, and no repairs were ever carried out.

As is so often the case, the female proved to be the bolder of the two, and fed the chicks with great regularity. These warblers are delicate, dainty little birds, and the food that they brought was in keeping too – the minutest of little black caterpillars, and once a little round thing which looked like a seed, but was probably a cocoon. Away from the nest, the male put a bold face on things, and swung through the twigs almost overbalancing himself as his tail wagged to and fro; but when he got near the nest, he meekly handed the food he had brought to the hen, who completed the perilous approach and fed the chicks in turn.

Somehow they reminded me greatly of the long-tailed tit of southern England; but at close quarters, their lovely hazel coloured iris is a striking feature. No museum specimen can ever convey the life and sparkle in the wonderful eyes of wild birds. By contrast, another odd garden bird which differs in having hardly any tail at all is the crombec, which when you think of it is an odd name too. We used to see them in our garden, around the forest edge, and they behave rather like the British tree-creeper, creeping about on the limbs and continually poking into crevices. Birds which do this sort of thing, like tree-creepers and woodpeckers usually have quite noticeable stiffish tails which they use as a prop – but not the crombec. He seems to manage quite well without. Nor is its nest anything like what one would expect. It builds in creepers, or on the outmost twigs of a bush, and the nest is a peculiar sort of hanging cup, without a top, rather like a sunbird's nest cut in half.

The nest is patched all over with dead leaves, and looks exactly like a bunch of nondescript rubbish hanging down, a most effective camouflage. The nest is also deep, and when the bird is sitting, it appears to sit on its almost non-existent tail, with beak pointing straight up in the air, a curious sight. I was never able to watch the birds from a hide at the nest, for with the two I did find, the birds had built cleverly but not well. They both fell down in heavy rain, and although I tied them up again the birds deserted.

Once you are actually out of bed, getting up early in the morning anywhere in Kenya is a most repaying affair. The air is cool and fresh, and as the sun rises the cloud banks are shot with pink and gold, the tired leaves of the day before seem to shake themselves afresh and everything is vitally alive in this cool dawning hour. Those who say that birds in Kenya never sing, never get up early enough. That still hour of dawn is the time to hear the finest songster of all, a common bird in Kenya gardens known as the white-browed robin chat. This early morning song rivals that of the blackbird at home; but he is a temperamental artist, for he will sing only in that early hour, and perhaps for just a few minutes again as the sun goes down and twilight peace descends. Throughout the hot and sunny day, all you will hear from him is a most monotonous three-toned whistle.

The white-browed and the black-tailed robin chat are not easy to distinguish in the field unless you look carefully at the two centre tail feathers as the bird is flushed. The latter has much darker webbing on the shafts. A third species, the ordinary robin chat, is frequently seen in gardens, and like its white-browed cousin it frequents more open bushes and hedges than the black-browed bird which haunts the dark undergrowth of the forest floor much more. The ordinary robin chat is quite different in plumage too, for it has a grey belly with only a rufous bib, the other two are completely rufous underneath.

All three kinds sing, but the white-browed is the finest of the

Stone curlew approaching eggs, Watamu 1953

lot. In addition to its own sweet rich song, it is a wonderful mimic too. One bird I heard singing late in the evening in the Kericho area, in addition to its own deep melodious notes, interspersed these with a perfect imitation of chuckling bulbuls, the characteristic call of the emerald cuckoo, the curious antiphonic whistling used by Africans, and to crown it all, a magnificent rendering of ourselves whistling our own black labrador to heel. An amazing performance.

Any domestic sort of bird with a red breast is liable to be called a robin by nostalgic Europeans wherever they are, even though that may be the only resemblance. These robin chats are no exception, but their nests indeed are not unlike the neat cup of our own robin; but they are usually built in bushes, and not in banks, jampots or the gardener's old coat left hanging up. They are rarely more than ten feet from the ground, but nearly always in fairly dark bushes or hedges. Without a flash, I have never been able to get a good picture of the bird at the nest, but in spite of this I watched once with great pleasure at close quarters a pair who had nested in the depths of a thick cypress hedge.

Their behaviour was typically chat-like, and they were tame and confiding. The hen bird returned within a very few minutes of my hiding up, and fed the chicks most deliberately on fat white carabid beetle larvae, pushing the juicy food well down the chicks' throats. After each visit, she dug deep into the nest with her bill and worried and tugged at something, but I could not see what was annoying her. The cock, who was in much finer plumage than his careworn mate, was a good deal more circumspect at first, and approached the nest with caution, with occasional uneasy flips and a deliberate slow cocking of his tail, just as a robin will do. After a while, the hen decided to brood the chicks, and as she sat, the cock came back several times more. The sitting hen, on his arrival, would tilt up her head, open her beak and shiver her wings like a chick begging for food, at which the cock would gravely pass the food he had brought over to her, in that gracious pair-bond ceremony so often shown by married birds. The hen held the offering for a second or two, then bent her head down and gave it to the chicks under her, the cock standing the while on the edge of the nest and looking approvingly on. Of such is the intimate charm of being alone with birds.

I was amused once however, to see the cock, who clearly considered that the hen had held the food he had passed over for quite long enough, take the grub back again and feed it to the chicks himself. Twice too, when she was sitting, the cock called her off with a few liquid low notes from a bush to the right, and when she had slipped off, came to the nest himself and fed the chicks; but he never brooded them himself. They were completely undisturbed by people moving in the next-door garden, and that whole Sunday morning remains in my mind as one of the most quietly satisfying I have ever spent.

As at our later Nyeri home, all through the hot days, the wood was quiet at the bottom of the garden with no song at all; but one of the few birds which can be heard in these burning hours are the forest bulbuls – several different kinds of them – whose monotonous chuckling calls can be heard most of the day. Some are called greenbuls and some bulbuls, but they are all alike in being birds of the deep tangled undergrowth and forest floor. All one often sees of them is an indistinct flash of olive-green as they skulk among the leaves.

The Kenya highlands olive bulbul, or as I prefer to call it, the red-tailed bulbul, is a common bird in the wilder garden and is an inveterate chuckler throughout the day. Their nests are flimsy cups in a branching tree fork a few feet off the ground, but are not easy to see, since they are usually patched too with dead leaves and look like a tired and dusty tangle of débris over which the forest spiders have spun their webs.

One bird with chicks which I photographed was ridiculously tame – so much so in fact that I could actually lift her off the nest, and the more the tree shook, the tighter she sat. This excessive boldness was however rather odd, and was shown only at the nest itself; when she left to collect food for the chicks, outside a range of perhaps two feet from the nest she was shy and very hesitant in coming back. She fed the chicks on a single fat green caterpillar each time she came, and I reflected what an enormous destruction of caterpillars there must be at nesting time; they are perhaps the commonest food of all insect-eating birds who hunt for food in bushes and trees.

Unlike the robin chats, they never came to the nest together, one leaving before the other arrived. Once when the female had left the nest she flew straight at the hide and perched within a foot of the lens – a very embarrassing position, as I was perched on the top of a very rickety step ladder. She inspected both me and the camera very closely, but as I did not even bat an eyelid under this scrutiny she was soon satisfied that we were quite harmless and returned to the nest, and I breathed again.

Like many other birds, I noticed that the cock called the hen off the nest, with a low chuckling note when a few feet away. Sometimes they collected food from the ground just at the foot of the tree, turning over leaves to do so; once they had found a juicy caterpillar, they thrashed it against the nearest branch. I have marvelled that a small chick does not bring up all its last meals when the parent tries to stuff its throat again; several times these birds brought a caterpillar so big that they had to try several times to stuff it into the already overfull chick, who was then usually left gagged and helpless with a fat tail hanging out of his beak which he simply could not swallow, while his parents went off to look for still more. It is extraordinary too how selfless most birds collecting food for their chicks seem to be; there is seldom any indication of 'by Jove, I really must have this really luscious one for myself' to be swallowed surreptitiously with a guilty look. Often however with this pair I did note that they would take food out of one chick's beak and stuff it down the other if the first really could not cope. Once they brought a small white moth, which was also thrashed to break its wings; but caterpillars were the usual diet, and the cock seemed to be much more successful at finding these than the hen.

The hen of another pair who had a nest with chicks nearby, was the only bird in Kenya, other than a plover, who had tried to lure me away from her nest with the 'broken-wing' trick. As I approached, she fell helplessly out of the nest and fluttered and struggled through the twigs, and hardened as I am to the wiles of birds it was so unexpected in a bird of this kind that only her chuckle of triumph as she flew away showed what a fool I had been in trying to catch her as she fell! This form of distraction display is indeed rather uncommon in passerine birds, and one wonders how it is that perhaps only one individual of a kind will behave thus and none of its relatives ever give any indication of being able to do so.

Photographing in the dappled light and shade of forest trees is usually a hopeless proposition in the strong equatorial sun and my results were no exception. They were uniformly bad. In full sunlight I am not sure that it is not worse. Not far away I found a very open nest of the much more common yellow-vented bulbul, the 'toppie' so frequently seen in cultivated land. The incredibly ugly name of geelgat has also been coined for this bird, but it is a shame to inflict such a name on a really pleasant little bird whose cheerful presence enlivens many a bird table and garden, even though it may be a pest to fruit growers.

Anyway, this nest, like so many of its kind, was full open to the blazing midday sun, which caused acute discomfort to the chicks when the parent was away food collecting. When at the nest, she shaded them with outspread wings, while squatting, but their restless heaving under her soon sent her off again. She was so tame that I used no hide at all, and stood in full view the whole time, but the photographs I took were again very bad indeed, with burnt out highlights where the sun glossed her plumage and clear spaces in the shadows from the harsh vertical sun. As the sun climbed in the sky it became hotter and hotter, so I picked a large green leaf and placed it over the chicks for shade. She made no effort to remove the leaf at all, but clearly knew the chicks were underneath, for she occasionally lifted one corner to keek at them. It was a most odd sight.

No garden in Kenya is complete without a pair or two of the dainty little white-eyes who somehow seem to take the place of the tits at home as garden birds. They are lovely little birds, their large white eye rings giving them a quaint air of surprise the whole time, and their trilling little calls can be heard all day long as they hunt for insects in the trees.

Their nest is in keeping with their ways, and is a masterpiece of neatness made of lichens, moss and hairs slung like a little hammock in a fork, in which are laid two eggs only of a beautiful hedgesparrow blue, but very long and oval. We used to find their nests frequently in the forest trees, but many of them were too high to be of much use photographically; but with one, I tied down the branch on which the nest was slung, and from a hide nearby I found them very tame. They had a most curious way of feeding the chicks which I have never before seen or noted in other birds; each time a single large caterpillar was brought back and held over each gaping beak in turn while the juices were squeezed out, before finally giving the remains to one of the chicks. Modern babies have nothing on bird chicks who are fed on pre-digested chlorophyll and caterpillar juice! This pair also frequently came to the nest together, and they once did a thing I have also never seen before, when both parents tried to shove their respective beakfuls of food into one chick simultaneously; this was just too much altogether, and the chick refused point blank to swallow either. Though silent at the nest, they spent a good deal of time preening and billing each other over the chicks, a perfect Darby and Joan.

Not far from this particular nest I found a nightjars' nest in an open patch of dead leaves on the forest floor, just like so many I had seen at home, with the two pinkish oval scribbled eggs lying on the bare ground. The close sitting bird became quite one of the sights and was pointed out frequently as a garden attraction to visitors; like all these birds, her plumage blended marvellously well with the dead leaves and twigs around, and as anyone approached she half-closed the large tell-tale eyes to make concealment more complete.

Flocks of waxbills, fire finches and cordon bleu are common in any garden in Kenya, and scattered millet or crushed maize is an infallible attraction for them. They are lovely little things, and well known even to folk who have never been abroad, because they are familiar inhabitants of any zoo aviary or cage-bird shop at home. Their quick incessant little chitter enlivens any place.

As I have mentioned elsewhere in this book, I have had little success with these feathered imps at the nest; the whole of this group seems to become excessively shy at nesting time, and one needs lots of patience to watch them at their nests. Though so tiny, they must be treated with every respect, and the most elaborate precautions taken if a photograph is wanted. All of them build a domed ball of a nest of fine grass with a short entrance tunnel, usually in a dark thick bush or hedge – never an easy type of nest at which to photograph a bird.

The only one of the group with whom I have really succeeded is the Masai waxbill – he of the delicately barred brown plumage and pillar-box red bill. Their nest is a somewhat curious structure, a ball of very fine grass with a long tunnel entrance, and almost invariably perched immediately on top of it a 'cock's' nest of the same sort of structure, but without much of a tunnel. Watching the birds at the nest, I have been struck by the great attention both the cock and the hen pay to this false nest above, and they spend a good deal of time creeping round it like little mice, pulling out a grass blade here, pushing in one there, taking a new piece in for a lining and so on. (Plate 11). In between times of course they also fed the chicks in the real nest below, and as is the way with so many seed-eaters this is done by regurgitating a thick white fluid. The cock will also bring small white feathers to the brooding hen as well, presumably a pair-bond offering.

With one pair I watched, the female used to spend minutes on end in the nest and whenever I made some odd noises in the hide to make her poke out her head again, she would come right out and creep around the nest poking and pulling at it, as if it must be the nest which was creaking badly as she sat! She never seemed to associate the noises with the hide.

Stripe-breasted swallows nested in the verandah eaves of the house, but never in a really good enough light to photograph them well; in addition, they build a nest with a long entrance tunnel of mud, so that one can never see what goes on inside. The swallow tribe nearly always nest in such awkward dark places, where only flash can cope with the lighting.

I remember once spending a pleasantly idle day watching for hours a colony of square-tailed swifts nesting on the beams of a bridge spanning a waterfall near Nairobi. These colonies are extraordinary things, the nests being plastered one on top of the other at all angles, and stuck all over with feathers and grass mixed in with the mud; each half ball of a nest is made of mud, with an entrance near the top, and in the cluster the floor of one forms the roof of the one below. Due to the down draught of air created by the fall under the bridge, the wheeling twisting flocks of white-rumped birds had strictly one-way traffic only, downstream of the bridge. Most of the birds had half-fledged broods, and I was intrigued to see how easily the birds could find their own nests in the huge untidy clusters in the girders of the bridge; they seldom made a mistake, and each flew direct to its own entrance hole, occasionally perhaps landing on the outer wall of a nest a few inches away, but soon crawling in to its proper nest without hesitation. If landing on the wrong nest whose owner was at home, it was surprising there were no squabbles; all was most peaceful and orderly, but how the birds coming and going avoided collision I do not know.

Like many of these types of birds, these swifts have a habit of flying to the nest and then suddenly twisting away as if they had changed their minds. Although they were normally silent at the nest itself, when wheeling in the air away from the bridge they kept up a constant reeling cry, so like swifts at home. Other birds, who were not visiting the nests, cleaved and turned in tightly twisting knots in the air above in a form of communal aerial play. How I longed for a flash outfit that day! But it was hopeless to think of even trying to get pictures in the dull light under the bridge.

Mentioning flash recalls one eerie evening Alex and I spent crawling around in the roof of the new Native Hospital in Nairobi, photographing a barn owl which was nesting there. The weird snoring noises in the roof had become somewhat unnerving to the theatre staff engaged in delicate work in the operating theatre below, until one bold soul climbed up and traced their origin to a family of barn owls in the eaves above. She had five chicks, all different sizes as is the way of owls, and in daylight hours allowed a very close approach, sitting quietly with half-shut eyes.

I did not want a picture of her thus, but wide-awake and standing by the chicks, or perhaps feeding them, and this she would do only in the dark hours. So one afternoon, about an hour before sunset, Alex and I climbed into the roof. She still sat there with half-closed eyes as the slanting rays of the setting sun found chinks and crannies in the tiles and sent shafts of light to pierce the surrounding gloom. We focused on the nest, and as twilight fell, set our cameras for open flash. Pitch darkness soon filled the eaves, and as we shone the dull glimmer of a torch on the nest, the sitting bird suddenly became a wild shy thing, and slid softly out into the night on ghost-like wings, leaving the chicks hissing and wheezing in their nest.

Then began an eerie ordeal; we could not see outside, but we could hear the weird and melancholy cry of the owl outside, and we judged it to be sitting on the gable to our right. In the inky darkness we could not tell when she would return, and we sat in the deep silence broken only by the scuffling of the chicks as they scrabbled on the boards. I was certain the bird could see us even in the darkness of the roof and was not at all hopeful of any result; but as we strained our ears, Alex suddenly whispered to me, and we could hear a faint but different rustling by the nest, and as I cautiously switched on the torch we saw the owl sitting by the chicks, its facial disc now wide and black round eyes staring at the light. We were too late; in the momentary click of the beam she was gone again, winging quietly into the night once more.

We crouched among the timbers to wait again, and after half an hour or so, the same faint rustling told us she was back again. Not daring to risk the torch again to see what she was doing, I fired the flash at random, and in the sudden white flash we saw that she was there again, crouching over the chicks. The brilliant light sent her off again, but a short while after we did the same again as we heard her return; but she had brought no food and as it was getting by then very late, we came down from the loft and walked through the long deserted corridors of the hospital to our waiting car.

On developing the films later, we were bitterly disappointed to find that the pictures were practically no good at all. A low roof beam which we had not noticed cut off the top of her head when standing upright by the chicks, and in one or two I had double exposed the negative while setting the shutter for open flash, which I had not tried before.

The following year, the same pair nested again in the same place, but a plague of small red mites which invaded the aseptic spotlessness of the theatre below was thought to be due to the birds, so out they went and we did not have another chance.

If the owls are birds of the darkness, then surely the hoopoe is a bird of the brilliant day. It is one of those birds, which, when you see it, makes you realise with a little start that you are really in the tropics. Though indeed it nests in southern Europe (and rarely in the south of England too), and these European birds visit us during the winter, yet there is a resident Kenya species too whose pinky plumage, chequered black and white wings and fanlike crest seem to me to hold the essence of the brilliant tropical sun. For it is indeed a bird of the sunlight, and open garden lawns in blazing midday sun patched here and there with deep shadows are essentially its home.

Nearly everybody who sees a hoopoe thus, walking about on the short turf of a lawn, remarks what a striking bird it is. It is common in Nairobi gardens, and has developed a curious habit there; many Nairobi houses have roofs tiled with red mangalore tiles whose nooks and crannies are beloved of spiders and many other small insects too who shun the light. Hoopoes often run along such tiled roofs, tapping vigorously at the tiles with their beaks, to drive the spiders out and as they scuttle across the roof to seek shelter, the bird catches them with great dexterity.

There is nothing the hoopoe likes more than a dry and withered lawn, brittle and crisp in the hot weather of January to March, where the grass roots are tunnelled with the red dusty runs of termites. In such places it can find a rich abundance of juicy food, and the wriggling white ants are easily pulled from their holes. Then too, is the time when the dry ground becomes pitted with the neat round holes, lined with smooth silken webbing, of the trap-door spiders, and I have often watched the birds exploring each in turn. They are often successful, and extract the protesting occupant with a great air of triumph, holding it aloft with wildly waving legs before tossing it back down their throat.

Though sometimes they nest in tree holes, the shafts of termite nests are equally favoured, and it was in one such that I once found a nest in a garden at Fort Hall. The finding of this nest had led to the gravest doubts about my intentions and character amongst our neighbours there. We had only recently moved into temporary occupation of a house there, and I had already noticed a pair of hoopoes who seemed to spend a long time on the lawn of the house next door to ours. So one afternoon I crouched down behind the low thorn hedge which separated the two gardens, opposite a gap, and glued my field glasses to my eyes to see what the birds were up to. Being engrossed in this quite harmless pursuit, I had failed to see that immediately in my line of sight, behind the birds, was the front verandah of the next-door house, on which the owner was sitting, also looking at me and no doubt wondering what on earth I was up to; being a young and very attractive lady, my actions must have suggested that I was up to no good at all, thus spying on the house in this surreptitious fashion. However the matter was soon cleared up, and this young couple assisted with great interest later as I erected my hide near the hole in the ground where I had watched the birds popping in and out. Our friendship with these kind folk, thus so strangely started, was of short duration; for the husband, not long after, was most tragically ambushed and killed by a Mau Mau gang not far away in the course of his duty as an Administration Officer.

The birds were nesting in an old termite shaft, which went down vertically for some eighteen inches or so, and then turned sideways. By peering in with a torch, I could just see the tail of the sitting bird, and a few grass straws, beside which were lying a half egg shell, and one whole egg of a chocolate brown colour. The chicks were obviously hatched, but I could not see how many, or what state of fledging they were in.

I spent several very pleasant hours watching these birds from the hide. As far as I could make out however, one bird sat the whole time, and the other passed food down to it, leaning over the hole and presumably handing it to the sitting bird who climbed part-way up; but I could never make out what actually happened. Certainly the male, for so I called this bird who did all the collecting, did not enter the hole himself. (Plate 12).

He was kept extremely busy rushing about collecting food on the lawn, and I was most interested in his technique. All the food he collected was entirely subterranean, and he would jab his long curved beak into the dry and dusty ground, about up to the 'hilt', and with a rapid pneumatic drill-like motion poke around; the probing became particularly vicious if he found a tasty grub, which was then pulled without delay to the surface and pecked and stabbed till it lay quiet, then picked up at the very tip of his bill and either brought to the nest or swallowed whole himself.

His energy was quite extraordinary; he fairly rushed around all over the place probing and stabbing apparently quite at random, and hearing seemed to play no part at all as it does with worm-hunting thrushes at home for example. There must be an incredible number of subterranean creatures to make such random probing worth while, but now and then he would find a particularly good spot to which he would return time after time. The food collected seemed to be almost invariably spiders or some sort of white grub which was brought one at a time to the nest; sometimes taking a short flight low over the grass, if he had been collecting some distance away, and pitching at the lip of the hole; and at other times he walked direct to the hole if he had been foraging nearby.

I was also interested to see what function the wonderful fan-like crest fulfilled. I had often watched these birds before, and noted that as they alight after a flight, the crest is erected then depressed, just as a blackbird at home cocks his tail on alighting after flight. Normally the hoopoe's crest is carried flat, and projects backwards like the claw of a hammer head, and the raising of a crest or cocking of a tail is usually taken to be a form of social recognition, identification or greeting signal, sometimes as a sign of alarm; but it conveys its meaning quite clearly to other birds nearby.

With this hoopoe too, it was quite clear that the raising of his crest was an identification signal to the bird sitting in the darkness below – in fact, he politely raised his hat to his wife as he leant over the hole to let her know that he was there. Thinking over the matter in the hide, I could well understand what purpose this action served. The bird sitting below has her field of vision restricted to a small circle of sky; in this circle of vision almost anything was liable to appear, such as an inquisitive dog, a snake, or almost any sort of potential enemy which might require evasive action. How then was she to know that the dark shadow peering over the rim was in fact her husband bringing the rations home, and that she should come up the hole to meet him instead of cowering at the back? Why – by seeing him raise his hat, of course, a signal that all was well. Sometimes I think she cannot have been looking up when he arrived, because as he peered in and raised his crest, nothing seemed to happen, and after a second or two he would get rather agitated, stamping on the ground, clearly too, a signal to her by vibration to wake up and do her share.

I tried sometimes to get him to erect his crest in alarm by making a sudden noise, but it never worked that way, and the crest stayed flat no matter how much of a fright he got.

For two whole hours one hot and sultry day he trotted backwards and forwards bringing food every five minutes to the hole, and never once did the hen show herself; and indeed, I saw them out together only once – the first time I had found the nest. As these were the only pair I have ever watched, I do not know if this is the normal procedure or not. Very occasionally, he would collect food from elsewhere, but most of the time the lawn in the immediate vicinity of the hole seemed to be the most profitable source of supply.

I suppose it is indeed rather queer to consider a vulture as a garden bird. Most people regard them as the acme of repulsiveness, ghoulish creatures to be regarded only with loathing; but they do in fact carry out one of the most useful scavenging roles in hot tropical lands, and the clean picked white bones of a carcase are a great deal more hygienic than a lump of rotting flesh, as the Tibetans realised long long ago.

Of the seven vultures which occur in eastern Africa, six are birds of the great game plains and open rolling hills, where they can see, as they circle round from an immense height up, where the next feast is likely to be; but the seventh, the smallest of the lot, the hooded vulture, has become a very domestic sort of bird, and performs most useful sanitary duties in and around towns and houses, in the company of kites and marabout storks.

They are particularly common, where offal is regularly available, and nothing seems to come amiss. I regard them really with something like affection, since I got to know them well when nesting near our house. They also have the distinction of being the only wild bird I know who can blush furiously at will! A really rather charming trait.

Their nest was about forty feet up in a forest tree in this garden, a broad flat structure in a fork, with a stout foundation of large sticks, lined with smaller twigs and a shallow depression in the centre. After six weeks solid sitting, the female at last hatched her solitary chick, a weak woolly little thing clothed in nigger-brown down all over, with a hooked grey-blue beak. The nest was remarkably clean, decorated almost daily with fresh twigs and one or two new green leaves, and the chick, like most raptorial chicks, was house trained from the start and always did his business over the side of the nest, whitewashing the trunk and branches below.

With a bit of a struggle we erected a couple of huge forest poles against a nearby tree, thus making a tripod on top of which the hide was built, this being reached by climbing up a wildly swinging rope ladder. But once up it was most comfortable, and the life in the tree-tops round about full of interest.

Barbets, bulbuls, plantain-eaters, pigeons and all sorts of other birds came around, and as is the usual case they were particularly fearless up there, since a bulky great thing up in a tree spells no sort of danger to them. Nor did these other birds pay any attention to the vultures themselves, whom they obviously knew for the harmless scavengers they are – not like the fierce sparrowhawks and buzzards in the nearby trees.

When I climbed up for the first time, the female was sitting on the nest, and her mate on a branch nearby; but he heaved himself off with a great spreading of wings and circled slowly overhead, while the hen sat on. It was curious to see how little attention she paid to the bulky structure in the tree nearby, but anything moving in the forest down below immediately put her on the alert, and as she craned her scraggy neck over, she peered into the depths below at any rustling of the leaves beneath.

I was quite content to sit, and watch her sitting too; at close quarters she was not the least repulsive looking, but had instead a dazed, surprised sort of look about her. Vultures of all sorts nearly always look somewhat dishevelled, as if they have had a night out, and she was no exception and her feathers hung loosely on her, like a somewhat shabby cape. As I watched her, the male came circling low over the nest, and as the hen looked up, a rich purplish blush spread over her grey-white face and throat as she followed his flight; paling again as he swept away. He did this several times, and I could tell when he was near by the maidenly blush which suffused her face as she watched him approach; really a rather comical sight in this most unlovely and unloved sort of bird!

He never landed at the nest however, and after an hour or so I felt we had reached a stalemate over this sitting game. So I tried quietly to make her move, but my movements and noise finally got louder and louder, and I had to create a terrific hullaballoo and shaking of leaves before she lazily rose and stood at the side of the nest, dazedly contemplating her chick. After much thought she suddenly vomited up a piece of rather rotten meat on to the nest, and did this seven or eight times in succession. After looking at the results for a while she picked some of it up again, and re-swallowed it; but made no attempt to feed the chick, who pecked at the revolting lumps in a weak and feeble way.

Nor did I ever see her feed the chick at all on several subsequent visits to the hide, and I do not know how it is done. Indeed most of the time she merely sat hunched up on a branch by the nest, apparently sunk in deep and abstract thought; occasionally shaking her head as if the whole thing was too much for her altogether. But I think that the hordes of tree-breeding mosquitoes up in the tree-tops there were really responsible for this negation of all things; for at times they made life a misery for me in the hide, and I saw too that they swarmed round the bare skin of her face.

In spite of this curious lack of interest in her chick, the offspring grew well, and finally flew away; but fledging and parental care last for many weeks as with all these big carnivorous birds.

Reading through the foregoing pages again, I realise all too well that I have given a very unbalanced picture of those birds which live so close to man; and I am conscious too that I have not even mentioned many birds which are perhaps better known as garden birds than those of whom I have written above. But where can one stop? The list goes on and on, and to mention all of those who have sat for me in many different gardens would make a weighty tome, and perhaps too tedious reading. I can only hope that the few already mentioned in this chapter whose doings at the nest have so enchanted me, will quicken interest more and more in the very unknown ways of these others who frequent the wilder garden. A garden always is a lovely place, but to know even just a few of the secrets of its birds, will make it lovelier still.

CHAPTER 4

CORAL REEFS AND COCONUT PALMS

NOT so many years ago, the coastal strip of Kenya was almost the White Man's Grave; you were commiserated on being posted there; spine pads were *de rigeur*; huge doses of quinine were dutifully swallowed daily to combat the fearful fevers arising from the hot steamy shore; to go about without a topee was courting certain death; so you set your teeth and stuck it out for your tour of three years.

Tempus fugit – and with it the old ideas. From Mombasa north to Malindi, and south to Shimoni, the Kenya coast now bids fair to outdo the Durban beaches to the south as a playtime holiday resort. For Kenya folk the soft balmy sea air is a cure for those taut jagged nerves brought on by the thin air and blinding sunlight of the highlands behind. The warm sunshine, the cool monsoon breezes, and the lazy blue sea lapping silver beaches force you to relax, and worry itself becomes just too much trouble to worry about; so down to the coast every year stream hundreds of holiday folk in search of sea, surf and sunshine, and there is indeed no more restful cure to be had.

Reef-pottering is one of the simplest and greatest delights of the coast. The coral reefs exposed by the tide, patterned with brown, gold, green and red; and split by innumerable fissures and pools each filled with the clearest of clear blue water, offer a world of their own. Each pool, each tuft of seaweed turned back, each pebble moved gently to one side, reveal creatures of infinite shape, colour and form, of beauty almost unique and colour exquisite. Better pens than mine have paid full measure to the gorgeous beauty of such tropical reefs, and I cannot attempt even an imitation of such descriptive prose. Only to see it once is to believe. Many parts of the coast are

Crested cranes, male and female (Old Gammy-leg) at nest, Sagana 1952

one's childhood visions of Ballantyne and *Coral Island* come true. The white surf creams on the outermost reef, driven by the monsoon winds; but in the calm lagoon behind, the soft blue sea pulls and washes the fine white sand of beaches with a sibilant hiss, as if each tiny wave was reluctant to come higher up the gentle slope. The sandy ridges are crowned with rows of graceful, rustling palms, the pendant leaves tattered and torn with the easterly winds, the trunks supple and bending with the weight of hard-skinned nuts clustering the crowns.

The moon as it rises seems more silvery, more radiant than anywhere else, and moonbeams cast a shimmering path of light leading out over and beyond the white line of breakers into the deep blue of the night; the palms whisper, rustle and bow in the breeze, and the fantastic whimsical baobabs lift crooked hands to the stars – to me, they are just like those trees which peep at us from the pages of our childhood books, each bearing a face; some malevolent, some kindly – but all part of the fanciful dream world of fairies and gnomes.

Tropical sleepy lagoons and romance are inevitably linked; but I wonder how many of the holidaymakers lying on the beach or pottering on the reefs ever stop to realise how much more romantic are those tiny birds which whistle and twist in quick flocks on the sand? For they are indeed, travellers from a far land; and each one, twice yearly, without the aid of compass or radar, accomplishes a journey which shames those of ours as we step into the comfortable Constellation or Argonaut which takes us to London in a day from Nairobi. These little birds come from the far outermost ends of Europe, beyond the Arctic Circle, from Siberian tundras behind the Iron Curtain, from Spitzbergen, Iceland and the Land of the Midnight Sun to the warmth and sunshine of these equatorial coasts to escape the frozen grip of northern winters. They begin to arrive on our coasts in that season so aptly called the *meleleji* in the dialect tongue of these parts; that calm season in November which our Meteorological Service almost poetically describes as having 'winds light, variable, and the sea slight'; when the blustering southerly *Kusi* monsoon has died, and the steady and warmer northerly *Kas-Kazi* winds have not yet begun to blow.

They stay, feeding and fattening for the return journey again, when in March the internal rhythm of the northern spring urges them north as the monsoon swings southerly again. I often wonder why they take wing at all; the feeding on the reefs and beaches must be tropically abundant and ample, and surely enough to tempt them to stay and lead the idle lotus-eating life so suited to such tropical coasts. But the breeding urge is stronger than any attraction they may find here, so back to the northern wastes they go, for only there can they court, build nests and rear their chicks as is their immemorial habit. Far travellers indeed; but indeed, not all in fact do go each year, for on the coast in the middle months of the year one can often still see curlews and whimbrels who will not move again till spring again follows spring. Most, however, have evolved a 'Design for Living', a summer in the north and winter on the Equator, thus getting the best of both worlds. But just as we pay heavily too for any such privilege, so do the birds pay much more seriously in lives, and the annual toll of these migrants is heavy indeed. Wind drift, exhaustion and predators all the way, each take their share however stout the little hearts may be.

Of course not all birds of the Kenya beach are such long-distance travellers. Many, such as the terns, have only come a short way south from their breeding grounds, and others such as the sandpipers, some plovers, and stone-curlews are resident all the year round; but the big mixed flocks one sees are usually all far-travelling migratory birds.

All parts of the coast are not equally well-favoured. Some shores undoubtedly have richer feeding grounds than others, and particularly where the sand has an admixture of mud. The birds will congregate in tens of thousands where such conditions prevail, as at the Tana and Sabaki estuaries, Mida Creek, and the shores round Kikambala where the sand is blackish and muddy.

What sorts of birds comprise these migrant Kenya flocks? The commonest, I suppose, are travellers from the plains of Central Asia – the Mongolian sand plover; a nondescript little plover with ash-grey colouring above, white forehead and white underparts. They, in this non-breeding season, are typically social and form the bulk of the small quick-twisting flocks which skim over the beaches. These flocks contain, too, occasional individuals of their larger cousins, the great sand plover, also from the Asian steppes and distinguished by its larger size, heavier bill and more solitary habit.

Those who have lived by the sand-dunes and shores of the British Isles will easily recognise the ringed plover – a bird too of the mixed flocks, but occasionally solitary in habit. But the ringed plover here in Kenya, though so alike to the British bird with its quick explosive *puuleep* whistle and flash of white wing-bar in flight, is not the same as that on British coasts, for ours is again a long-distance migrant which comes to us yearly from away beyond the Arctic Circle, north of latitude sixty degrees north, and spreads its individuals in a wide fan across the world in the tropical and semi-tropical islands and lands from Barbados in the west to India in the east, and southwards too to the Cape in the non-breeding season.

Of the larger plovers, perhaps the grey is the commonest – occasionally in twos or threes but more commonly single. It too, like the ringed plover, is a tremendous traveller from the Arctic to the Equator and beyond to the southern part of Africa. Its spotted dark grey appearance, squat plover shape and short bill are characteristic, and when put to flight, look for the jet-black axillary patches under the wings; these distinguish the bird as no other feature can.

The black and white plumage and striking red bill of the oystercatcher always takes me straight back to the shingly banks of Scottish Highland rivers where I first saw them, but they are not the commonest of Kenya coastal migrants, and are surprisingly silent here. Memory, and now actual fact again, recalls their piping call on many a fishing ploy on Scottish rivers.

The huge family of waders finds many representatives on the beaches of Kenya. The long curved beak and long legs of the curlew are unmistakable to those familiar with the marshes and moorlands of home. The female is a giant among the birds of the beach, but again the wild bubbling call so characteristic of the wild places at home is seldom heard to the full on our coasts, except when spring restlessness affects the flocks in March. We get two races of curlews in Kenya – those from eastern Europe and those from western Europe, but the distinction in the field is almost impossible, and a matter for the expert.

The seven-whistler or whimbrel is much more vocal than its relative the curlew, and its characteristic note is often heard far into the night. It gathers in large flocks on the estuarine mud, but look for the light central streak down its crown; a certain distinction from the very similar plumaged curlew. Amongst the rarer British birds, the 'blue-riband' nest to find is that of the greenshank, that wild and elusive bird of parts of the central and west Highlands of Scotland. Only this last year, I spent many happy hours in its headquarters in the Cairngorms Nature Reserve, watching pairs, and their shyness is a challenge to one's fieldcraft. Their spotted grey and white plumage, long greenish legs and tip-tilted bill, with the unmistakable call, will be forever one of the richest memories of wild moorlands and pines; their elusive flight as they circle up many hundreds of yards away from the watcher is tantalising, and yet fascinating, to a degree. To those whose memories of the bird are thus, their behaviour and presence in large flocks on the Kenya coast is quite a shock. Here, they gather in scores, the plumage paler perhaps, but the bill and the white rump are quite distinctive, though their whistle is a poor substitute for the wild breeding call of the summer at home. They are tame too – not at all the shy birds of the Scottish glens and corries – and flocks can be watched with impunity standing only a few yards away in the open. What a contrast; and they are indeed one of our commonest winter waders from November to March.

One of the smaller waders to winter on these tropical coasts is another whose upturned bill and bright yellow legs are quite unmistakable – the terek sandpiper, a bird again from northern Europe. It is a queer little creature, and in some years may be abundant, yet in others uncommon. It mixes with other small waders, but never in flocks. While the terek's bill turns up, that of the curlew sandpiper turns down. Small flocks of these on the coast are often in a queer motley of dress; many still show the russet and chestnut of the breeding season, but the white rump is distinctive. It too comes from the Arctic to winter in tropical sunshine.

Perhaps only three other waders complete the list of the

common types. The little stint is indeed a little bird, and astonishingly tame; its small size is quite characteristic, as is the very whitish and larger stumpy appearance of another bird from the farthest Arctic north – the sanderling. It too comes in mixed flocks. The short stumpy figure of the turnstone, with its odd irregularly chequered plumage of black, chestnut and white and bright orange legs is characteristic. It occurs singly in the mixed flocks, and is a nostalgic reminder of winter migration at home where the sea-pink grows on the rocks and in the saltings backing on the mudflats. It is just at home amongst mangroves and coconuts!

As the tide ebbs and exposes the reefs and mud-flats, so the flocks of waders waiting near high tide disperse and become scattered singly all over the shore as feeding time comes round. Such singly feeding birds are usually shy and quick to take wing; but as the tide turns again, the flocks coalesce once more as the deepening water drives them further in, till once more at high tide they stand hunched and dejected round the line of spring-tide wrack, all facing the wind. This is the time to study them, and every day on the same stretch of beach the composition of these flocks will alter as parties travel on further south in the fall, or north with the spring.

One year, an exceptionally good migration year at Kikambala, Alex and I constructed a hide near the high-tide mark; part dugout in the sand, part built up and roofed with palm branches and twigs. It was an abominable place. The fine white sand trickled down one's neck from the roof, blew in fine streams off the beach, got in one's hair, eyes and nose, and worst of all into the camera itself. But it was well worth it. Each afternoon as the spring tides drove the birds higher up the beach, we sat in the hide and watched them as they came nearer and nearer. On the Kenya coast high-water springs is always conveniently about 4 p.m. in the day. It was great fun, and we had curlews, whimbrels, greenshanks, sandplovers, tereks, curlew sandpipers and all the rest standing and feeding not six feet away.

It was interesting too to watch the various ways of feeding as the flocks retreated before the flowing tide. All the flocks started down wind and worked up towards us against the wind.

Curlews, whimbrel and greenshank, as befitted their stature among the lesser fry, stalked slowly here and there with slow deliberate pokes into the dampening sand as they felt for food. Turnstones and tereks ran quickly along the edge of the wavelets, pecking and dibbling in the bubbling foam as each wave receded on the next. Ringed plovers ran hither and thither, stopping and starting as is their wont, turning over the wet weed from time to time. Solitary curlew sandpipers, on the other hand, always rushed about at a furious pace, poking their bills deep in the sand at an incredible rate, as if it was the last meal they would ever have, and their whole life depended on it. As the hissing foam lapped the foot of the hide and paused to collect its breath after the uphill climb up the beach, so the birds gradually ceased feeding and stood hunched head to wind, only the high feeding sandpipers still bobbing about. Then at some quiet signal, as the tired tide sank gratefully and slid down the beach again, so a little wave of restless movement spread through the waiting flocks, bills were again unsheathed from wing-coverts as the harvest the tide had brought was gathered by a thousand hungry birds.

One of the most exciting things about bird watching in the migrant season at the coast, is the uncertainty of knowing what will turn up next. This particular November was no exception. One day, far out near the end of an *usio* barrier trap, Alex and I spotted a solitary wader; it was largish but more slender than the whimbrel we had been watching, and had a curiously upcurved bill. Manoeuvring to get the light right, we saw that it was spotted and streaky with dark and lighter shades of brown; the bill was dull pinkish with a black tip, and as we deliberately flushed it we looked for its main distinguishing feature – was its rump white and tail black, or was it barred? Did it have a white wing-bar or not? For we had realised already it was a godwit. The black-tailed godwit, white on the rump, blackish tail, and white wing-bar, had been recorded only infrequently from the Kenya coast, the related bar-tailed never officially before. As it rose in flight we saw that its tail was spotted and barred, and there was no white wing-bar. So indeed it was the rare bar-tailed godwit, and we felt enormously pleased. It stayed on our beach for a good many days, and even on occasion joined with the birds near our hide, so that we had supremely good views of it at really close quarters. As I watched it, I thought that here too was a bird familiar with places I would never see; I wondered what it thought of our warm Kenya coast compared with the desolate wastes of Omsk, Tomsk and Lake Baikal.

Then too, on the beach near the swankiest hotel at Malindi, I spotted one day a large flock of those curiously pigeon-like birds, the pratincole, and a few notes on their plumage soon identified them as the Madagascar pratincole – a bird I had not seen myself in the Red Island, but here in hundreds on one of its peculiarly irregular irruptions to the East African coast. Their trill-like note on flying and alighting was heard for several days up and down the beach, then one day the whole flock suddenly went, as mysteriously as they had arrived.

Lesser black-backed gulls – another migrant from northern Europe – mix curiously with the resident sooty gull as they stand and wait for the offal to be thrown from the fish-gutting station on Malindi beach. The resident birds are however of no less interest than these far-travelling migrants. The reef pools feed egrets and herons of two or three different kinds, and most parts of the coast have their resident pairs of chestnut and white fish eagles, with their wild-sounding cry; certainly one of the handsomest of the East African eagles. The curiously odd-looking woolly-necked storks stalk over the squelchy sand-banks at low tide, and play tug o' war with the shiny great worms which burrow here – but the bird always wins anyway.

Out in Mida Creek, perhaps one of the best places for shore birds, a small flock of greater flamingoes is almost resident, but in the dozen or so there, there is not the same wild beauty and flame-coloured flashing of wings of the massed thousands on the Rift Valley Lakes. Here too at Mida one day, I watched a flock of large birds, the black and white pattern of which resembled the avocet flocks of these Lakes; but their short, heavy black bill marked them distinctly as crab plovers, another occasional visitor to the coast.

Back from the beaches, the most noticeable birds of the coconut plantations and high tide scrub are undoubtedly the pied crow, and the gorgeous lilac-breasted roller. Crows breed in the palm-tops at almost inaccessible heights, while the rollers dive and twist with harsh calls over the short scrub, returning occasionally to sit side by side in a low branch as is their habit. This scrub too conceals a hundred and one lesser fry, some peculiar to the coast, some only to Kenya as a whole; but they require patient watching.

Along the sea coast I find the countless terns confusing in the extreme. Many of them breed on the islands north of Lamu, and travel south when nesting is finished. Huge flocks frequent the mud-banks of the Sabaki estuary, and the sand-bars beyond the outer reef just south of Malindi. These flocks comprise several different species, and individuals of one species in every state of plumage from first-year young to non-breeding adults. Their identification in the field is a matter for more expert bird watchers than I, though a few of them I can distinguish fairly well.

The size and black-tipped yellow bill of the lesser crested terns are fairly distinctive, and they tend to be more solitary than their relatives. They are much given to sitting at high tide on the posts of the numerous barrier-traps which stretch at right angles to the shore. It is amusing to note that from December to March they face north into the northerly winds, and from August to December, when they have left their breeding grounds, sit facing south into the southerly winds. The very dark appearance of the white-cheeked tern is a clue to its identity, and the harsh low call, long white outer tail streamer and black beak of the roseate mark it out from the others. This latter bird, so rare and uncommon a breeder at home, and so numerous on the East African coast, seldom shows the rosy flush on its underparts as described in the books; this depends on the light, which is so seldom right.

These smaller terns all chitter and hover and dive splashily after fish just as they do in home waters, and their cries too are nostalgic. As breeding birds in Kenya, terns are confined almost entirely to islands off the coast, whence they have presumably been driven by relentless harrying by the coastal African, which still goes on year after year; but the flocks are still huge.

Above the yellowish muddy waters of the lagoon at the

Sabaki estuary, one can always see that indefatigable fisherman of all African waters – the pied kingfisher. His method of fishing is a unique combination of kestrel and gannet. Twenty to thirty feet up, it will hover on rapidly beating wings, almost 'sitting' on its tail, with beak pointing straight down. Its eyesight must be incredibly keen to see anything in these turgid waters, but as soon as a fish is spotted, the wings close sharply with a snap, and the bird falls like a stone into the water. The fish, if the dive is successful, is brought up across the beak, and with a curious hesitating shake in mid-air again, the bird tosses the fish down its gullet, while still on the wing. Its mastery of the air is complete and superb. If by chance the fish moves away, while plummeting down, the bird recovers itself with an upward swoop a few feet from the water, and resumes its hovering patrol elsewhere.

Our visits to the coast have seldom coincided with the main nesting season, so I have rarely done much photography at the nest there. One September however, I did have a grand chance of a series of a bird, which is not specifically coastal in habit, but occurs on both the shore and on inland water beaches.

The stone-curlew, as I prefer to call it, goes under all sorts of aliases, such as big-eye, thicknee, water dikkop, and the African resident is a close relation of those which are found in the eastern breckland of England. The first two of its aliases refer to peculiarities of its anatomy, but the name of stone-curlew is surely prettier, though in fact, the bird has little to do with the real curlews. It is a curiously silent sort of creature, except for its clear whistle when it takes wing, and it is much addicted to just standing about on mud-banks in an odd sort of hunched up position.

Watamu – the place where this bird and I met at close quarters – is one of those places which resemble so closely the lagoon of our boyhood romances, and conjures up visions of bloodthirsty pirates, with cutlasses swinging under the Skull and Crossbones and brass studded treasure chests filled with pieces of eight. Nowadays alas, it is all too well known and has been facetiously re-christened Blue Lagoon by holidaymakers from nearby Malindi – a name not nearly as attractive as its real Swahili, or rather Arabic, one.

The entrance to the lagoon is guarded by two little islands of the curious mushroom-shaped wave-eaten coral so often found along the coast. The tops of these are crowned with short turf and low scrub, and the exciting thing about them is that they can be reached only at low tide across the reef, unless of course you prosaically have a boat. But wading across on the ebbing tide is much more fun, and one day when I reached the larger island, I walked round it, and found at last a fissure which gave access through the jagged coral overhang above, and at the expense of a few minor cuts finally reached over the edge.

As I did so a stone-curlew walked gravely and silently away in front of me and stood hunched up at the top of the ridge, where it joined another standing nearby. I have a curious instinctive feeling about this sort of thing, and somehow I felt quite certain this pair was not up here doing nothing. Searching around the area soon proved fruitless however, so I lay down behind the low thorn scrub as far away as I could and watched the pair. One soon returned to where I had first flushed it, and with that grave, pre-occupied air so characteristic of their kind, squatted silently down near some old sun-bleached branches.

The spot was easy to mark, and I soon had the satisfaction of looking down at the first nest of the species I had seen. It was a wide circular scrape in the soft sand, under the branch, and contained two very oval eggs of a sandy-ground colour, splotched and streaked with dark chocolate brown; as I approached, the bird ran off quietly again and stood mute on the ridge.

As I have mentioned elsewhere, it is most difficult to judge the state of incubation of such wader and plover eggs, and knowing that the young would run as soon as hatched, the next low tide saw me across to the island again with the hide, which I erected in its final position some eight feet from the nest, taking note of where its shadow would fall. Most Kenya birds are obliging in this respect, and allow one to make such drastic alterations in the neighbourhood of their nests, with little disturbance to them.

Next morning I returned again with the welcome assistance of my father, who hid me up, and climbed down the low cliff again. The next three hours were some of purest delight, such as comes only of watching a shy bird at confidentially close quarters. The hen (I write thus, though in truth I could not tell, for the sexes are alike) returned almost at once, walking and running back to the nest in zigzag stages with the usual plover 'bob' from time to time – a displacement reaction which finds its fullest expression in the 'false feeding' of so many plovers when really anxious. With a good deal of final hesitation however, she entered, almost crouching, under the arch of the dead branch (Plate 13), stood lost in wonder over the eggs a while, then fluffed out her breast feathers and sank on to them. Her mate ran up behind and stood about six feet away; but I was denied the chance of a 'change-over' picture, since as he came a little closer the hen rose from the eggs and walked off, leaving him to approach by himself and sit on the eggs. The same long-distance change took place a short while later, the female returning very quickly as a few spots of rain splattered down.

The semi-crouching position with neck extended forwards is quite typical of the species on approaching the nest; indeed a picture of a bird of the same kind taken by my father many years before on an island on far-distant Lake Victoria is almost similar to mine. This is actually reproduced in Volume 1 of Mackworth-Praed and Grant's *Birds of Eastern Africa*, and incidentally my father used to relate a gruesome tale of this particular occasion when that photo was taken; having no hide material to hand, he dug a long trench in the sandy beach where the nest was, lay down in it with the camera ready and got his African attendants to cover him up entirely save for head and arms – a useful if somewhat uncomfortable dodge. After some while, lying thus, and waiting for the bird, he was alarmed to note a heavy weight being placed on his legs, and twisting cautiously round was frozen with horror as he saw that a very large crocodile had gone to sleep on the sand across his legs! An uncomfortable position indeed. But with mighty relief, after a short while, my father felt the old croc pull himself off and heard him waddle to the water again; and he himself lost no time in vacating that spot also! Such peculiar perils do bird photographers run in in the tropics.

Many plovers and waders shuffle the eggs with their beaks as they settle, but my bird made no attempt to do so. As always, her movements were grave and deliberate, though once or twice I heard her give a low muted pipe with closed beak, as she approached the nest. After a short while I talked to her in a low voice, as I often do with my bird subjects, and she listened a while, allowing me to take a series of portraits; but after a while too, the large sheep-like eye closed, and she dozed in the sun.

This same sun, pleasantly warm in the open with a sea-breeze blowing, soon made the windless hide an absolute inferno, and the view of the blue sea, white beach and waving coconut palms on the shore beyond became blurred with the sweat trickling down my face. With one eye on the incoming tide, I was glad when my father finally appeared to release me.

A few days later the eggs had hatched, and we found one long-legged chick scrambling about on the reef-rocks below. I suppose the little chaps must tumble down the low cliffs somehow, but quite high falls seldom worry such little things. The parents left the island a few days later and their chicks went with them.

As a zoologist, I find these tropical coasts almost too distracting for really serious bird watching. Poking about in rock pools, turning over boulders on the coral reef, examining the wonderful variety of corals, molluscs and sea-shells, and studying the habits of the jewel-like fish that live in these green-shaded grottoes, keeps my attention too fully occupied at times to watch the migrant birds as they pass.

For serious bird watching however the coast would be hard to beat; the watching of migrant behaviour, noting of unexpected arrivals, and nesting of the resident birds are all facets of the game well worth a deeper study. Then too, I am quite sure a good net-catching technique could be developed at favourite resting spots along the high-tide mark for ringing of birds. Ringing of migrants in their winter quarters has hardly ever been undertaken seriously, and the results would be well worth while as Dr Eggeling has shown along the migrant-haunted shore of Lake Victoria in Uganda. There is so much still to be found out.

CHAPTER 5

RAINPOOLS AND REEDS

THE ROADS of Kenya are internationally notorious, and a source of steady income to garage proprietors. The pot-holes are bigger and better than anywhere else, and the regularity of the corrugations would make a cardboard manufacturer green with envy. The dust clouds on many a main road resemble a London Particular, and the appearance of an ordinary European at the end of a day's travelling would make an observer from Mars think he had landed in North America in the early 1800's by mistake; or perhaps he might feel quite at home, instead of away from his Red Planet.

True, indeed, the blessings of Mr McAdam are gradually reducing the thickness of the red linings to one's lungs there, but it seems an unaccountably slow process. Elsewhere the benevolent P.W.D. still digs enormous holes at the sides of the roads to excavate the crumbly red murram or ironstone gravel which surfaces the major network of Kenya roads, and which, when laid, soon settles down to the existing pattern of pot-holes and ruts by now moulded into the many layers below.

This murram slightly stiffens the gluey red mud which otherwise forms in the irregular rains, but in the holes from which it is dug this same rain forms lovely clear pools, beloved of malaria mosquitoes and bilharzia snails – but other animals too, which have been a great source of interest to me in the past. For in such temporary pools one also finds a rich assortment of zoological oddities – all the so-called 'temporary pond fauna'; most of these are unique in their way of life, for the eggs they lay must be dried for many months, when the pool dries up at the end of the rains, before they can hatch out again at the next filling by the rains. Thus one finds a strange, pulsating community of one-celled protozoans, microscopic rotifers and odd crustacea, all living their brief temporary lives when the pond is full, and drying to red dust again as the rains weaken and the sun sucks the water back again to heaven. Such a pool teems with life; transparent shrimps, which swim on their backs, jostle with queer crab-like creatures which crawl on the bottom and others which jerk through the water like miniature cockle shells. Slowly turning green protozoan balls are eaten by trumpet-shaped rotifers; and through all these myriads of organisms float the ghostly, glassy forms of the big clawed frog tadpole and the smaller, blacker wrigglers of the common frogs and toads.

The birds know, too, of this richness of under-water life, and these murram pits are favourite haunts of kingfishers, hammer-head storks and other water-loving birds, who find in them an abundant and well-spread cafeteria system with food just for the taking. Often such pits are left with a steep bank of red earth above the harder murram and this is tunnelled easily by the hole-nesting ant chats, martins, saw-wings, kingfishers and the gorgeous bee-eaters.

One day – I see from my diary it was the 9th June to be precise – when such a pit near the house had been filled with abundant rain that year, I startled a kingfisher out of a hole in the bank above the water; its pillar-box red bill, beautiful blue back and slight crest as it flew away identified it easily as the malachite kingfisher. Bending down and peering in through the guano-plastered rim of the hole I could just make out some white eggs. A week later these had hatched, and having plenty of leisure in those days (I was on leave from wartime duties) I was able to build a rough hide on the opposite bank, and I settled in it later on to see what would happen.

The birds were shy and took a long time to come back – vegetation soon withers in the hot African sun and there were great chinks all over the hide. When one finally did so, I saw a flash of blue streak past the hide and dive into the hole before I could say knife. This sort of thing happened repeatedly, so that I began to despair of ever seeing the bird properly at close quarters. Elsewhere in this book I have mentioned the useful expedient of placing a small piece of the nesting material at the entrance to the hole, when birds are too quick; its presence, while not blocking the entrance at all, will very often make the owner hestitate that vital fraction of a second before diving in – enough to give at least a chance of a picture. But here was a poser, for these kingfishers use no nesting material at all, the eggs being placed on the bare earth at the end of the tunnel; so I compromised by hanging a large leaf near the entrance.

This completely non-plussed the birds, who repeatedly flew to another hole about two inches away and tried to get into it. This wrong hole was only a few inches deep, and was clearly no good at all, so both birds finally settled on a root projecting below the nest and sat there gravely bobbing their heads up and down, considering the matter, and occasionally letting out a chattering squeal. Finally, the great decision was made, and one at last flew to the right hole, where it discovered to its obvious astonishment that the leaf was not blocking the hole at all, and it could push right in, which it did. The other then flew up, hovered in front of the hole and pulled the offending leaf away. Peace was restored.

The root on which they sat was not a good place to photograph them, being at an awkward angle, so a few days later I placed another stick upright in the water under the nest, hung another leaf near the nest hole, and hid up to await events. Repetition of the leaf trick infuriated the pair enormously and they flew repeatedly at it, apparently not realising they could still get round it; but they refused point blank to sit on the stick so considerately placed for them below the nest. The matter was a complete stalemate, so I removed the obnoxious leaf and settled in to watch them again. One bird returned and flew straight to the hole, but backed out sharply, as if the leaf was still there; but it was interesting to see that neither tried the wrong hole again. At the next try, the bird obviously realised that it was making much ado about nothing, and dived straight into the hole and got on with the business.

This started a perfect orgy of feeding, both birds feeding the chicks ten times in as many minutes. As they flew in, the chicks greeted them with a noise like a kettle boiling over, this being soon stifled by the slimy tadpoles stuffed down their throats.

As each bird finished feeding the chicks, it slid backwards

out of the nest and fell straight into the water below, where it dipped about twice and then wiped its beak on the gravel. This happened on every visit, and appeared a very necessary hygienic precaution because by now the walls of the hole were simply filthy with excreta. Quite often as I sat watching, a thin stream of the very liquid droppings would pour out of the hole, the tunnel being on a slope up, as all such nest holes are, or else a sudden squirt out would indicate that the parent itself had relieved itself in the hole. The lower lip of the hole is soon covered with white, and all told their sanitary habits leave a lot to be desired.

I noticed that the birds never came straight to the hole, but landed on the ground by the water edge about six feet away before flying up; but my carefully focused perch was still completely ignored. Such a pair of birds must cause enormous slaughter among the juvenile amphibian population of such a pool, since the food brought was metamorphosing tadpoles of the clawed frog, caught by diving in the pool. These were delivered alive to the chicks, being brought head-in-gullet and tail hanging out of one side of the red beak. The high feeding rate slackened after a time, but I sat on entranced at the industrious pair; but not once did they sit on my stick, so sadly I packed the camera away.

The next time I tried, I hit on a ruse which deceived them completely and was highly successful. It is common experience, when photographing a bird which is still shy after all proper precautions are taken, to notice that the immediate vicinity of the nest is the most alarming zone for the bird. They will perch on twigs all round, or walk nearby, at a distance much closer to the hide than the nest itself, and sometimes even I have had a shy bird perch on the camera lens itself while still refusing to visit the nest; it is the nest zone itself and not the strange square object and the black eye pointing at it which is to be avoided. So this next time I turned this experience to good account and placed my perch stick a good six feet away in the water to the side of the nest, and focused my camera on it there instead of pointing it at the nest.

This new position for the stick, away from the nest, was very much to their liking, and within a short time I could be quite

Madagascar magpie robin, male at nest, Sakaramy 1943

certain that within a few seconds of hearing the plop that signalled a successful dive, the bird would fly back and sit on the stick. (Plate 14). The victim in its beak would wave its feeble new legs hopelessly in the air, while on the stick the bird would sit bobbing its head up and down while pondering the next short flight to the nest. The feeding of the squalling mob over in the indescribably dirty hole, out the bird would slide into the water below; a short dip and a shake, then up to the stick again before going off for the next load of rations. So within a very short time I had all the pictures I wanted, both with and without tadpoles.

I used to wonder whether in the hole the single tadpole brought each time was divided amongst the chicks. These *Xenopus* tadpoles are large, and would indeed be a slimy whole mouthful for one chick; but in such holes, as in a domed nest, such features remain hidden to the observer, although recently there have been some ingenious German experiments by an ornithologist in that country who substituted a glass panel for the wood cut out of the back of a woodpecker hole and was thus able clearly to see all that went on.

The malachite kingfisher is dependent on aquatic food, but few people realise that in Kenya there are several kingfishers, such as the grey-headed and the chelicuti, who live entirely in the dry country away from water altogether and whose staple diet is insects and lizards. The little pygmy kingfisher, a not uncommon bird in Kenya, forms a link between the water and the land kingfisher, for he is not infrequently found near water and feeds on insects caught near the water surface; but never dives underwater to catch prey as does the malachite.

Amongst the water kingfishers is the largest of all, the giant kingfisher, who is a handsome creature of chequered black and white, with a chestnut chest and a heavy black beak. Like the malachite, it captures its prey by diving into the water from a perch above, on which it may sit motionless for minutes on end closely watching the water below with its large black eye. Though usually seen in pairs, it is really a rather shy bird and most trout anglers know it only from its loud raucous cackle as a black and white streak twists through the forest. For it is essentially a bird of the lovely forested trout streams of Kenya, and when undisturbed, a pair occupies perhaps a mile or more of a river. In the days when these clear sparkling waters above six thousand feet were completely devoid of fish life (for trout were a comparatively recent introduction), the diet of these birds was entirely freshwater crabs which they catch most expertly under the water and crush and thrash to death on a nearby branch. Though still crab-eaters to a large extent, they have now, alas, discovered how tasty a fat young trout can be. When running the trout hatchery on Mount Kenya, we had to control these birds severely since they found in our rearing ponds an ample and easy food supply; though indeed it was surprising how seldom we found a trout in their stomach. They became exceedingly wary and gun-shy after a time, though replacements always seem to be forthcoming for those that are shot, in spite of their wide spacing along the river lengths.

Indeed, their distribution along any river must be largely controlled by the presence of suitable earth banks in which to nest. Their nesting tunnels are immensely long, up to twelve feet or more, and are always dug on an upward slope. They do not foul the nest entrance to anything like the same extent as the smaller malachite does.

One year, a pair had the effrontery to tunnel in the bank immediately behind the Hatchery Superintendent's house; but as here there were no available trout in quantity in the pools, we let them be, and from the window of the house we did occasionally watch them bringing small trout to feed their chicks. The bank was so close, that I could sit in the house and photograph them from the window left slightly ajar. But alas, I was quite unsuccessful, for they shot into the hole each time like a bullet from a rifle, and absolutely nothing I could do would persuade them to stop for a second or use any perch anywhere near.

The pied kingfisher is indeed the King amongst Fishers. I have described their hovering methods elsewhere in this book. They however, can be persuaded to use a perch since like all water kingfishers, they like perching above the water and dreaming about fish when not actually catching them. Thus I was able to photograph a pair at our Fish Culture Farm, who found our pond *Tilapia* much to their liking. They took little notice of the hide I had placed by the stick planted for their use by the water's edge. This stick would accommodate only one at a time however, and thus led to some pretty change-over pictures as one bird thought the other had quite long enough sitting there, and swooped up to take its place, the other flying off with a loud chatter to resume hovering.

They seldom caught fish direct from the perch, preferring to hover, though once or twice I watched them tumbling off to catch some small fry beneath; but this performance lacked the precision of the power dive from a height, and was rarely successful.

Except during the months of May to August, the whydah grasslands are also the main feeding grounds of the graceful crested crane, the fitting emblem of the Uganda Protectorate. In pairs or in flocks they spend their time stalking through the grass picking up grasshoppers and lizards they disturb, and occasionally even snakes which they kill by stamping on them. From May to August however, the flocks split up and the pairs take themselves off to the more remote swamps they can find; for they are mainly swamp-nesting birds, choosing tall reeds or grass in which to flatten down a large circular area, in the middle of which the flat untidy mound of decaying reeds cradles two chalky, greeny white eggs.

At this same Fish Culture Farm, two pairs of cranes had their residence. In the middle of one particular reedy patch, John and I could see the head of one bird fairly constantly sticking up like an umbrella handle in a certain spot. When we judged the time ripe, the African staff swept through the swamp, and I was delighted next day to receive a telegram at my own headquarters, which read 'Result operation Crane two egg nests'.

I had been looking for good nests for a long time, and two nests with eggs seemed almost too good to be true. I lost no time in getting down, and John showed me both nests in triumph. One was where we had been watching the bird, in tall rank grass very squelchy under foot, and the other in a nearby reed swamp where the water was almost too deep to wade. Both had two eggs; clearly the one in the reeds was not really workable, so I put the hide near the other in a horrible wet and soggy place. The birds had trampled down such a wide area of grass round the nest that I had no difficulty in getting a good close view from twenty feet away.

Next morning in high expectation I settled in the hide, wearing gum boots and having prudently brought a big box to keep my behind dry. This rather cramped the space in the hide, but was nevertheless quite invaluable. My expectations were soon to be delightfully fulfilled, for no sooner had John walked away than I heard the whoosh of great wings overhead and the bird pitched at the nest. It stood over the eggs, twisting and curving its snaky neck and peering at the hide. I was interested to see that she – if indeed it was she, for the sexes are alike – must have broken her leg at some time for there was a great callus at the ankle joint, and the foot between here and her toes all out of alignment. She was promptly christened Old Gammy-leg and immortalised in film. Shortly after, another great whoosh of wings heralded the arrival of Himself, who pitched in the grass about twenty feet behind the nest, and after much deliberation stalked through the grass to stand beside his gammy-legged wife.

The two of them stood silently side by side for quite a while just doing nothing at all, as birds so often do (Plate 15); and then their behaviour became strange and yet comical to watch. Like Annie, when She Got Her Gun, whatever she could do, he could do better. If she looked to the left, he looked to the left; if she looked to the right, he looked to the right; if she preened under her wings, he preened under his wings. (Plate 16) So it went on, this strange imitation play, until I myself became quite bemused and wondered if the stifling heat in the hide had affected my eyesight and I was really seeing double.

After a while she bent down and poked at the eggs in a disinterested way, and then sank on to them, doubling her long legs under her and dosing off with half shut eye. This sitting spell did not last long, for soon she got up and stood idly at the side of the nest again. This was the only time she sat on the eggs, and I was rather surprised. Admittedly the sun was hot, but when I felt the eggs later at the end of the session I was still more interested to note how really warm the eggs had kept all the while with the heat generated by the decaying swamp vegetation below.

The male finally stalked away and took wing, and Old Gammy-leg stood silently by the eggs again. In a short while, I heard the whoosh of the cock's wings again and before he landed, Old Gammy-leg broke into a weird and ungainly dance, flapping her wings and prancing up and down in the grass till he landed. These cranes often break into these curious dances when in a flock, and the action is a ritualistic form of social display; but it is impossible to tell which sex performs, or if both do so.

Time wore on again with both birds still doing nothing, so I finally made a slight movement in the hide at which both birds looked enquiringly. After some consultation, they both sprang into the air and with long necks extended flapped heavily out of the grass calling with their resonant nasal honk. I crawled out of the hide, well satisfied with the morning's work, and from the house on the hilltop I could see a little later on that Old Gammy-leg was back on the job.

Time did not permit of further sessions, but a week later when I visited the spot I was sad to see that some African children – the curse of such work in the Native Reserves – had interfered with the nest; the eggs had rolled out and were stone cold. The other pair fortunately hatched, and the long legged downy chicks with their ridiculous little head tufts – forerunners of the glorious golden crown of the old bird – were seen scrambling out of the reeds.

Not far from these crane nests, there were some nests of the grosbeak weaver in some tall bulrushes, the black plumaged males in attendance on the bulrush heads. This is one of those curious birds who build several nests all close together, but in usually one only are the two greenish eggs laid. Like all weaver's nests they are intricately woven structures of fine grass, which are started as a circle of grass binding two upright stems close together. This entrance ring is made first, then the lower landing edge is made particularly strong and thick, and the dome and bag of the nest are added last. Like many such weavers the hens are dull and inconspicuously striped, and slip silently off the nest long before one gets near.

In this small group of nests I soon located the occupied one, which had two chicks. The nest was high, nearly six feet above water level, but the water was fortunately not deep, and had a reasonably firm bottom. So I put the hide at full extension, and next day prepared for a long standing wait – perhaps one of the most tiresome positions to keep up for long, unless one happens to be one of the curious Dinka tribe in the Nile Valley of the Sudan who can stand for hours on end on one leg, the other tucked up like a stork.

I was not hopeful; I had tried one of these birds before in a swamp at Kabete, and found them to be one of those exasperating types like the whydahs, whose males never visit the nest, and whose females feed the chicks by regurgitation – this necessitating long waits of an hour or more between visits while she digested her meals.

This Kabete nest had not been a success; the light had been bad, and the mosquitoes ferocious, but I had made one interesting observation there. The nest had been in very tall reeds, and even at the fullest extension of the hide, it was still silhouetted against the sky, an impossible position from which to obtain a good photograph. So I had cut the two main supporting reeds, tied them to poles and lowered the whole nest by over a foot; I was then most interested to see that when the hen returned, she flew straight to the nest in its new position. Often when this is done and the nest moved, the owner will return to the old position and try to land on a non-existent nest; just one of these curious traits which show how different the bird mind is to ours. Their whole life is ruled by set reactions to a perceptual pattern in a sometimes quite automatic way.

However, this Sagana bird was no exception to the usual behaviour of the species. As before, only the hen came to the nest at very long intervals. She would then cling to the entrance ledge, and for several minutes head stretched and 'chewed' till a nasty looking green mess oozed from her bill. Dinner was served; so she popped her head into the nest and distributed it to the chicks, but I could not see exactly how this was done in the deep domed nest.

Her tail and wings flicked continuously, making photography

difficult, and she was quite silent at the nest except for an occasional low guttural note. The black cock kept up a poor wheezy song in the reed tops nearby. Chick excreta was removed in the mother's bill and dropped at a distance. On one occasion she returned immediately after dropping one sac to pick up another from the nest; perhaps she could count two! Then too, on another occasion she suddenly noticed a piece of dried dropping on a reed stem below the nest; this had actually been there some time, but automation took charge, she picked it up and flew off with it. One wonders at the apparent inefficiency of such reactions; but probably nest cleanliness is more important than at first seems obvious where inconspicuousness is the rule. Once at the nest, I noted that feeding of the chicks is a lengthy business, taking ten minutes or more, and astonishingly large quantities of food are regurgitated.

In many ways, these grosbeaks resemble whydahs more than weavers. The sexual dimorphism is well marked, and the hens only take part in nest duties. Both birds are quite silent when the nest is disturbed. The nest entrance is open at the side, and not on the underside with a deep porch as in most weavers; and regurgitation to feed chicks is much more a whydah than a weaver habit.

Near the Kabete nest, I had noticed also a much more handsome relative, a Camburn's golden weaver, which is really pure gold all over. The bird was tearing strips of reeds off for nest building, and this was most ingeniously done. A firm beak grip was taken of a leaf half-way down one edge, and taking hold the bird would fly off, tearing away a strip all down the edge nearly two foot long. A good many other weavers have similar habits when collecting nest material, and the origin of this habit is a matter of interesting speculation; how did they first find that strips could be torn off in this fashion?

These gorgeous golden weavers do not always nest in swamps; they are not colonial weavers, but like most of their kind the males still build extra nests surplus to immediate requirements. In the nesting area of a pair, perhaps two or three nests are found in addition to the one occupied. Their rather clumsy nests usually have no lining, but in the occupied one we found nearby in the swamp, the entrance porch (directed downwards in true weaver style) was tastefully decorated with flowering heads of a docken, the nest itself being at the end of a flowering sparganum reed stalk overhanging the water. The two eggs are very oval and a beautiful blue. With this species, there has been some suspicion in the past that eggs or chicks are moved from nest to nest, but I have never found any evidence of this.

My usual cloth hide was erected nearby, and the birds proved much more obliging than the tiresome grosbeak a few yards away. When the chicks had hatched, the hen, who is more greenish yellow on the cheeks and lores than the cock (though both have the same bright golden yellow iris), returned about five minutes after I had hidden up, with a large insect in her beak. She flew straight to the nest, and clinging to the underside, fed the young most deliberately, taking a long time to pass over the food.

Her visits thereafter were most regular, about four to the hour. The food brought was always insects, held in the beak. I could not identify these properly; some were large, some small, but all appeared to have been chewed up considerably before being brought to the nest. Chicks' droppings were removed on each visit, but the young were not at all properly house-trained, and often defaecated straight out of the nest till the rushes below were white with droppings.

The golden cock did not visit the nest this session, but shortly proved himself a perfect nuisance. At first he settled on the reed stalks nearby and called occasionally with a typical weaver 'boiling-over' noise. Then for some extraordinary reason he took it into his head to fly to the top of the hide, where, peering through a gap in the seam, he suddenly saw me. I froze like a statue, but this odd sight inside the hide shocked him beyond measure and he flew off full of alarm and despondency calling with a sharp *cut-cut-cut* note. This he kept up incessantly for about half an hour, constantly hopping about the reeds close to the hide, usually embarrassingly close to my mosquito-netting window through which he would peer to see if the horrible sight was still there. He was the first bird who had ever done this to me, and I found the strain of keeping quite still very trying, for normally the seclusion of the hide offers a certain freedom of quiet movement.

Each time the hen visited the nest, he redoubled his efforts to warn her of the frightful danger she was running into, but she, like the sensible spouse she was, ignored his cries of *wolf, wolf* and carried on feeding the chicks as usual in a quite unhurried way. This terrible racket attracted a horde of inquisitive rubber-neckers who flocked along to see what it was all about; the reeds round about were alive with swamp warblers, Speke's and Reichenow's weavers and bulbuls, all chattering away and clearly saying *Where is it – What is it – can't see a darned thing myself!* It was a most embarrassing situation.

The next day I spent the whole day in the hide, as this swamp was full of bird life, quite apart from the weavers, and from the hide I could see all sorts of interesting things. The weavers themselves were most active, and feeding rose to six visits an hour in the morning, dropping again to four in the afternoon. The hen took life most seriously, and fed the chicks silently and deliberately. The stupid cock again alarmed himself twice unnecessarily by peering into the hide, but did at least this time help occasionally at the nest, performing his duties most hurriedly and then rushing off in alarm telling everybody what frightful risks he had run. I really had to laugh at him more than once, and he didn't like that either!

If the hen returned while he was still near the nest, he greeted her with his sizzling call, to which the chicks would respond at once by sticking out their scraggy necks and begging for food. Sometimes they would do this if the main nest stalk was touched, but not always. The vibration had to be right. Try as I would, I could not get the birds to perch on the stalk for me, both flying straight to the nest each time they came. Food brought was again large, green and squashy, and was probably caterpillars. The racket kicked up by the cock again attracted the usual horde of idlers and hangers-on, and the cock had a busy time chasing away a Reichenow's weaver who would settle too near the nest. It was altogether a most lively day. A few days later, I had the pleasure of watching the chicks being fed by their parents away from the nest which they had just left.

The little brown coloured swamp warblers have a most

characteristic deep single note, and the broad rounded tail in flight is quite typical. I once found a nest of these birds built in the head of a papyrus stem in a swamp near Ruiru. It was a deep cup woven into the flower stalks, lined with fine grass, and contained a single egg of dusty blue ground colour with indistinct reddish speckling. The birds seemed very tame, and returned to the nest as I stood only a few feet away. Next day there were two eggs in the nest, and as the birds seemed surprisingly bold I put up the camera by the nest and crouched down in the foul smelling swamp below. I had no hide, being on military duty at the time.

For some time, the birds hopped round the reeds, uttering their deep *chok* note, rather like that of the English whitethroat, and occasionally gave vent to a few clear and startlingly loud notes of song. After a while they grew bolder and the hen settled on the eggs. Finding I could not work the shutter satisfactorily sitting below the camera, I rose slowly up and stood beside it in full view, and as long as I made no sudden move the bird did not mind in the least. Frequently the cock would fly up to the sitting hen and fondle her beak – one of those intimate scenes so delightfully frequent when watching a pair; and sometimes they would change places on the nest. By now the sun was blazing hot and the sitting bird panted with beak wide open.

As the war by then was being fought really a long way away, the inhuman military machine soon had me moved, and I was unable to follow the further fortunes of this pair.

One way or another I seem to have spent a good many hours sitting in swamps and by puddles of water watching birds nesting, drinking or bathing. It has all been great fun. Although indeed much of my time in Her Majesty's Service has been spent at various kinds of watersides, my official preoccupation with the fishy inhabitants thereof has left me with too little time to spend in hides at such places; and I have little pictorial record to show of the ducks, geese, the darters, ibises, lily trotters and gulls which teem in such African waters. One of these years we have promised ourselves a long, leisurely bird watching safari right down the Great Rift in Kenya, to study and photograph the countless thousands of waders, plovers and water birds to be found in that area – from Rudolf and Hannington to Nakuru, Elmenteita, Naivasha and beyond; a trip when time is no object, but only the birds.

CHAPTER 6

MADAGASCAR INTERLUDE

IN LATE 1942, His Majesty's Government generously paid my fare to the fabulous 'Red Island' of Madagascar, and supported me there for a whole eighteen months. The fact that I was only one of several thousands whose fare was so paid at the same time, and that I was a very small cog in a very large machine whose function it was to persuade the then Vichy Government of the island that it was really very foolish to re-victual Japanese submarines there, in no way detracted from the anticipation of visiting a new and exciting bird area.

The journey across I remember well. After a most secret embarkation at Mombasa, we travelled in a little Dutch coasting steamer, the *General van Geen*, which was no longer able to travel on its usual run round the Javan and Sumatran Islands and had in consequence been moved to the East African coast. In spite of having travelled many nerve-wracking months in submarine-infested seas, the crew of the ship with characteristic Dutch thoroughness still managed to keep the interior spotlessly clean, the brasswork gleaming, and the linen immaculate; the voyage was pleasant and uneventful.

The lack of bathroom was somewhat puzzling at first. The gleaming square copper tank in what was clearly the bathroom was obviously too small to bath in; it was not until we discovered the curious ladle beside it that we realised its function was merely to hold the tepid water, which one poured over oneself with the ladle in question.

The Dutch are past masters in the art of adapting themselves to living in the tropics, an art which the British have never acquired. Amongst the better things they have devised is that useful bed-fellow known as a Dutch Wife – a long, hard-rolled pillow over which one slings a leg so that perspiration does not become excessive and uncomfortable at night time. The purpose of this curious article having been explained to my cabin mate, I have amusing recollections of him fighting with his Dutch Wife at night, and hearing muttered imprecations to 'get in there, Gertie – lie still now – be quiet!'

Another characteristic of Dutch life in the tropics is the enormous and soporific 'rice tafel' meal at Sunday midday. After this gargantuan curry repast, I presume the ship steered itself for several hours, since I doubted if the crew were capable of doing so.

Bird followers of the ship were surprisingly absent, and the haze of golden days and velvet tropical nights on the voyage was broken by only one incident of note.

This was caused by one of our amateur submarine watchers, Oloo Obunga by name. The Captain, rightly, had decreed a twenty-four hour submarine watch, since we were not in convoy but alone – subject to that curious ruling that only if a ship contains so many of one unit should she be accompanied by an escort. Had we been sunk with all hands, our loss would have made a tidy hole in the 'odds and sods' replacements for the Red Island forces – but total numbers apparently do not matter in war, the size of the part being more important than the whole. Be that as it may, owing to shortage of man power, some of the African Askaris on board had been impressed for this duty.

Most of these were simple fellows, straight from their smoky mud-huts and odoriferous companionship of goats, and now turned into soldiers and clad in the full panoply of war, right down to regulation oversize boots. The whys and wherefores of this latest phase of European madness were beyond them. Most of them had never seen the sea, or anything like it, and the thought that it might conceal boats which travelled underwater and could strike you down from afar was beyond their comprehension. What therefore, they really looked for on their two-hourly vigils on the bridge I cannot imagine.

Oloo, then, was detailed one night for that grim watch between midnight and 2 a.m., and time clearly hung heavy on his hands. Even thinking about nothing becomes boring after a time, and a row of little switches beside him on the bridge gave food for thought. Speculatively he flicked one down; and instantly the strictness of the total blackout was split by a stabbing beam of light from the masthead searchlight, and a radiant path across the water beckoned all lurking submarines to have a crack at the *General van Geen*.

Pandemonium and confusion reigned. Oloo was bellowed at in a strange mixture of Javanese and Dutch to switch that blank-blank light off. Dholuo being his native tongue, the curses and instructions were quite unintelligible. He realised from their urgency that he must have committed the gravest of blunders, and stood paralysed with fear at the consequence and unable to do a thing. One of my N.C.O.'s was finally dragged out of bed, and in curious broken English asked to explain to that so and so the enormity of his offence, and convey intelligible instructions to switch the damned thing off. Meanwhile the helmsman zigzagged wildly all over the Indian Ocean to confuse the waiting submarines until peace and order were restored, and finally the voyage pursued its former even tenor.

We landed at Tamatave on the east coast of Madagascar, a few days after the main assault was over. Red and Blue Beaches had been stormed, Diego had fallen, Majunga taken, and the remaining unwilling Vichy forces penned in the south of the island. The guns were silent, and already the local population was clamouring for grossly over-estimated compensation for damage done by the victorious troops – which I imagine in the usual incomprehensible British way probably was paid in full.

I suppose a book about birds is no place really to indulge in such reminiscences, but as I write, memory rolls back the curtain of time, and the fourteen years which have passed since I left the island seem never to have existed. I remember those eighteen months mainly as a time of good fellowship in the pleasantest of company. We were a very small unit, and a very happy one. Our work took us to many different parts of the island, and we saw and we marvelled at much that was different there from the Africa we knew. The Malagasy are Melanesian in origin, not African, and our African Askaris noted with interest their well-built brick villages with double storey houses; the hundreds of thousands of acres of flooded rice fields with thin, wonderfully engineered, furrows leading the water seemingly from hill top to hill top; and perhaps most of all, the astonishing polyglot and polychromatic population which makes up such French Colonial possessions, where race and colour matter not one whit, and all live together in apparent harmony.

Yes, one could write a whole book of reminiscences there, as memory kaleidoscopes a succession of pictures across my mind. The incredible hotels in the capital Antananarivo, where it was wise to whisk the sheets smartly back and liberally dust the bed with pyrethrum powder before settling for the night; where the revolting English habit of having breakfast had to be relegated to a dingy backroom. The astonishing collection of junk in the Queen's Palace Museum, where scores of stiff brocaded dresses worn by former Hova Queens rustled side by side with fantastically stuffed birds of paradise and skeletons of dodos, and where the unmentionable picture on the lid of a queen's snuff-box was the main attraction for visiting troops. Clean, healthy, bush camps away in the wilds; gold, beryls and topaz to be had for the picking; our tame ringtail lemurs, with their quaint habit of sunning themselves in front of the camp Tilley lamps, drawing their tails under their armpits and flicking the scent forwards; the quaint Emmett-like trains on that stiff pull from Tamatave to the capital; turkeys at two shillings each till we got tired of eating them; bombing great fat carp in the rivers; and Christmas 1944, far from our own homes, with one of the unit bringing tears to our eyes with his masterly rendering of 'Nellie Dean', and he who performed the astonishing feat of becoming drunk and then sober three times in one day. Above all, the snakes – hundreds of them everywhere and not a venomous one amongst them; Cai, with his two tame boa-constrictors which frightened the life out of me; earthworms two feet long and thick as your thumb. And so on and on.

As before in the East African campaign, I was thankful for my interest in birds, which whiled away many a long hour for me in the dreary round of garrison duties, enlivened only occasionally by irate inspections by choleric generals whose job it was to keep the troops on their toes, by Gad Sir.

The scent of the fantastic Star of Madagascar orchid hung

heavy in the air as we entrained at Tamatave, in a great sticky heat, for the cool central highlands which we reached next morning after many puffing stops and starts. We awoke to a vista of thousands of acres of flooded rice, dominated by the rocky outcrops of hills on which stands the capital Antananarivo.

The Red Island is indeed a fabulous place. It has everything, from two hundred and fifty inches of rain a year on the east to two a year on the west. Water which spouts from the tops of the hills and is the life-blood of the rice-growing Malagasy; they pay for this heavily with the chronic malaria which ages and finally kills them years before their time. Graphite, gold and precious stones almost for the taking; a wild abundance of varying scenery and climate from the heavy rain forests of the east to the dry rolling grassland of the west; magnificent turbulent rivers rivalling those of the Scottish Highlands. Some of these are stocked with great carp, others with fat rainbow trout, the capture of which would certainly cause raised eyebrows if not apoplectic fits in the Club at Stockbridge. For the contents of the 'fly-box' are usually alive – big green and gold frogs and bright yellow grasshoppers, and – horror of horrors – the rod may even be reel-less. Even I, whose job it is to deal with fish, fisheries and fishing, was somewhat taken aback at the methods employed *pour le sport*.

Our first stay was a 'jungle-camp' some kilometres south of the capital, at a place called Sahavondronina; the Malagasy names are beautiful and euphonious, but apt to recur in repetitive manner in widely differing parts of the island, since they are usually descriptive only of some main topographical feature of the area, and hence features common to many different places.

Most of the central highlands have been widely denuded by man of the primeval forest which once covered them, and are now bare and eroded, or planted with unexciting rows of eucalyptus trees. With the destruction of these ancient forests went the indigenous fauna, and birds are now scanty in the populated central regions. I doubt if the casual observer would see more than a few species in these highland areas, of which the commonest would be the cattle egrets, pied crow, fody finches, yellow-bellied wagtail, green bee-eater and kestrel – all

White-winged scrub robin by nest, Magadi 1940

birds which have adapted themselves to man's change of the land.

As is well known, the Mascarene sub-region is of the greatest interest zoologically. Here was the home of the roc and the dodo, the giant lemurs – and now that archaic living survival – the coelacanth *Latimeria chalumnae*, now being caught in increasing numbers off the Comores. Even today, there is still a most striking and original indigenous fauna of birds which are found nowhere else in the world, now mixed with migrants from neighbouring Africa; and the curious indigenous lemurs and rodents are quite unique.

Mr C. S. Webb, now Superintendent of the Dublin Zoo and author of that delightful book *A Wanderer in the Wind*, lived for many years in the island, and played a not unimportant part in causing our landings there. He collected the curious Mascarene fauna for years for the London Zoo, and his long, gaunt figure, surmounted by a battered topee, and full of dry humour, was an ever-welcome visitor to my various camps there. Many were the facts and curious tales he told me about the wild-life, and to him I owe a deep debt of gratitude for checking over the curious birds which I saw and which were quite strange to me.

As always, shooting did not attract me, and so I collected voluminous notes on the birds – surely one of the best ways to get to know them since they must be watched and studied alive to obtain accurate field notes on plumage, call-notes and behaviour. Field glasses and camera were constantly in use.

The bird watcher in Madagascar will inevitably be struck by the paucity of species, and also the paucity of individuals. There is there not the rich abundance of the African mainland and one has literally to look for birds. Admittedly however, I could spend but little time in the best birding regions – the eastern rain forests and the great Lac Alaotra, where birds were more frequent. Perhaps the most striking absence is that of the large raptorials and scavengers so common in Africa. This is probably because of the primeval absence of game in the island – where thousands of square miles of perfect game country exist. The smaller birds such as bulbuls, weavers, sunbirds, chats and warblers are but feebly represented, but there are at the same time other features of extraordinary interest showing parallel evolution with Ethiopian birds. Thus, some of the arboreal types of coua in Madagascar are very reminiscent in habits and appearance to the totally unrelated turacos of Africa – which are not represented at all in the island. The Madagascar vangids are clearly parallel in appearance, habits and ecology to some of the unrelated African laniid shrikes. But reverse instances also occur; thus many of the Mascarene rollers are terrestrial birds, their relations in Africa being arboreal; while some of the pittas are essentially arboreal, unlike their ground-loving African counterpart.

Sahavondronina was an area of relict forest among the populous highlands, and hence was particularly good for studying some of the Mascarene oddities. It was here I watched my first coua – the great blue coua, perhaps the most striking of the lot as it flops from tree to tree. The smoky-blue head and back, slight tufted crest, conspicuous white eye-ring, and long broad deep purple tail are quite characteristic, as is its loud penetrating call.

Here too, I found my first Madagascar nest, and had my first photographic session with a curious little bird called *Dromaeocercus seebohmi* – literally Seebohm's emu-tail. It is a bird which is confined to swampy hollows in such high-plateau forest, and is a dowdy little creature about the size of a willow warbler, with a long tail of which the two outer tail feathers appear much frayed like an ostrich or emu plume – hence its name. A pair of these were nesting in a clump of marsh grass near my tent and had two newly hatched young. This was in the third week of November, the usual nesting time in Madagascar.

From an extremely damp and unpleasant hide built in the shallow stagnant water nearby, I spent a good many hours watching and photographing the pair. The female was very shy and took a long time to return, finally flopping into the nest tuft with a low note, and creeping about for all the world like a mouse before venturing to the nest. She fed the chicks most deliberately with minute beakfuls of insects. She repeated her visits only twice in the hour, but next day was much bolder except when warned of my uneasy movements in the hide by the male who sat behind me and called every time I shifted my sodden feet. Himself was a good deal more shy and came to the nest only twice; but I had to leave the area before I could get to know them better.

At Sahavondronina I recorded a good many birds which were new to me, either Mascarene races of East African birds, or others indigenous to the island. A list of these would make dull reading, and indeed I have recorded full notes on them elsewhere in the pages of *The Ibis*. A good many of the birds then were nesting, though I had little time to do much photography. An interesting find was a chick of the Madagascar snipe – a large heavy bird which is much more reminiscent of a woodcock than a snipe. Somehow I found the long grey-blue toes of the chick extraordinarily funny to watch as it clambered weakly through the tall grass.

Stonechats were nesting, and the long bubbling call of the Madagascar coucal was heard all the time – so like the call I knew so well in Kenya. Newtonia flycatchers (much more like a white-eye than a flycatcher), brush warblers, Madagascar bulbuls, Madagascar white-eyes and red fody finches were common.

The latter are perhaps one of the most characteristic birds of the highlands; for abundance I suppose they rival the house sparrow in Britain or the weavers of Africa. The scarlet heads, backs and chests of the cocks are most distinctive, and blend remarkably well with the dying scarlet leaves of the eucalyptus trees. As with the dioch finches of Eastern Africa, the flocks are so numerous and destructive when the rice is ripening in the wonderfully terraced fields that the Malagach construct little huts on stilts in those fields in which a child sits all day long scaring away the birds. They also catch considerable numbers by some means I could never discover, and sell them twenty or thirty at a time for about a franc each, imprisoned in little cages made of raffia slivers. I suppose they were eaten; I used to buy them, and let them go again, much to the annoyance of the local population I suppose.

In spite of their abundance, their nests seemed curiously rare, and I found only two. One was in a low overhanging bush above a forest stream, and was domed, with a porch like a Reichenow's weaver nest. It contained fledging young, but a large and active wasps' nest on the same branch a few inches away precluded further investigation. A deserted nest with a single pale blue egg, and a few feet away, also had an angry-looking wasps' nest near it – there is clearly an association here, as with some East African birds. A further, empty, nest a few feet away contained, of all extraordinary things, a cluster of large danaid butterflies sleeping in it.

The yellow-headed Sakalava fody replaces the scarlet bird in the northern region round Diego and these nest in colonies like many African weavers. But unlike the latter, the colonies are extraordinarily silent, without the constant bustling about and sizzling noises one associates with the African birds. The nests hang in long strings, one nest being attached to the side of the entrance tube of the one above, and so on. There must be harsh words exchanged if the owner of the topmost nest does not make his foundations strong enough.

From Sahavondronina we moved to Fianarantsoa, further south; a quaint, almost medieval town perched on a set of precipitous hills, with the valleys between cultivated with the inevitable rice, even right in the town. It was in consequence shockingly malarious. Our camp was pitched overlooking the local cemetery, where rows and rows of gravestones, all inscribed the same, constantly reminded us grimly of the other great scourge of the island – the dreaded plague, which sweeps the inhabited part of the island with devastating effects from time to time. Rat control appears to be beyond the power of the authorities, who rely almost entirely on mass inoculation of the protective attenuated live vaccine they have developed. In Antananarivo it was a common sight to see great fat rats scuttling into the gutters in broad daylight. Like the daily dose of quinine, they are regarded as inevitable.

At Fianarantsoa we sat for several months, making pleasant excursions down to Tulear on the south-west coast, where the wild call of the curlew sounded strangely out of place on the hot steamy foreshore. On the road to here one day I saw for the first time the quaint running coua – a bird of large smoky-grey appearance and curious sideways hopping movement; and my first troop of wild ring-tailed lemurs.

North too, we went occasionally, to the wealthy health resort of Antsirabé; to the capital Tananarive, and eastwards down to the coast again at Tamatave, where bits of my far-flung unit were still stationed.

One night at Fianarantsoa, the sky held a queer lurid glow and the wind moaned strangely. I remarked to Cai as we turned in, 'Fine weather for a cyclone'! This was only too true, and that night a furious cyclone hit Tamatave, an unfortunate town which had been razed before by these demoniacal wind-devils which roar in from the south-east Indian Ocean. As soon as we heard the news, I went down to see what had happened, for some of my unit were stationed there. My N.C.O. Ash had had a hair-raising time. The storm had hit the town in the evening, with a wind of over 100 m.p.h., and had lasted all night. Corrugated iron sheets were ripped from the roofs and tossed about like sheets of paper. Steel helmets had to be worn, and the terrified African troops had tents whisked off them like umbrellas, and spent the night lying flat on the ground. Houses tumbled down like packs of cards, and the devastating wind cut a mile wide swathe through the town and forests behind, twisting and breaking the trees all about ten foot from the ground, till the cutting resembled the work of a giant scythe in a forty foot stand of corn. Most luckily, the cyclone was not followed by the usual tidal wave, which spared many lives; but the death roll was still high enough. Big boats were tossed on the beach like driftwood, and the harbour strewn with wreckage. The shacks in the town resembled the east end of London in 1941 with great gaping holes and piled up rubble strewn everywhere.

I was particularly interested in the effect on the birds, and all I could see were the ubiquitous introduced Indian mynahs, crested drongos and pied crows. All the smaller fry such as white-eyes and grass warblers had vanished completely.

Fianarantsoa, like all the denuded highland country, was very poor for birds, and I was glad when we finally took part in the mass evacuation of troops from the southern and central island to Diego in the north. This move took place by road from Tananarive to Majunga on the west, and then up the Rue Stratégique on the west coast to Diego. The going was hazardous, and the Engineers did a marvellous job in ferrying the hundreds of vehicles across the blown-up Betsiboka bridge and the numerous westerly flowing rivers which cut the road as it wound its way north. On all of these the bridges or ferries had been blown up or destroyed to delay the earlier advances of the British troops. Many and wonderful were the temporary arrangements made to deal with these, and luckily at the main obstacle – the Betsiboka river – the water was so low that pontoons could be pushed across by man power – wading, stumbling and cursing in the sticky sand of the river bed.

I was privileged to be on the small staging camp committee which reconnoitred the route before the great move, and the three of us provoked a classic paraphrase from Major F. W. – one of our party – who remarked that never had so few mucked up so much for so many. But all went reasonably well. I travelled up and down that road shepherding convoys for hundreds of miles that month the move was in progress, and it was a great opportunity to see new birds and new country. Alas however, I was never able in that restless job to stay long enough in one place to get to know it really well.

Down in those dry western forests and rolling grasslands I was able to watch for the first time some of the uniquely Mascarene birds, though nesting and photography was out of the question. The Betsiboka river is the haunt of thousands of small crocodiles, which were at one time the source of a quite profitable skin industry. They lie in scores on the riverine sandbanks, and their constant companions are flocks of white-faced tree ducks – not indeed purely Mascarene birds, and their *pee-wee-woo* whistle was welcomingly familiar. I often heard it well into the hours of darkness at Ambanja as they flighted in V-formation overhead.

The harlequin quail was another East African bird commonly seen; but here they had the curious habit of running about on the thick forest floors, loth to take wing – a habitat I have not seen them use in Kenya.

The only large raptor common on the island – the augur buzzard – was frequently seen on the road, the peculiar round winged, short tailed appearance being quite characteristic. Other large birds frequently seen in flight were the Vasa parrots. Their greyish black appearance, curious truncated look in flight due to the deeply hooked bill, and slow flapping flight is very reminiscent of a crow, and markedly different from all the East African parrots. They have a wide range of metallic sounding notes, and are capable of imitation. Once, at a camp near Port Berge, miles from any water, I was very puzzled at hearing a fish eagle calling constantly with its wild cry in thick forest. Following up the call I finally tracked it to a big Vasa parrot on a tree-top. The imitation was deceptively perfect, but I cannot imagine where the bird had learnt it. The Malagach are said to split their tongues and teach them to talk, but although I saw several tame ones in Malagach houses, I never heard one utter a single word.

Flashes of bright green streaking off the road were usually all I could see of the grey-headed green love birds. They were shy, but often fed on the road with small parties of fody finches.

The patches of dry forest on the road often contained solitary specimens of the beautiful crested coua and red-capped coua, which run along the tree-branches like the turacos of Africa, and in general appearance indeed resemble them strongly. For many kilometres along the Rue Stratégique the landscape is monotonously similar, and lined with thousands of the traveller's palms – satrana as it is known locally. Above and all round them wheeled thousands of palm swifts, just as they do in Kenya; and here too I saw a harrier of sorts flapping and gliding low over the grassland as is their wont, although no harriers have so far been recorded from the island.

The vangids are common on the west, and resemble the shrikes of Africa. Chabert's vanga resembles the pied shrike of Kenya gardens, but the white-headed vanga is more like a barbet. The blue vanga is one of the most exquisite of birds, and the glistening cobalt-blue of the back, and contrasting white underparts make it quite unmistakable. I should very much like to study these birds at their nests, but I had no time to look for any.

The Madagascar bush-lark is curiously misnamed, because it far prefers the open eroded grasslands, as do others of its kind, and it was particularly common in the bleak and desolate area near Mahatsinjo on the Tananarive-Majunga road.

This month of restless travel finally came to an end, and we ourselves came to rest at Sakaramy – a place about half-way between Diego Suarez and Joffreville, on the Montagne d'Ambre. It was a pleasant place, up out of the heat and the maddening winds of Diego itself. Before us, there was a wide sweep of open rolling grass with patches of forest, not unlike the country round Molo in Kenya. These plains spread downwards to the unpopular town of Diego which lay before us spread out like an aerial photograph. It lies on the south shore of the huge and most perfect natural harbour in the world – a narrow, close-guarded entrance leading into a vast blue inland lagoon, deep enough and wide enough to anchor almost all the capital ships of the world. Cap Diego poked into the north side of this anchorage like a finger, and on it the red dusty strip of the huge airfield was clearly visible from our cool heights.

Behind us rose up the still cooler heights of the d'Ambre massif, with the little rest resort of Joffreville nestling at its base – a place of shade and quiet relief to one worried with the dust, heat and dirt of Diego some twenty miles lower; and therefore of course, the residence of the brass hats of Garrison and Island H.Q. The forests clothing the mountain behind Joffreville were damp and cool, but only deceptively pleasant. For they were the haunt of millions of leeches, which lurked poised on every bordering twig and grassblade on the narrow forest paths. They strike and stick as soon as any warm-blooded creatures brush past them, and their bite was maddeningly painful and bloody as all leech bites are. Only the tip of a lighted cigarette applied to them would ever cause them to drop.

There followed an orgy of camp building which was fun at the time, and then came plenty of time to indulge in bird watching. Here in the Northern Savannah country, the bird life was really rather poor, but as I had more leisure and opportunity then, I came to know the local bird life better than elsewhere on the island. Fortunately too, we stayed there over one complete nesting season, so the camera was kept busy too.

From the top of the Queen's Palace at Antananarivo, one can see thousands of acres of flooded rice fields surrounding the town, all dotted with innumerable specks of white – each a cattle egret. They are indeed one of the most noticeable birds in the central plateau, either in rice fields or following grazing cattle – one bird to one beast. Here again, at Sakaramy they were present in thousands. After an October grass fire had nearly destroyed our camp, the egrets could be seen converging from all directions, attracted by the smoke. They stood round the edges of the blaze, picking up grasshoppers and other insects driven out by the flames; and later when the fire died down, they stalked in hundreds over the blackened but still smoking ground, picking up other tit-bits of food – their plumage still white and immaculate in spite of the clouds of ash disturbed by the wind. Then too, was the heyday of the kestrels, which wind-hovered for minutes on end over the burnt ground, catching the grasshoppers as they leapt and eating them in mid-air. These kestrels were aggressive birds, and one of them repeatedly attacked two tame ring-tailed lemurs in my camp for no reason at all.

November brought the welcome relief of rain, the country turned green overnight and nesting was soon in full swing, and lasted for three whole months. A pigmy kingfisher obligingly tunnelled and laid its three white eggs in the bank of the camp rubbish pit. Alas, it soon attracted the attention of my sweeper askari, who dug out the tunnel and triumphantly brought the three eggs plus bird to my office – knowing that his Commanding Officer showed this peculiar form of the general European madness. To his astonishment, eggs and bird were regretfully returned, but the bird inevitably deserted and the askari thought me even madder than before.

One of the major triumphs of our camp construction was the 'Danish' floor of our Mess-room – designed by Cai of course. This was a masterpiece, made of thousands of hardwood sticks, cut to about a foot in length, squared at the top and sharpened at the other end. These were driven in close to each other in the ground, making a distinctly unusual form of parquet flooring. Cai swore it would last for ever, and I could well believe it; it certainly saved much dust. Cutting of the necessary sticks in the neighbouring forest formed a useful punishment for the minor offenders who paraded before me daily in the Orderly

Room – the number of sticks being increased with the severity of the crime; and so in time the floor was complete. But all such offenders were ordered to look out for birds' nests as well as they toiled in the forest, and the rewards were sometimes rich as far as I was concerned.

By this means a nest of the Madagascar white-eye was found not far from the camp as late as 21st March. When I saw it, the nest was of the typical white-eye type, underslung in the fork of a branch, and very flimsy in construction. There were two eggs, rather elongated, and uniformly pale blue in colour; as the two parents were trilling anxiously nearby I left them. On revisiting the nest ten days later I found the eggs had hatched, and one parent sitting very close. I therefore made the usual rough sort of bush hide nearby (my proper hide being an inconvenient item for military baggage) and returned again to hide up the following day shortly after midday.

The bird most obligingly returned a few seconds after I had settled in, but immediately she had done so, a heavy thunderstorm broke and she sat tight for half an hour, getting very wet and swaying heavily in the wind. Not wishing to disturb her, I also sat on; my hide was by no means waterproof either, so I was soaked to the skin in a matter of minutes. By half past three it had however cleared and I dried out in the sun again. The bird immediately left, and then fed the chicks four times in ten minutes, bringing small green caterpillars and being most deliberate at the nest. As with so many birds, she announced her arrival by a short trilling and a low *tuk-tuk* note.

The next day I had another session with them in the last two hours of the morning. The female alternately fed and brooded the chicks. After a while the male appeared and then ensued a period of that delightful devoted attention by both which is one of the joys of close watching at the nest. They both took it in turns to visit the nest, the male feeding the chicks and then brooding them until the female appeared; then he hopped off, while the female attended them, and so on for an hour or more. It was very curious to see how the male always sat facing the hide, and herself facing away. I could tell as soon as the mate was nearby, because the sitting bird would suddenly stretch its neck eagerly, look round and hop off as soon as the other arrived. The acute awareness of a bird at its nest, even engaged in other duties, was well shown once when a kestrel flew close overhead; the sitting hen cowered quickly, but did not leave the chicks. Between the pair, they averaged eight visits to the hour with food.

By now, some of the flimsy material used to sling the nest was beginning to give way – a miscalculation birds seldom make. The whole structure appeared most precarious, and it was most instructive to watch the sitting bird shifting its weight around as the wind swayed the branch. As often with a contented bird, the hen would doze off while sitting, closing up the lower eyelid till the eye space was a curious white patch.

Four days later, when I revisited the spot, I was distressed to find this nest also gone the way of so many at Sakaramy – the fabric destroyed and the chicks missing. The destruction rate of nests in Madagascar was as high as it is in Kenya, and there I am sure the local snakes were to blame. In particular, my suspicions fell most darkly on Cai's two pet boa constrictors which had the free run of our camp. These gave me many an unpleasant moment, when I met them unexpectedly, either curled up on a roof beam in the Mess, or in my office, fairly licking their chops in anticipation of a tight squeeze round something. The fact that they are harmless, and are indeed the ones which children play with in zoos, did nothing to allay my uneasiness whenever I encountered them; I still don't like snakes! It is one of the odd things about this odd island that these large snakes are in fact boas, related to the South American boas, and not pythons which are the African equivalents.

Our camp buildings were constructed entirely of locally grown materials, and we were particularly proud of our walls, which we made of two layers of sisal poles split lengthwise and so overlapped that they were practically draught and weather proof. A pair of magpie robins which frequented my office building also found these double walls very much to their liking, and at the end of January furthered our already intimate acquaintance by building a very neat little cup nest between two layers, about four feet off the ground and lined snugly with donkey hair.

Almost any black and white bird is inevitably called the

magpie something or other, and these are no exception; but in fact it is only the cock bird who is resplendent in glossy black and white, and the hen is much more dowdy and coloured greyish brown and dingy white. The English robin too finds its counterpart all over the world, often on no stronger ground than that the imitator has a reddish breast or is similarly domestic in habits. In fact, however, these Madagascar birds in many ways resemble flycatchers more than the related chats, though the song is indeed most robin-like, being short, slow and tinkling as if the bird was reluctant to let each note fall. By closing one's eyes, one could be transported straight back to a frosty February morning in a garden at home by this sweet sound. Sometimes too, a glimpse of the bird would suggest a robin, as it stood motionless on a twig with head tilted for a second; then cocked up and depressed its tail before flying off to another twig – *Ah me, no worms just here, I'm afraid*!

This nest when I first looked at it contained three black naked chicks a week old. Two days later Cai's evil reptiles had also found it and gobbled up two of the chicks. They returned for the other when it had fattened up a bit nine days later, but not before I had found out a lot more about their home life from a nearby hide.

The hen was exceptionally bold, and treated my efforts at secrecy with complete contempt, in spite of repeated warning notes by the cock whenever she approached the nest. I could not in fact get her to pose for long enough before she slipped behind the crack in the sisal poles, so I partially blocked the crack with a natural looking dead leaf. This she ignored completely, merely diving in over the top of it as she returned; I then tried the expedient of removing the whole pole in front of the nest, replacing it again at the end of the session. This did not worry her either, and certainly gave me all the pictures I wanted.

The solitary chick was fed almost every twenty minutes, the parent birds clearly overestimating the capacity of their offspring's stringy gullet, and trying to stuff into it each time a single very large item, either a beetle grub about one and a half inches long, or a big green bug, or a large black beetle. This required determined efforts each time, the chick finally sagging in a pop-eyed manner to the bottom of the nest as it was finally gagged. Indeed, I do not blame the parents, because as soon as they left the nest again in search of more food, the chick became restless once more, and gave vent to a constant succession of the most unchicklike squeaks, gurgles and whistles, which I would not have believed it to be capable of making had I not been hiding close to it. Such a noise could clearly not be tolerated for long, and back the parents came again to gag it once more with a leathery grub.

The arrival of the parents was announced by a low sweet song from a bush behind me, so that I had plenty of time to get ready. The cock distrusted me however, and was always most hurried at the nest, without the calm deliberation of the hen. (Plate 17).

From the wide low window of my office, I often found relief from the tedium of making up innumerable weekly returns by gazing at the wide view beyond. I used to wonder, for example, how often the military powers that be think that the troops changed their religion; week after week I used carefully to detail the same return of the number of Mohammedans, Seventh Day Adventists, Atheists and what have you in my small unit. To my knowledge, the Mohammedans were still Mohammedan after a year or more, the atheists still atheistic – but should one week ever be missed, back would come a sharp reminder from G.H.Q. that they were unaware how many atheists there were in my unit that week, and would I please inform them forthwith or sooner. The military mind, or machine, is quite incredible, but, in spite of this I suppose we always win the war in the end.

The view indeed was magnificent. Diego Bay shimmered glassily blue in the dancing heat haze above the town. In the nearer distance, the shimmer was steadied by the darker forest patches, and these were washed in turn by the metachronal waves which rolled over the tall yellow grass in the foreground. Along the forest edges I often used to watch that curiously, but delightfully, named bird the kirombo cuirol, undulating in its flight, its whistling call keeping time with its swoops. Its head always seemed too large for its body.

As the rain set in, so the grasslands turned green once more and became alive with the little wing-snapping cisticola warblers who circled high in the sky and came clicking down in spirals to earth again. Their name of cloudscraper warblers is indeed an appropriate one. These birds frequent only the grassy ridges, and not the hollows. In the course of time, between orgies of garrison pen-pushing, I had tracked down quite a few nests from my office window. These, on inspection, were typical grass-warbler nests, a deep domed cup tied over the top with green grass blades, the whole resembling a miniature gourd. The nests are well lined with soft vegetable down and contain usually four or five eggs. Many of these nests went the way of nearly all in that area, but in one the chicks did hatch out and I was able to watch the affairs of the home from a hide a few feet away.

The hen (although indeed one cannot really distinguish the sexes, and often it may be the cock who shows more solicitude for the chicks), amused me. She was the first bird I had seen get really angry with her chicks, and it was entirely her own fault too since she stuffed them at such a rate that the little things were completely satiated and lay limply at the bottom of the nest with squashed caterpillars hanging grotesquely out of their beaks. This was not good enough for her, and back she came with more a few minutes later; and through the walls of the nest which I had thinned slightly I could see her stamping and *chukking* at the chicks as she tried one after another with the unwanted morsel. Poor things, she was finally stuffing them with really large caterpillars at the rate of eight visits per hour – but most of the time they were just *f.u.r.t.b.* as we used to say as children – full up and ready to burst.

The wing-clicking flight of these small warblers is very characteristic, although I was several times deceived into thinking the bird had arrived by the flicking flight of large grasshoppers nearby. As with many birds, her attention to nest sanitation was most scrupulous. Although she twice removed excreta in her beak, at all other times she swallowed it – not really the unpleasant procedure it might be imagined, as the excreta of most small chicks is enclosed in a sort of gelatinous sac. Before leaving the nest after each visit too, she looked carefully all round and under the outside of the nest as I have often watched other birds do. This is probably to destroy marauding ants, though Madagascar appeared singularly free of such notorious types as the East African 'siafu'.

A few days later our acquaintance was once more sadly cut short, and I found a large hole in the top of the nest and the contents gone – possibly a rat this time. Nearby however, I stumbled on a pair with new-fledged chicks just on the wing, and it was pleasant to know that at least one pair of birds had completed the full cycle.

Yes, Madagascar was a fascinating place, and these intervals with birds at close quarters, and time off spent in just watching birds was a welcome relief from the tedious round of singularly Inactive Military Service. All this was under the peculiar conditions of wartime occupation of the island; now that fourteen more years have rolled past, I should love to visit the island again and renew old acquaintances among the birds I knew there, and make new friends too the while.

The island too, will always remain in my memory as the home of two of the noisiest birds I have ever heard. One of these is an odd creature called the sicklebill; the pundits are uncertain whether to relate it to the shrikes or the starlings, but in behaviour and appearance it resembles neither in the least. Indeed, they resemble most the East African woodhoopoes or kakelaars. With their long curved bill, black and white plumage, their habit of running up trees and along branches, poking into crevices and hanging upside down by their claws, chattering the whole time, and with their slow, laboured flight from tree to tree, the resemblance is striking. They travel along the forest edges in parties of a dozen or more, and suddenly invade a patch of trees with a loud chatter, and then pass on, perhaps not to be seen again for several days. Their row is quite indescribable; their chief note is a loud chopping *chow-chow-chow*, and this is mixed up with the weirdest medley of cries, groans and almost laughs.

In this they are rivalled, if not outclassed, by another queer bird of passage there, the broad-billed roller, whose appearance is no less striking than the noise they make. The large yellow bill, russety back and breast, patch of deep violet on the shoulder, deep violet primaries, blue rump, and brown tail showing a white band above in flight, coupled with the squat roller shape and exceptionally large black lustrous eye are quite unmistakable. From November to January, the forest round the camp resounded with their clamour and even the phlegmatic African Askaris were stirred to remark it. The main call is a harsh, loud and penetrating chatter, mixed with a call extraordinarily like that so-human call of the Scottish grouse – *go-back, go-back.*

One bird calling is the signal for others to start, and the row is quite deafening for a few minutes, then all suddenly stop together. They are curiously inquisitive birds, and will often fly closer to have a good look at you. They were paired at the time, the pairs flying together, and the behaviour of the two was often clownish in the extreme. They conversed the whole time with each other in grunts and chatter, and suddenly, at some witty and clearly Rabelaisian remark by one, the other would throw its head back, with beak wide open and head shaking in mirth, and give vent to the most astonishing laugh, in which the other bird then joined.

The clatter and chatter and grunting of these two most extraordinary birds was my final farewell to the island, as I left the camp early one cold dawn and the Sunderland furrowed the blue waters of Diego Bay, carrying me back at last to my regulation issue of chalk-stripe suiting and – home.

Ibis Point, Lake Magadi. Wood ibis, marabout storks, flamingoes in distance, Magadi 1940

CHAPTER 7

LAKE MAGADI

LAKE MAGADI is a wonderful place. Lying near the southern border of Kenya, where the Great Rift Valley has dipped from the cool Naivasha highlands to the rolling thorn tree plains of northern Tanganyika, it looks from the air like the imprint of a silver hand in the midst of the yellowing waste.

Its glistening, shimmering surface spells water – but water fit for the survival of only a few kinds of birds and animals in this blistering, heat-dazed valley. For 'Magadi' means soda, and the lake is now one of the most concentrated and richest soda deposits in the world. Many aeons ago, the vast Lake Kamasia which filled the whole of the Rift Valley in Kenya slowly shrank in size with increasing desiccation of the land; and as the deeper parts became isolated one from the other, there formed the chain of Lakes now known as Baringo, Hannington, Nakuru, Elmenteita, Naivasha and Magadi. The shallower of these lakes formed great natural evaporating pans for the concentration of the salts leached from the surrounding volcanic soils, until, as at Magadi, the sodium atom and its satellite molecules of carbonate, sulphate, chloride and hydroxide controlled the very existence of the plants and animals which have won their survival in the salty waters. The hot volcanic springs which still flow in this area bring further deposits of salts to be evaporated by the scorching sun and enrich the layers already there. Now, only those living things who by mutation and evolution have been able to adapt themselves to a world of soda can survive in a curiously close-knit community of algae, fish, insects and birds who live in and on the caustic waters.

Man has come too, as he inevitably does, to exploit such

natural riches, and now the grey dusty banks of the lake support a small community of Europeans, Asians and Africans engaged in digging out the semi-solid soda and feeding it for purification and its hundred and one modern usages to a great iron-roofed factory on the shores of the lake. This enterprise is one of the subsidiaries of a great chemical concern and the men who work there deserve every admiration for earning their living in such parched and soda-laden air.

As is the way of modern exploitation, Magadi is now served by road and rail from the capital city of Nairobi, some eighty miles away; and while neither are fast in the modern sense, one gets there just the same in the end. The road I know well, for Magadi has long been a favourite haunt of mine for bird watching and photography. It climbs through the rolling parkland west of Nairobi up to the cold and windswept shoulders of the Ngong hills, and then drops down and down and down, past the famous prehistoric site of Olorgesailie to the heat-laden dusty floor of the Rift where lies Magadi.

If I was ever asked to show Africa to a visitor, I would not take him to the coral fringed coasts where the blue spray breaks on silver sand fringed with coconut palms; nor to the cold and rolling grasslands of the highlands, dotted with little white settlers' houses; nor to the patchwork native reserves, nor the montane forests – no, I would take him to the top of the Ngong hills. From there, I would bid him look westwards across the seemingly limitless Rift, into the blue distance of the Mau escarpment, across the endless miles of yellow plain broken with the grey and ochre of flat-topped thorns and the little rocky hills scarred by numberless waterless channels. Mile upon mile of empty, desolate land, whose vastness is exciting and awe-inspiring, but not forbidding; a gigantic panorama whose beauty is heightened at dusk, as the flaming scarlet and gold of the dust-laden sunset gives way to the deep blueness of the tropical night; that, to me, is Africa, and this view from the Ngong hills is the essence of the African emptiness on a tremendous scale.

All of these Rift Valley lakes are abundantly rich in wader and water bird life; many are resident, some are migratory. The soda flats of Magadi, Elmenteita and Hannington; the water lily patches and papyrus swamps of Naivasha, the tussock swamps of Nakuru – each have their own rich quota of delight for the bird watcher. I have often promised myself a leisurely photographic safari down these Rift Valley lakes in the nesting season; but the opportunity has never yet arisen, and no doubt it will be 'one of these days on retirement' – and a special trip back to Africa to do so.

As with so many African birds, the breeding season of the Magadi birds depends on the rainfall. Most of the birds, except the birds of prey, breed during or just after the 'long rains' in March, April and May. If these rains behave themselves, which they seldom do in Kenya these days, the end of May will usually see the height of the breeding season, at that exciting time when the early courtship and nest making is over, and the hard sat eggs are beginning to chip with the struggles of the emerging chicks.

For that reason Empire Day, 24th May, which is a holiday in Kenya, holds a very special place in a bird diary for the year. If it falls on a Monday, which it all too seldom does, it always means for us the grand prospect of a long weekend with the Magadi birds. The Powers that Be are often generous in allowing the Saturday morning off too, so the Friday evening sees the car laden to the roof with all the impedimenta of safari, which must include the all-important drums of water since such is not obtainable on the shores of the lake. 4.30 p.m. signals the start of the eighty mile trip from Nairobi, and the car is eased gently over the numerous pot-holes and bumps on the road to the Ngongs – a broken spring would be disaster at this stage. Beyond the hills, the road is reasonably good and maintained by the Soda Company so the miles spin pleasantly by.

'Spotting' the various roadside birds which one finds in abundance in this low thorn-bush country is a great sport on such a trip, particularly if the rains have been good and the open grassy spaces are carpeted with a lush ephemeral green growth of new grass, starred with the white, yellow and blue of the various plains flowers which grow up, flower and die seemingly overnight when the first rain soaks the parched ground. At such a time the grasslands and the thorn tree clumps are alive with birds; the various larks, pipits, grass warblers and *Quelia* finches in the long grass, and the thorn trees with weavers, barbets, scimiter bills and countless other small birds for which a passing glimpse is insufficient for identification. The long thin upper branches of a certain *Acacia* are hung with the curious double entrance nest of the grey-headed social weaver – one entrance blocked if the nest is used for breeding, both entrances open if for roosting only; the closely woven gourd-shaped nests of the vitelline weaver hang solitary from the smaller trees, while the largest thorn trees are festooned with great tangled masses of Speke's weaver's nests, many of which are often used or parasitised by the smaller finches such as the cut-throat.

Occasional coursers pick their way elegantly across the stony ground, various raptors perch on the thorns, and there always seem to be one hundred and one things to stop and investigate; the road itself is worth a long weekend! But the destination is Magadi itself, and the idea (which we have never yet achieved) to get to our camping place before nightfall, so many things have unwillingly to be left. As dusk falls, the nightjars fly down for the evening squat on the dusty road – a curious habit which I cannot explain, for they do not seem to indulge in dust baths as do many other birds; there is a suggestion they swallow grit from the roads to fill their gizzards. The headlights of the car pick out their eyes as two glowing red spots many yards away, and at the very last minute, when it seems that the wheels must certainly crush them, they flip off the road past the windscreen with that peculiar wavering moth-like flight of theirs. It is seldom one really hits them when travelling at normal speeds.

During the rains the various dry dongas across the road are liable to be flooded with the rainfall off the hills – flash floods which dry as quickly as they rise, and on the 1952 trip we ran into two of such which caused us some anxiety. With the water over the running boards and across the floor, the faithful Land Rover stuttered within a minute of entering the stream, but by coaxing her across we made the other side just as the engine faltered and died completely; so here we had an enforced wait while the distributor and plugs dried in the heat of the engine.

Coming back that weekend we were not so lucky, and the engine died in the middle of a deep running drift; we perforce had to wait on our mechanical island with the swirling water all round until the engine dried sufficiently to start again – the time being enlivened with the snack remains of our camp food, and heated arguments as to whether the water was still rising or falling. There is always the danger on this road during the rains of being marooned between two such drifts, but fortunately the wait is never very long.

The road runs along the higher east shore of the lake, and as night closes in, in the distance the lights of the small Magadi township twinkle a friendly welcome. But our destination is beyond the town down at the south end of the lake, so driving carefully over the causeways between the evaporating pans below the town, we pass up the single main street and out across the airstrip and inevitable golf course whose fairways are sparse tussock grass, the 'greens' the sandy brown circles of so many courses in Kenya.

At this point we invariably lose our way in the dark, and take the wrong turning in each track, and great are the arguments as to whether we should keep nearer the lake or farther away. While thus arguing on our last trip, we narrowly avoided two bunkers on the golf course only to sink a minute later up to the axles in the one and only soft patch of mud for miles around – a little isolated bog not more than a few feet square. Unhitching the trailer, which was also bogged to the axles, and engaging low range in the gearbox, the Land Rover literally chewed its way out of the muddy mess. By dint of shoving and sweating, the trailer was rehitched, and popped out like a cork under the tremendous pull of the car now on more solid ground. By now, it was about 9 p.m., so we thankfully hitched the tent fly between the car and a thorn tree on the ridge overlooking the Lake, fixed up the camp beds, had a quick supper and fell into refreshing sleep in the soft balmy air which brings such cool relief after a burning day at these low levels.

Next morning was all plain sailing of course in the daylight, and we were not far off the road after all. Our usual camping place by the side of a dry stream bed on the southern shore of the lake was quickly reached, the tent fly slung between two trees and the camp made shipshape. A tent itself is rarely necessary at this altitude, and flysheet only slung between the trees provides the necessary shade during the day. The nights are warm and soft, and sleeping thus under an open sky with the silver twinkle of the stars in the velvet blue of the sky above is one of the greatest joys of such a trip.

It is pleasant to be up as the sun tips over the Kajiado escarpment, and the early mornings here have a refreshing coolth which reflects itself in the chorus of dawn song as the larks and pipits spiral up from the grass on quick quivering wings. Across the soda flats, where the channel of the hot springs meanders down to the lake, the massed ranks of the flamingo flocks groan and grunt in the clear morning air as they paddle about in the warm shallow water. Now and again sheets of scarlet and pink flame across the sky as more and more drop in to join the paddling crowds.

Canny creatures, these flamingos: as one walks slowly towards them, there is an imperceptible drift away, so that the distance between never decreases. Here and there one will uncoil its long neck above the crowd, looking like a walking-stick with the crook held upwards, and carefully judge your approach. At some silent signal, a whole forest of walking-sticks rise up together, and with a sudden flash of scarlet the flock rises and takes wing, to settle a safer distance away. Down go the walking-sticks, and with upturned bills they start dibbling away again at their feet, and the groaning and grunting commence anew.

There is a marked difference between the feeding habits of the lesser and the greater flamingos. The lesser, which are far more numerous, wade slowly about, dibbling with inverted heads just in front of their feet and occasionally swinging their neck from side to side and covering quite an area of ground. The greaters, which feed solitary among the thousands of lessers and stand a good shoulder above them, stand in the one place pivoting slowly on their long legs which mark time quickly in the same spot, stirring up a cloud of bottom muck; the long neck and curiously down curved beak then stretch down between the legs and the stirred up muck is sifted with a quick dibbling movement. When the possibilities of the one small spot are exhausted, up goes the neck again, the bird stalks a few paces away, and the treading starts all over again. Their food is different too, since the greaters eat far more insect food than do the lessers.

Pelicans occur in small numbers in these hot springs, and they love to sit on the stones of the raised causeway across them. This is the pink-backed pelican, and I can never tire of watching them. Now and again one will alight on the water with outspread wings and neck tucked in, for all the world like a Sunderland flying boat, and make a ponderous belly landing throwing up a shower of spray on each side. Once afloat on the water, Alex calls them Spanish galleons, and indeed they are. They float about with a bulbous hull, a high raised poop, and the head and great beak resemble the carved figures on the bowsprit. No description could be more apt.

There is no shortage of food for these great ships of the Magadi fleet; it is there all round and under them in the myriad shoals of little silvery fish which live in these hot springs. One scoop of the great pouch like beak and down go several hundreds of these fish at one gulp, although on Magadi I have never seen the pelicans driving the fish in an ever-narrowing circle as they do on Lake Victoria and elsewhere.

These little silvery cichlid fishes, *Tilapia grahami*, are one of the most astonishing adaptations in nature. They are clearly descended from some ancient Kamasian cichlid, which as the lake waters shrank and became more and more isolated from the other lakes in the chain, gradually adapted themselves to the increasingly saline and caustic conditions till now they swarm in countless millions in all the hot springs at the southern end of the lake. The males in breeding colouration are a most glorious sky-blue, and could they be adapted to fresh water, would make most attractive indoor aquarium fishes. Though they will indeed adapt themselves slowly to increasing amounts of fresh water, they are unable to live in water which is completely fresh, and die after a short while. The biggest are only two to three inches long, and their nesting habits (for they surely nest as do the other cichlids) are still unknown. From the scientific point of view, their physiology must be of considerable interest in the method of osmotic regulation of their body fluids, and in excretion, since they live in a very caustic medium which would kill other fish in a matter of seconds. They are probably exclusively algal feeders, and can be seen browsing on the thick green slime which coats the bottom in these channels.

Millions of wriggling black midge larvae also feed on this bottom slime, and the algal felt and midge larvae in turn form the food of the flamingos. These midge larvae and their little two-winged adult stages which cluster at the water edges also form the food of the many thousands of waders which frequent Magadi, particularly in the migration season. Mixed flocks of these wading birds can be seen all round the lake shore, running hither and thither poking and dibbling in the soft mud as is their habit.

Nest finding at Magadi is great fun, and demands a special technique of its own, involving the use of a car. The mud and shingle flats which ring the lake are for the most part hard, though somewhat hummocky here and there. Avoiding these hummocks and obvious soft patches, the technique is to drive slowly over the mud in a car, with one keen-eyed person sitting on the bonnet or front mudguards using field glasses to spot a sitting bird. As soon as a sitter rises and runs off, the car is stopped, and with eyes glued to the spot where the bird rose up, the party walks forward and with any luck finds the nest. This is best done in the early morning before the heat haze starts dancing and shimmering on the mud flats, distorting the ground and distance.

I have, it is true, found occasional nests on the shingle by squatting or lying down and watching the suspicious behaviour of pairs through glasses, but one often finds one is sitting just by the nest itself wondering why the birds will not return! Merely walking over the ground, just looking for nests, is nearly always a sheer waste of time since the cryptic colouration of most of the wader eggs here is perfect, and the nests mere scrapes in the shingle. Walking over parts of these mud flats is however a disconcerting experience at first, since one is accompanied by little cracks and explosions at each step. Closer investigation will show that all the little pebbles are cemented to the ground and to each other by a film of crystalline soda, and as the weight of one's foot alters the pressure on the mud surface, this thin cement cracks, and the stones released from the tension may fly up several feet in the air in front and behind – poltergism which needs no supernatural explanation this time!

There is not a great variety of resident breeding birds at Lake Magadi itself. Those there are may be divided into three groups depending on the habitats they select for nesting. On the extensive flats and shingle banks the commonest breeders are the Magadi or chestnut-banded plover, Kittlitz's plover, the blacksmith plover, and latterly, avocets. The marginal sparse tufted grasslands fringing the shores are used by singing bush larks, several species of grass warblers, long-tailed doves, occasional guinea fowl and coursers, while the pin-tailed sand-grouse and the abundant finch larks nest on both the shingle and the grass. Black-bellied sunbirds and cardinal woodpeckers utilise the small scrubby trees in this grassland, together with a host of other bush nesting birds.

At both the south and north ends of the lake, there are swamps unconnected with the main lake, which are probably the breeding grounds of the black-winged stilts, cape wigeon and various other duck and snipe, though I have not yet had the opportunity to investigate these. It is probable also that the pelicans and the lesser flamingos may nest near the north end of the lake, but this is unconfirmed.

The commonest breeder on the mud flats is undoubtedly the Magadi plover itself, an interesting little plover which is confined entirely to the soda-lake of Magadi, and the somewhat similar Lake Natron in Tanganyika. Curiously enough its presence has never yet been confirmed on the other soda-lakes of the Rift Valley, and its nearest relative is a related race which occurs in far away south-west Africa – a most unusual distribution. On Magadi it occurs in hundreds and probably thousands, and is frequently seen in pairs or small flocks running along the stagnant water's edge picking and dipping for its food amongst the débris of pink flamingo feathers and algae washed to the edge by the wind. On the dry mud and shingle flats, they run hither and thither for all the world like little mice scurrying about, and the brown of their backs blends perfectly with the khaki coloured mud.

The blacksmith plovers are boldly conspicuous at close quarters with their striking black, white and grey plumage. They are usually paired, each pair holding a very definite area of territory on the shingle. Like the redshank at home, they give first warning of any intruder on the flats and on the slightest provocation are up in the air wheeling round with their metallic *tink-tink* note, from which the bird so aptly gets its name. The Kittlitz's plovers occur in isolated pairs running swiftly over the stones, where their mottled dun plumage again blends perfectly with the background, and they, like the Magadi plovers, seldom take wing.

The isolated brackish pools of water on the flats are the haunt of the elegant black-winged stilts, and occasional pairs of cape wigeon float peacefully on the oily surface. These pools too, are the feeding grounds of the striking black and white avocets, who have, within the last two years, started breeding at Magadi.

At the breeding season, these shingle flats are divided into definite territories by the various plovers and waders. The Magadi plovers are somewhat catholic in their choice of nesting site, and may breed almost anywhere in the wide expanse, in shingle, on the plain mud, but always in a dry place. Their nests are astonishingly like those of the English ringed plover, the merest scrape on the surface in which the two disproportionately large pointed eggs are laid. Their stone ground colour, with purplish and black speckling and splodges are similar, too, to the ringed plover, and cryptic to a high degree. Indeed, only the unusual regularity of their shape will betray their presence at close quarters. I often wonder how the birds themselves find their own nests, but as Konrad Lorenz has shown, most wild animals are highly sensitive to apparently minute differences in their *Gestalt*, or world around them, and I suppose to birds of this size the immediate surroundings of the shingle and shapes of the stones are as distinctive to them as ranges of hills and plains are on the greater scale to us. Sometimes their nests, particularly when placed on plain hard-baked mud, are decorated with a ring of the little flat pinky pebbles so common at Magadi – which often makes them quite conspicuous; but more often there is no attempt at nest-building whatever.

The blacksmith plovers often select sites near some fairly conspicuous landmark, such as a shingle bank, or near, or on, the stone causeways marking the track across the southern bays; again no attempt at nest-building is made, a shallow scrape serving to hold the two to four dark brown, black speckled eggs, which resemble those of the English lapwing. The Kittlitz's plovers have the very curious and interesting habit of partly burying their eggs in the sandy shingle until just the tops are visible. When the bird leaves the nest, particularly if it is disturbed, a few quick scuffles of the toes serve to cover the eggs completely before the bird runs away; all that remains to indicate their whereabouts is a ring of slightly finer sand. These can sometimes be picked out from the surrounding shingle by a keen eye. Whether this habit serves for concealment, or for preservation of an even temperature of the eggs is an interesting speculation though one cannot suppose this plover has adopted this habit with either end in view. It would not appear to lead to any greater survival than the cryptic but otherwise exposed eggs of the Magadi plover for instance.

Photographing birds on these shingle flats is perhaps one of the most trying ordeals one can endure in this sport. I well remember the first time I tried. We had found a particularly picturesque Magadi plover's nest, with the two eggs lying in a little ring of flat pebbles close by some curiously shaped hummocks of soda-encrusted mud. As at that time, I had no proper hide with me, I set up the camera as low as possible nearby, covered it with an old piece of cloth, fixed my distance release and retired some forty feet away with a string connected to the shutter and lay down on the mud, covered by an old blanket and a mackintosh.

This distance release is one of the intricate and practically useless gadgets I have made from time to time to fit on the camera. It is a sheer fluke if it ever goes off when I pull the string, and yet at other times a mere puff of wind will set the shutter off when least expected. I get a lot of fun designing and making such gadgets, but very few of them ever prove their worth, and sooner or later are relegated to the junk-box! This method of photography is in any case bad practice, since one can never be sure what position the bird is really in from a distance, and worse than that, it inevitably means exposing oneself and thus disturbing the bird, in order to reset the shutter. I certainly do not recommend it, unless as a last desperate resort when all else fails.

It was about 9 a.m. when I settled down, and as the sun climbed higher and higher in the brazen sky my position under the thick covering on the exposed flats became more and more unbearable. I got cramp, the sweat poured down my back and into my eyes, half blinding me, my shirt stuck to my skin, and the stench of soda nearly sickened me. All the while the owner of the nest ran about quite unconcernedly a few feet away from the eggs, and showed no sign whatever of wanting to return. Once indeed, I thought the bird had returned, and pulled the string, but fortunately as usual the shutter did not click, and on raising myself slightly I saw that the dancing heat haze had deceived me, and the bird was in fact still several feet away from the eggs.

At length I could stick it no longer, and staggering off the ground at about 11.30 a.m. in sheer desperation I sat down right beside the camera, and covered myself with the blanket again, determined not to be beaten. To my astonishment, within a minute or two of my settling down, the bird came running back to the nest in that engaging way these plovers have, and with no hesitation stepped right over (Plate 18), and straddling the eggs fluffed out her breast feathers and squatted over them. The sun was blazing fiercely overhead, with sun temperatures well over the 100°F. mark, and within a very short while I had obtained all the pictures I wanted.

Since that time, I have used nothing but my standard hide in the orthodox way within a few feet of a nest on these mud flats, with a comfortable seat and plenty of ventilation. That experience also taught me the secret of the open-nesting birds at Magadi – that they are much more willing to return to their nests about noonday than at other times, and their first reaction at this hot time is to shade their eggs as quickly as they can. Most of the plovers there seldom sit on the eggs as closely as they do elsewhere; they usually just stand over them, with flank feathers fluffed out, moving from time to time to keep the eggs in the shade of their bodies as the sun moves overhead.

The air temperature is more than sufficient to incubate the eggs naturally, which indeed would become hard-boiled if exposed directly to the sun for too long there. I imagine they must also sit more closely in the cool of the night, but have not checked on this point.

The Magadi plovers do not seem to indulge in those delightful change-over ceremonies at the nest which other plovers show, and I have never been able to obtain a picture of a pair together at the nest. The blacksmith plovers certainly do so, and though there is little actual ceremony, the mate will stand beside the sitting bird for some time before the latter leaves. While sitting with the Magadi plovers described above, I spotted a sitting blacksmith not many yards away, who later was most obliging at her nest, and gave me two or three opportunities to portray the two together. It is one of the indescribable thrills of bird photography to see the one of a pair gradually approaching the sitting bird – will it, or won't it come near enough to get the two together? – and as excitement mounts, the climax is reached as the two finally stand side by side for a short while by the nest; not always, alas, in the most favourable attitude or position for picturing. Often however, the sitting bird will walk off before the other has approached close enough; but the few occasions are compensation enough when one can see the two together within a few feet of the hide, and perhaps obtain the picture of a lifetime.

This first visit to Magadi proved exceptionally good. The rains had been early and long, and on our usual Empire Day visit nesting was in full swing, and there was an abundance of nests and eggs of many kinds, and a good many chicks already hatched out. Just behind our camp, in a tuft of long grass, was a nest of the white-winged scrub robin with new hatched chicks, whose parents proved most assiduous in their duties, and gave some classical moments of bird photographic sport although their tail flicking habit proved rather tiresome, and caused a lot of failures of otherwise good pictures. As in so many instances, there was a convenient triangular stone nearby which afforded better opportunities to perch for a portrait than at the nest itself. (Plate 19).

Within a few hundred yards of the camp, we found several

Magadi plovers' nests with eggs, and several chicks – little grey-speckled downy creatures with the same cryptic squatting habit shown by most plover chicks. The pin-tail sandgrouse (which the local African labour used to trap in set nooses at the small waterhole above Magadi township as they came down to drink) were nesting almost colonially at the upper edge of the shingle, but efforts to picture the birds at the nest were quite fruitless. I began to think they never incubated their eggs at all, since there was never any sign of the birds whatever when hiding by the nest, even for hours at a time.

Several long-tailed doves' nests were found in the grass tufts, incredibly flimsy little platforms of sticks and grass perched insecurely a few inches off the ground, each with two small perfectly oval white eggs. The owners of one nest proved obliging for one member of our party, but I subsequently found them most shy; after watching them fluttering about a few feet from the nest after I had hidden up, without returning, I soon left them to sit in peace, as an anxious bird is never a good subject.

Finch larks' nests were common, neat little cups embedded in the shingle and hardened with soda, and usually shaded on one side by a large stone under which the nest was tucked. One pair of these proved easy subjects, and gave me a lot of fun and some good portraits since they were not at all shy. They had chicks, and dropped straight down to the nest from above on each visit, so that I had to be alert the whole time.

Subsequent visits have never proved quite as good as this first. The rains have failed or delayed with dreary consistency since then, but on my second visit, in the good company of Alex and Bill, we did find a few nests, though we were clearly too early for most. With his usual amazing faculty for finding nests, Bill discovered a Kittlitz's nest within a few minutes of arrival, just by the side of the gravel causeway over which we had just passed. A hide was erected nearby the same evening, and as usual the birds proved relatively tame when we tried them the next morning, returning to stand over the eggs within a very few minutes of my being hidden up. For most of the time she merely stood over the partly buried eggs, and made no attempt even to squat over them or fluff out her feathers.

When I gently disturbed her once or twice, it was interesting to watch the way she kicked the sand over the eggs before leaving, but she was always back within a few minutes again. She made no attempt to uncover the eggs deliberately again when she returned, and they became partly uncovered in time as she shifted her standing position from time to time. Sometimes she even stood on the eggs themselves.

Bill, who had had official sanction to collect a few specimen eggs of certain species for study purposes, spent most of the time in rather fruitless searches; and by the time we left was muttering darkly about catching the birds and squeezing the eggs out of them! He did however, find another blacksmith's nest also by the causeway, where the hide was later erected. These birds are somewhat wary, and the usual full precautions must be taken when hiding up to them, but the extra trouble is well worth while to ensure a contented subject who returns readily. When all is quiet, and the bird finally approaches unsuspiciously, one experiences the unforgettable thrill again of seeing a wary bird only a few feet from the hide. Having relatively long legs, they squat over the eggs on their ankles, never sinking right on to the eggs. (Plate 20). At close quarters these birds are a joy to watch with their sleek plumage and lustrous eye alert for any movement from the hide. In such short term work for only a day or two at a time, the hide, a conspicuous enough thing in all conscience in such open expanses, is never really accepted as entirely harmless, and it behoves one to make all movements even inside the hide as cautiously as possible; with some birds even sound is alarming and will send them precipitately off the nest in alarm.

At close quarters, the carpal spur on the wing of the blacksmith is very noticeable, but it appears a useless structure and I have no evidence that it is used for offensive, defensive or any other purpose.

On our last visit, again paid with Alex and a new companion John, the work was partly official as I had to collect several hundred *Tilapia* fry for transference elsewhere; but this did not take long. The main bird purpose was to study the avocets, a pair of which had been found breeding for the first time in Kenya some two months earlier in one of these southern bays.

We had no real hope of finding such unusual nests again, but the trip was in fact to have triumphant conclusions in this respect, as I shall relate later.

Having the versatile Land Rover on this trip was a blessing, and we were able to cover much more ground than normally over the mud. Again however, 24th May proved too early, and though most birds were paired and in territory, nests were still few and far between. The sandgrouse were particularly disappointing, as I had set my heart on getting them too this time; though we repeatedly flushed pairs from the shingle, we found no nests at all. The stilts were again also wading in pairs, but since they are marsh nesters we did not try to find them, as undoubtedly they had not started yet either. On the other hand the finch larks appeared to be finished, and we found many empty nests, though these tend to be so well preserved by the soda that they may well have been last season's nests.

We located several Magadi plovers' nests however, most of them with one egg only. At one of these we both had a successful time, and the little plover again captivated me with its dainty mouse-like ways. To see them running to the nest from some distance away, finally approaching with little stops and starts, till they finally cover the eggs, is a thrill not easily forgotten.

Three pairs of avocets were in evidence, two in the area where the first nest had been found, and one some distance away. This latter pair occupied a small island of gravel near the west shore, a little distance out in the lake. As their behaviour was most suspicious, Alex waded through the shallow water to the island which was only a few feet across. He discovered a shallow depression in the shingle there, an obvious nest, which on a flying visit there a week or two later contained eggs, but at the time it was a disappointment to find it empty.

On this trip, we rigged up a temporary hide of sticks and sacking by the hot springs to try and get some pictures of the flamingos, and when John and I had hidden Alex up here, we

PLATE 23A. Avocet approaching nest, Magadi 1952

PLATE 23B. Avocet settling on eggs, Magadi 1952

LATE 23A

PLATE 23B

Plate 24

carried on over the next ridge to where we had previously seen a pair of avocets wading in a shallow pool. They were still there when we arrived, and though we searched the area we could find nothing, and the pair did not seem to be particularly alarmed. As however it was nearing noon, and knowing the habits of the Magadi birds, I suggested to John that we retired a few hundred yards away to a ridge overlooking this pool. This we did, and lay watching the pair for some time through glasses.

Within a very short time, we suddenly noticed one of the pair wade out of the pool, and with nervous steps walk across a little gravel spit near the water's edge. In mounting excitement we watched her stop at one place, sink forward on to her breast on the gravel, fluff out her flank feathers and settle with that typical side to side shuffling of a contented brooding bird.

John and I carefully marked the spot, and jumping to our feet, raced down the hill with a triumphant if somewhat undignified shout of 'It's in the bag!' The bird rose when we were many yards away, but with our eyes glued to the spot we raced on, and within a few seconds were looking down with great joy at a shallow scrape in the shingle not far from the water's edge containing the two large pointed dark brown and black speckled eggs – one of the main objectives of the trip, and as far as we knew the second avocet's nest with eggs to be found in Kenya!

As the bird seemed amazingly shy, I dumped an old mackintosh on the ground some fifty feet away from where I reckoned the hide would have to be, thus making a low mound for the bird to become accustomed to, and we then drove back to give Alex the great news. He had had a very good morning with the flamingos and was in great form. As our time was limited to only three days, we decided to erect the hide in its final position late that same evening (far the best time to place a hide, for in the hours of darkness a bird does not seem to worry much about such strange objects near its nest, and by the next day shows little alarm). The hide was therefore duly erected at about 6.30 p.m., the hard soda mud proving unexpectedly difficult to drive the poles into; and as there was a stiff breeze blowing, the hide was well pegged down with guy ropes at each corner, and stones piled on the cloth round the sides and bottom. A flapping hide can be the cause of serious unnecessary alarm to a shy bird.

That evening Alex fried some masterly eggs and bacon for supper, and we went to bed with the sun, in high hopes for the morrow, lulled to sleep by the monotonous reeling of the nightjars.

I was to have first try in the morning, and as John wished to go back and have a look round the town, we installed Alex at the flamingo hide again, and John hid me up at the avocets before driving on to Magadi. The birds were still wading in the pool when we arrived, and the eggs were warm to touch, though the bird had not been sitting when we first topped the rise and looked over.

A pair of cape wigeon also floated peacefully on the pool, and after carefully focusing and checking of all the items, I settled in the hide in tense expectation. The wigeon sailed past once or twice, and the avocets, at the far end of the pool, waded slowly nearer dibbling here and there, and daintily scything through the bottom muck with their curious upturned bills. They waded right past the nest bank, with an occasional glance at the hide, but seemed quite unconcerned about the eggs. Up to the other end they went, and then slowly back again along the water's edge. The hide was getting hotter and hotter, and with sweat pouring off me I wondered desperately if they were ever going to return. At length, at about 11 o'clock, one of them turned towards the shingle bank, and with hesitant steps and many stops to pick up imaginary food – the typical 'false-feeding' displacement reaction shown by many waders and other birds when anxious – it left the water, and came slowly up the shingle (Plate 23A), starting calling with an insistent, monotonous *took-took* note. Circling behind the nest it seemed to come on slower and slower, and with my heart thumping with excitement I felt almost suffocated in the hide. Finally it reached the nest, and with a large black eye fixed alertly on the hide, it stood over the eggs for a while; then sinking forward she arranged the eggs underneath her with her beak (Plate 23B), then settled and fluffed out over the eggs. It was joy supreme to see the beautiful creature sitting not ten feet away, and apparently not too worried about the hide; I scarcely dared breathe or release the shutter, but when I finally did so, she scarcely moved, and my whispered 'Got you!' she never noticed.

That heat worried her a lot, and she sat panting with open bill, still keeping up an occasional alarm call; though wary, she did not appear scared, and I was amused to see her throat feathers flapping in and out with her panting and call note combined. She moved a good many times, standing up, rearranging the eggs, shuffling about and sitting down again, only to repeat the performance all over again a few minutes later. She constantly cocked her head up at the sky, as if to see whether it would cloud over, but the sun blazed uninterruptedly all that morning.

The male (I call them thus though in fact the sexes cannot be distinguished), continued feeding and preening in the shallow water beyond the nest for some time. Then, in rising excitement again, I saw him too leave the water, and with much false feeding and head bobbing, walk forward to the nest too. Here he stood for a while behind the female, or slightly to one side, affording me superb opportunities to portray both birds together. (Plate 24). The alarm note of the female never ceased, and after a time she stretched stiffly up and walked off the nest, giving me a good chance again to observe the peculiar grey-blue webbing on her feet and the boldly contrasting black and white of her plumage.

The male then sat on by himself for a bit, then he too left for the water; the hen bird again returned shortly after and I had the great delight once more of seeing the whole change-over repeated again. There was no real ceremony however, and each bird appeared to take the other for granted, there being no recognition rites as with other birds; I was then able to shift the camera slightly, and take the birds feeding along, and leaving, the water's edge, where they stood perfectly mirrored in the oily surface. Within an hour or two, I had built up a most intimate understanding with this delightful pair, and I could talk to the sitting bird in a low tone – causing her to cock her head just as I wished. Though accepting the hide, they were still intensely wary, and once when a lone African passed walking several hundred yards away the hen walked off the nest hurriedly, not returning till he had passed out of sight.

This is the unforgettable thrill of bird photography; this complete acceptance of yourself concealed only a few feet away, and where this acceptance is by a particularly wary creature it is all the more thrilling. Avocets are beautiful birds, even at a distance, but to study the delicacy of feathering and the play of light and shade in the gloss of the black and white plumage at close quarters, is to realise that the camera never portrays what the eye really sees, and that it captures but a fleeting moment of the whole unforgettable scene. To watch how remarkably a bird can display its feelings in its momentary changes of expression, behaviour and poise, is to realise too how little the handling of a stuffed skin can convey any idea of the way of life of the living, pulsating, being it once was.

All these and other thoughts passed through my mind as I watched alone the entrancing behaviour of the pair before me. Most of the time I merely sat and studied them, only exposing film when I wished to capture a momentary pose that attracted me. The glare off the shingle began to blind me, and I wished I had brought my polaroid glasses. Just as I felt I had had my fill for the moment of this intimate scene, I saw John appearing again over the ridge, and on a prearranged manoeuvre he released me from the hide, the bird flying off and settling at the far end of the pool.

That afternoon I had a session with the flamingos, while Alex replaced me in the avocet hide. Although the birds were wading in the pool as usual when he started they finally flew off some distance away and did not return. He tried again the following morning, but again with no success; we were finally forced to the reluctant conclusion that the birds must have deserted for some reason. I was most upset over this unfortunate happening, which was unexpected too; for the birds, though wary, had learned to accept the hide, and I could think of no flaw in the technique. I could only assume that there must have been just too much coming and going near the nest with the change-over of watches.

In their European haunts, avocets are semi-colonial nesters, several pairs breeding in close proximity in the same area. According to an interesting hypothesis put forward several years ago by Dr Fraser Darling as a result of studying gull colonies, the successful establishment of the breeding cycle in such colonially nesting birds may depend to a large extent on the mutual stimulation afforded by several pairs of birds indulging in the same activities within view of each other. Carrying this idea a stage further, it may well have been that in the case of an abnormally isolated pair such as these avocets, even after laying of the eggs, the nest-egg complex was insufficient to hold them in the face of unusual disturbance of their environment exceeding a certain limit; thus desertion followed more readily than might have been the case had other pairs also been breeding close by. Whatever the cause may have been, I can only accept responsibility for this unfortunate ending; the only case which I have ever known in some twenty odd years of photographing birds. We have reason to believe however that at least one other pair of avocets reared chicks at Magadi that year, and there may yet be a breeding colony established. There have been sporadic attempts at breeding elsewhere in Kenya in the past, for chicks have been found, but no colony has yet been established for several consecutive years. Through breeding both north and south of the Equator, and migrating freely to Kenya in the non-breeding season, there appears yet to be some physiological or ecological barrier preventing their full establishment as regular East African breeders – this may well be the social stimulus of Darling, which is lacking when the migrants depart, leaving only a relatively few non-migrants behind; or it may be the almost unvarying length of daylight in these equatorial zones.

One of the common frequenters of the Magadi flats is the curiously misnamed wood ibis. It has nothing to do with woods, and is not an ibis, but a stork. Indeed it resembles the latter closely in its habits and appearance. With their striking red heads, and long yellow bills sunk on their chests, they forever seem to be contemplating the infinite, as they stand around the hot springs, and I have never seen them feeding yet. As one first drops down to the shore line from the grass ridge above there is a well known rocky outcrop sticking into the lake, which is whitewashed with their droppings. (Plate 21). For all their appearance of unworldly abstraction, they are

CHAPTER 8

GRASSLANDS OF THE DANCING WHYDAH

Part I. The Dancing Whydah

LONG BEFORE I first came to Kenya, some seventeen years ago, I remember my father telling me about the dancing of the Jackson's whydahs on the plains of Kenya, a sight which had struck him so many times as he passed to and fro from Uganda on his tours of duty there. The mental image of these wide areas of grass being covered with little bouncing black balls of birds remained with me for many years, and later when I had the chance to study them myself I found the truth more strange and interesting than I had ever imagined.

Jackson's whydah – so named after the former Governor of Kenya who found so much relaxation from official duties in bird watching in these parts – may be found almost anywhere in Kenya where suitable grasslands exist in the Rift or east of Rift areas. It is a bird of the wide grassy plains which are so much a feature of the Great Rift Valley itself and also of that wide shallow saddle which joins the northern Aberdares to the massif of Kenya; these are the plains of waving yellow oat grass and the stunted whistling thorns. But the bird is found too in smaller paddocks and pasture of the more cultivated ground near Nairobi itself, where I once had the most excellent opportunities of watching and recording its behaviour.

I am not systematically inclined, and shooting and the collection of skins does not appeal to me at all. There may be, I dare say, some birds still to be discovered and named in the lesser known parts of this Africa, but I am content to let somebody else make this sort of discovery. There are however, now so many of the commoner birds, so frequently seen in Kenya, whose behaviour and habits are so little known, that a wide field exists here for such a type of observation and enquiry on the living bird. This is what appeals particularly to me as a bird watcher, and this is the type of bird watching which has swept Great Britain with such a wave of popularity since the war. As long as you can record patiently and accurately, there is no need to be a scientist to do such work. This modern study of bird behaviour is entirely 'commonsensical', and the striking and original observations and deductions of Dr Tinbergen for example need no wrapping up in incomprehensible jargon; their meaning is unequivocally clear in the simplest of language.

Jackson's whydah is a social bird, with all the implications that sociality conveys; and it has developed a behaviour uniquely its own, but which can still be fitted into the great general pattern of bird behaviour as unravelled by modern means. This, let it be stated at once, requires no translation into terms of human behaviour to be understandable. Let us take a closer look then at these whydah dancing grounds and see what it all means.

During May and June particularly, in the central highlands of Kenya in such a grassland area, you can see perhaps a dozen or more of those little black balls bouncing up two feet or more into the air, and each seems to have its own rhythm which it may keep up perhaps for several hours each day with only short pauses for rest.

These black balls are the full plumaged males of Jackson's whydah, and this bobbing and bouncing is part of their breeding display. There are indeed a good many other whydahs of a social or semi-social nature in eastern Africa, but none of these others have developed the dancing display habit to such a full extent as Jackson's. Examining the dancing arena, there will be in an area of perhaps half an acre, up to a hundred or more dancing rings, and it is a fact that one bird may own two or three, while others have only one.

The dancing rings themselves are quite characteristic, and are separate entities, perhaps some three to four feet away from each other. Each ring consists of a central tuft of grass, surrounded by a circular, beaten down patch. The central tuft is about eight inches high, and oval in shape; on each side of the longest axis there is a characteristic cup-like recess, which is made by the bird. The circular area round this tuft may become trodden down to bare earth, and the mark made by these rings is extraordinarily persistent. A dancing area will still show ring traces a year or more after the birds have left; but in fact in many cases the birds return year after year to the same area, and use the same rings.

The displaying males are not shy, and a hide erected near a few rings is soon accepted; from several such hides, I have been able to build up a picture of the birds' behaviour and an interpretation of what it really means. The territory theory of bird breeding is now so well established as to need little explanation; but in brief the territory of a breeding bird is an area, small or large, of the immediate surroundings which usually the male bird 'stakes' out early in the breeding cycle. This imaginary area he will endeavour to defend against all rival males of the same species – sometimes losing ground a little here and gaining a little there. Defence of the territory is usually symbolic only, by song and display, and actual fighting seldom occurs; such song and display also serve to advertise the male and attract potential mates, who are recognised as such by their behaviour, only occasionally by visible plumage differences, by the reigning male. The final nest is often built in the territory, but not always so. Establishment of territory is one of the neatest devices known to ensure survival of the species, and create breeding space and order out of what might be chaos; but the territory alone does not always necessarily ensure the nutritional requirements of the pair and chicks. It does with some birds, with other species food is often found outside the chosen display area. Territory is indeed mainly sexual in function; it is a mating device, ensuring more even dispersion of the breeding stock and correlation of the breeding states of cock and hen, without extraneous influence from other birds of the same species, except in social breeders.

So it is that, in such birds as the ruffs, blackcocks and Jackson's whydahs, territory has passed far beyond its primitive physical survival value only for feeding purposes, and the males, which take no part in the nesting duties, establish symbolic, contracted territories which serve the function only of display and attraction areas where mating can take place with maximum effectiveness and minimum interference.

This is all however, anticipating the reasoning which has led to this, so let us see how the rings are used first, and watch the behaviour features which lead up to the establishment and usage of the dancing areas. In the non-breeding season, Jackson's whydahs roam over the pastures in mixed flocks of cocks and hens. Both sexes in this stage are in dull brown streaky plumage with short tails – for all the world like sparrows – and there is little to distinguish between them. As the 'grass-rains' break in February however, and these first few heavy thunderstorms presage the later onset of the long rains at the end of March, the males start growing their breeding dress of black. Long black curved tail plumes develop, the streaky body feathers are shed and replaced by glossy black feathers, the bill thickens and widens and becomes waxy white in colour; they become handsome, aggressive looking chaps indeed.

As these changes take place, the daily feeding rhythm of the flock is disturbed; the males tend to isolate themselves a little more each day, and to spend more time on the dancing areas, standing on tufts of grass and pulling at them with their beaks. Perhaps they even essay a tentative jump or two. The sexual break-up of the flock is imminent, and the hen birds bunch more together, leaving the males more and more on their own; but certain periods of the day are still neutral and all feed in the same area as before. The males gradually devote most of the day to the dancing grounds, and soon the whole area starts bobbing with black balls as the males assume full plumage and feel the display urge. It is however curious to note that even at the height of the dancing season, these glossy black males with their long tail plumes, still feed in peaceful communal flocks with the hens, away from the dancing area for short periods. Only in immediate proximity to the grounds does their behaviour become singularly male.

Cocks soon wear down their one, two or three rings by dancing up and down, but the ring alone is not the territory. Watch that cock for example as he drops down to his ring; about six feet away from it, you will see he suddenly arches the central plumes of his tail, and the two outer ones drop outwards and sideways; he will alight in this attitude, and take up his stance in the ring. Then watch that other male who crosses nearly over the ring with his tail plumes also arched – the owner of the ring jumps up and chases him away with pursuit flight. Curiously however, another male crosses the ring and actually drops down to it without being pursued by the owner; why the difference? If you were watching closely, you would have seen that his tail plumes were folded, not arched. This then is the territorial signal between full plumaged males – the way the tail is held. If expanded in the dancing attitude he will be attacked by the owner of the nearest ring; if held closed, he is ignored – or more commonly as we shall see later, treated as a female! On such little, apparently trivial, points does recognition of bird by bird depend.

By watching a full-plumaged cock approaching his own ring from several different directions, you will see that his territory – that invisible boundary over which his tail is arched before he alights – extends for some twelve feet all round his ring or rings. His appearance shows his ownership, and the attitude of the tail alone is the recognition signal.

By close watching of dancing males, it is clear that when two or more rings are found together, they all belong to the one male only, who may use them alternately for dancing, and keep them all in good order. Owing to the establishment of these fairly rigid boundaries, rings occupied by separate males are seldom closer than about twelve feet. These boundaries become accepted early in the break-up of the flock, and territorial squabbles later in the season are rare. But the feeding ground away from the dancing area is neutral and rivalry is absent here, full-plumaged males feeding together quite amicably. Furthermore, as I later found out, the females themselves are unaware of the territorial boundaries imposed by the cocks near their rings.

How does the male spend his time on these rings? Close watching from a hide shows many features of interest. The central tuft is clearly sacrosanct, and the cock never perches on it. He perches on the long grass at the edge of the ring, and spends a good deal of time calling, with a peculiar click and whistle note, and sometimes making a noise for all the world like a cow cropping grass. He pulls at the grass, and generally tidies the ring up. (Plate 22). Sooner or later he starts jumping, and jumps all round the ring, but always facing the central tuft. This jumping is of two kinds, a short twisting bounce, and a high leaping dance up to two feet in the air. High and low jumps alternate irregularly, but I noted that the cocks could seldom make more than six high leaps without a rest.

The appearance of the dancing bird at close quarters is quite unique. The head is thrown back, the neck feathers ruffled out; the central tail plumes are arched in a deep curve forwards so that they almost touch the head, and the two long outer plumes drop downwards and sideways. While rising and falling in the air, the bird makes a dull tinkling sound. The wings are quivered, and the legs beat the air, but there is no actual flight up and down.

When not leaping and bouncing about, the cock struts about on the smoothed ring, flaunting his tail from side to side, ruffling the neck hackles and posturing towards the central tuft with bows and scrapes. He butts the recess in the tuft, taking short runs at them with lowered head, then pressing into them and smoothing them out with his breast; and he also spends a good deal of time tidying them, picking out and arranging the grass in them as if they were a nest. So much attention is paid to this central tuft, that one day for experiment, I cut one away in the ring of a cock who was dancing well and then hid up again to see what would happen. The result was astonishing; he ignored completely the alteration of the ring, and continued dancing and posturing as before, except that all the bows and scrapes were directed to a non-existent tuft! Much as some birds – hole-nesters – have been seen to fly to a spot in mid-air where their nesting hole was, before it was experimentally moved lower down or to one side – in spite of the fact they could see quite clearly there was nothing there; such differences mark the working of a bird's mind.

All this display of birds dancing close together (for one bird dancing will often set off all the other nearby cocks dancing too), is clearly most intriguing to the hens, who will fly singly at random over the display grounds. The rings themselves also interest the hens greatly – for they will drop down to a ring, even if the owner is away.

Each male and each ring may attract several females in turn, and when a hen drops to a ring, the behaviour of the cock changes most dramatically. Jumping stops at once, and he circles to the opposite side of the tuft, stiffens with his head well back, ruffles his neck, arches his tail and quivers violently all over, shaking hackles and tail. He tinkles and hisses, circling round the tuft as the hen moves opposite him, and from time to time will rush round the tuft and flaunt his tail plumes in her face with a sideways flick. The whole performance conveys the impression of most urgent solicitation. (Plate 25A).

In most cases, the hen completely ignores this ardent display, but takes instead a considerable interest in the architecture of the central tuft, particularly the recesses, picking at the grass in each. Indeed, the central tuft appears to be of far greater significance to the hens than to the cocks, for they sheered violently away from the ring whose tuft I had cut down. It seemed to me quite deliberate avoidance.

The quivering fever of the cock increases in violence the longer the hen stays; if she suddenly flies off, the cock deflates like a pricked balloon; but if the hen remains and is ready, she crouches on the ring and the cock mounts ecstatically for a second or two.

Some males appear to be more successful than others at attracting the hens – why, I do not know, but this would be an interesting field for study. There is no doubt however, that they are polygamous and one cock will mate with a succession of hens over a period of days. As I have suggested elsewhere, I suspect that this arises because of the imperfect correlation between the maturation of the cocks and the hens. Some males mature early, others late. The early males may cease dancing and start moulting again while later males are just beginning to dance, and this irregular ripening of the males may be spread over several months. By contrast, most of the hens mature simultaneously, since all the subsequent nests are found at nearly the same stage of incubation, or building within a few days of each other. Since the sex-ratio of the mixed flocks is about 50:50, these fewer males who are ripe when all the females become ripe, are able to mate with several females each within a few days. The earlier or the later maturing males are unsuccessful because none of the females are ready to mate at these times. Whether or not the hens are promiscuous I do not know, for without colour ringing it is almost impossible to keep track of a particular hen; whether one mating with one cock, or several matings with one cock, or with several different cocks takes place is still unknown, though this point is mentioned again later.

The dancing urge in the males is indeed an early manifestation of the breeding cycle, and I have numerous records of very immature males, just showing a little black only in their plumage, dancing at rings. Their tails are as yet completely undeveloped and stumpy, and it is a ridiculous sight to see these young cocks bouncing up and down flaunting a stump of a tail, imitating a cock in his full glory. Indeed, since the tail is so undeveloped, and therefore cannot be used as a recognition signal, these immature males are often courted as hens by a full-plumaged cock on the same ring.

For the keen bird watcher with plenty of time, these Jackson's whydahs would make an ideal subject for an intensive study of behaviour by individual colour ringing on the legs. The flocks are very restricted to their own particular feeding areas, and could be easily trapped in quantity with a spring flap-net while feeding; and it would too, be easy to trap the cocks in the ring by a similar method.

Before we go on to consider the next stage of the cycle – the actual nesting – let me mention some other points of interest which a study of these birds has shown. I mentioned above that males in very 'immature' plumage would dance, but it is interesting to see how their behaviour pattern differs at this early stage from that of the full-plumaged cock. Two features are particularly noticeable. One is that they have not as yet established ownership to any particular ring or set of rings; these early males will drop out of the mixed flying flock and start displaying in any ring that happens to be handy. The ring obviously means something to them as such though they lay no claim to it. Secondly, to them the central tuft is not sacrosanct as it is to the full ripe cock; they will perch and preen on it, a thing which a full-plumaged cock will never do. Nor do these young males ever 'breast' the central tuft as do the mature birds. One other tailless bird of this type I was watching actually attracted a hen to the ring, and then committed the awful solecism of jumping at her instead of quivering; the little chap had obviously not learnt the right technique yet! They really know very little of the correct rules of the game at this stage, since when the female flies off the ring they will chase her and display to her elsewhere. This sort of thing just is not done in grown-up circles; if the hen departs, you leave her to it, and vent your frustration on the ring instead by pulling the grass about! There is thus a gradual development of the full behaviour pattern, it does not start 'ready-made', and by such small differences can the development of the display pattern be followed till it reaches the rigid symbolic perfection of full bird-hood.

Early in the season, just before the rains, beginnings of the sexual break-up in the non-breeding flocks can be traced. Instead of flying from feeding place to feeding place in an organised body, the whole flock tends to split into splinter groups which go their own way for a little while; and from these splinter groups, the earlier males begin to drop out from time to time as they pass over the traditional dancing grounds.

I was able on several occasions to watch the genesis of a ring. There appears to be no selection of a particular site. Most pasture grass is tufted anyway, and any tuft appears to be chosen quite at random by a bird starting to dance; there is of course a general preference for ring traces left from last season. Once a tuft is chosen however, the ring becomes beaten down within a week, but the formation of the central tuft recesses follows later as the full display pattern develops to include the breasting technique. Very often, after a spell of dancing activity, the cocks will give up altogether for several days, and the flocks join together again. The onset of the breeding cycle is not irreversible apparently, and in these earlier stages the display can be abandoned – I presume if the weather becomes unfavourable or the hens stay unresponsive. In these early days too, the ownership of a ring is still in doubt, even though some cocks may be in almost complete plumage. Thus, I have watched a male displaying to another male, who had alighted on the ring in the folded tail position and was therefore treated like a female, when both were suddenly chased away by the male occupant of a ring about three feet away, who had been too busy courting a hen on his ring to notice the intruders using what was apparently another bit of his property.

There is a very strict rule observed among these birds of 'one hen at a time only, please'; a second hen alighting on a ring will result in the cock becoming exasperated, and chasing both hens away. One can almost hear him mutter about importunate hussies. It simply is not done to barge in on another's courting session; but a hen happening to drop down beside any tuft, even if not on a ring, is fair game for any nearby male, and she will be quivered and displayed to. Perhaps this is how some rings start where they do. At first the pattern is random with birds coming and going in a mixed flock, but later, proximity of a hen to a tuft or a male is an immediate signal for her to be courted; or a passing male with arched tail is the signal for him to be pursued by the nearest full-plumaged cock.

I mentioned previously that I do not know whether the hens are promiscuous or not; certainly I do not know if they will allow themselves to be mated several times, but they will certainly allow themselves to be courted by different cocks, and I have watched several hens visiting dancing males in turn, but whether consummation occurred I could not tell.

As the season advances, sudden surges of activity are quite common, and as mentioned above one cock dancing will set off all the others in his vicinity, quite clearly a social stimulus effect so often observed in colonial birds. But by contrast, I have seen a full-plumaged cock alight close beside another who was already displaying to a hen, much to the latter cock's discomfiture. His display wobbled badly and finally ceased while he drove off the spectator. Clearly at some stage the courtship is not all-or-none, and can be upset by outside influence, and where display (or courtship behaviour) and aggressive ten-

PLATE 25A. Jackson's whydah, male, displaying on ring to female (right background of tuft), Kabete 1946

PLATE 25B. Yellow-throated longclaw at nest, Kabete 1940

Plate 25a

Plate 25b

Red-billed oxpeckers, feeding on sore on camel's leg, Kabete 1946

dencies come into conflict, the latter may win. I have not however seen a full-plumaged male being driven away by another, while the former was courting a hen on the ring.

I have not been able moreover, to detect any difference in the courtship behaviour of a cock when he is displaying to either a hen, an immature male, or another full-plumaged cock who may have alighted with a folded tail and therefore is treated as a female. But curiously enough, a full cock, such as the latter, being displayed to, may in fact behave like a hen as well – picking at the tuft recesses. He appears to be immediately dominated by the instantaneous display pattern switched on by the ruling cock, and shows female tendencies; other animals may in fact behave thus also, but this is an interesting case in birds.

Sometimes too, if a hen leaves the ring on which she is being courted, the courting male, in addition to deflating suddenly, will start tearing and plucking at the grass of the ring – clearly a reaction which releases the pent-up endeavour of the mating drive, or a so-called substitute activity, serving no purpose except emotional release, so often found in birds. This grass plucking is a frequent activity, and is one reason why the rings become worn smooth.

The actual courting of a hen on the ring falls into two distinct phases; the quivering of the cock is an invitation (like that of spawning salmon and trout), the flouncing of the tail plumes a dominating action which follows if the hen remains in the ring. It is rather uncanny to note how the courting male so closely follows the circling movements of the hen on the opposite side of the tuft, for it does not seem possible that he could see her over the tuft. Her presence is sensed only, and she is out of sight except for the sudden leap round the cock makes to flick his tail in her face.

Before any hen drops down, the dancing bounce of the cock is a clear advertisement to any passing hen to drop in and see him sometime; his call note, though low, may serve the same function since it is used only at the ring. This bouncing advertisement is a lure to attract the hen from a distance, the quivering solicitation is used the moment a hen crosses his territorial boundary, even though she has not yet alighted on the ring.

The cocks are however quite shameless, and will also try to lure away a hen who is already being displayed to at a nearby ring by another cock. One is irresistibly reminded of carnival touts. As mentioned before, I do not know what determines the hen's choice of which cock she will visit; on one occasion I watched a hen drop to a ring occupied by a tailless poor-plumaged cock, in apparent preference to two nearby equidistant rings occupied by two full-plumaged cocks; but here, 'choice' such as we know it, may not have been operative.

The function of the attitude alone of the tail as a recognition signal for aggression or ring ownership is so marked that I tried some experiments on this, firstly cutting two artificial cocks out of black paper – one in the folded tail attitude, the other with tail cocked and side plumes drooping. The 'folded tail' bird I placed upright in an occupied ring first. The owning cock returned and became very agitated, pulling at the white beak and tail, and finally breaking off the latter and dropping it a few feet away; he did not attempt to display to it. I then substituted the card with the cocked tail, and the owner ignored it. I kept ringing the changes, but could elicit no further definite reaction, except that the bird would occasionally attack the white beak portion of the 'folded-tail' card.

Like so many experiments of this kind, the results were quite inconclusive and made little sense. The sham seems to be recognised instantly, and evokes no real aggression or display. There is no doubt that any such experiment is wrong and unnatural in method, the sequence of events being the reverse of what happens in nature. Thus the artificial had necessarily to be placed in position *before* the owner returned, and cannot be placed *after* he is already there such as happens in natural aggression or display.

Subsequent experiments were equally inconclusive, and I am sure it would be necessary to impart an 'arriving' movement to the artificial if any normal reaction is to be evoked. The immobility of such cards is entirely unnatural, and movement, and the type of attitude during movement are much more a natural part of a bird's perception.

The effect of wind is amusing. A gusty wind upsets the bouncing of the birds, and a windy afternoon leads to too much upsetting of balance to be good dancing days; display is sporadic only in such weather.

Now all this dancing display and attraction has of course one end only – the successful mating of cock and hen, and this in turn is followed by nest building, egg laying and so on to completion of full cycle with the departure of the chicks. But here, my observations have a serious gap which I have never been able to fill.

Once the birds start nesting, the nests are arranged almost colonially, each within a few feet of another, until perhaps twenty or more nests can be found in one small area of pasture. Here however, is an interesting feature, for these groups of nests are not necessarily anywhere near the display area; they may be anything up to a quarter of a mile and more away, and are certainly quite unconnected with the ring territories pegged out by the cocks. Here is one serious gap in my records, since I have never yet discovered which sex actually builds the nests. I have certainly seen hens toying with grass, but never actually building.

The nests themselves are quite characteristic. They are built a few inches off the ground in grass tufts, and are domed balls of woven grass with a wide side entrance, whose lower 'landing edge' is particularly strengthened with finer grass. Curiously enough, in many of them the warm inner lining of fine *Pannicum* grass seed heads is completed before the nest framework itself is finished, a rather unusual habit for a bird.

The egg clutch is two, sometimes even three or four, and they are very oval, of a greenish ground colour flecked and speckled with dark chocolate and purple. In contrast to the open, blatant behaviour of the cocks, the streaky dun hens are shy and unobtrusive in their nesting area, and will leave their nests when an intruder is still a long way off, dropping out quietly and flying low over the grass. They are hard to see, and usually the nesting area has a deserted appearance when examined.

The cocks take no interest whatever in the nesting grounds, or any nesting duties. Their job is done, and they go off quietly to feed in mixed flocks again, and soon moult their fine plumes. Nests located in pastures with cattle suffer severely from cattle trampling, and the mortality rate is high; success is greater in pastures unused by cattle. In this respect, the hens make no effort whatever to mob or scold an intruder at the nest, and are singularly silent the whole time.

The dowdy little hens, who alone carry out all incubation duties and caring for the chicks, are somewhat dull and unexciting birds to watch at the nest. Like so many of these seed-eating birds, they feed their chicks by regurgitation of pre-digested grass seeds, and for that reason may be away from the nest for perhaps two or more hours between each chick meal. The seeds must be eaten first, and then left to pulp up in the mothers' insides for a while to become partially digested. The watcher must therefore be prepared to spend a good many hours in the hide to catch the few occasions during the day when the hen does return to attend to the chicks. The wait however is compensated, for when the hen does finally return, she will spend several minutes on end at the nest, bringing up each chick's meal in turn. This she does by astonishing contortions of the head and much back and forward stretching of her neck till the white pulpy mass oozes from her bill.

As the nest is domed, it is not easy to see how the chicks obtain this mess, and I do not know whether they put their wide gapes into their mother's bill or *vice versa*. As the chicks grow and fill the nest, so she has to perch on the outer rim to feed them, but her head is always inside the nest. As always, both mother and chicks are quite silent the while, and when the lengthy feeding process is complete, the hen picks the chicks' excreta from the bottom of the nest, and holding it in her beak flies direct off the nest and drops the sac in flight. I have not been able to persuade the hens I have watched to use any perches placed by the nest, although they have perched on the hide itself. Getting a good picture is not easy, with the bird's head stuck into the nest most of the time.

I seem to have written a good many pages on this one bird; but on reading it through I am unrepentant. The dancing whydahs are most fascinating birds; their curious habits seem to me so essentially a part of this land of curious things and watching them has given me many hours of the greatest pleasure, and yet how little we really still know of the wonderful jigsaw of behaviour of birds at nesting or any other time.

The dancing whydahs are only one of the many kinds of whydahs which occur in East Africa. They are however, the only one which shows the fullest development of the dancing display, and the most complete divorce of mating territory from nesting area. Most of the whydahs are semi-social flocking birds, and most of them are polygamous. Three other kinds commonly occur in the grasslands of their dancing cousins. One, whose cocks are also black, with long trailing tail plumes, is distinguished by a scarlet slash across the throat as the cut-throat whydah. These occur perhaps more in the longer grass, and the heavy flight of the tinkling males followed by a swarm of hens is a common sight; but I have no notes on their display or breeding cycle. Their nests too, are semi-colonial and similar in structure to these of the Jackson's whydah, but usually built higher up in the long grass stems.

In the breeding season, smaller flocks of black, shorter tailed birds with white patches on their wings accompanied by the usual swarm of hens denote the presence of the white-winged whydah, about which species too I have little information except that the hens are exasperatingly tedious also to watch at the nest, since, like hen Jackson's and cut-throat, the young are also fed by regurgitation from the mother's crop.

The various kinds of bishop birds are related, and are classic territory-holding birds, the males of which stake out large areas of grass and scrub within which the many wives complete the nesting cycle.

The pin-tailed whydah has however gone off on a line of his own. In the nesting season the slender black and white males with long thin tails and pillar box red beak are a familiar sight in Kenya; and each cock is accompanied by six or seven streaky hens. The cock is pugnaciously territorial and allows no other cock near at any time in the area he has selected, and the harem is most jealously guarded. The cocks, too, dance, but in a quite different manner; they dance and flutter aerially over the hens as they perch in low bushes, on the ground, and often on telegraph wires. To complete the strange difference, this species has abandoned the tiresome business of rearing its own young; instead the hens are parasitic and lay their eggs in the nests of various small waxbills and grass warblers. This widow-bird however is not a very close relation really of Jackson's whydah, nor however is it any relative whatever of the cuckoo whose parasitic habits it has paralleled. Undoubtedly a study of the pin-tail by anyone fortunate enough to have time to spare would be most repaying.

The big, handsome bright coloured males of Delamere's whydah which are more common in the Rift Valley than elsewhere, and the curiously 'hump-backed' paradise whydah are two species I know practically nothing about. As a group study, the bishop/whydah series as a whole would make a most fascinating story, and I hope that one day somebody will find the time and patience to complete the picture still hardly begun.

Part II. Pipits, plovers and others

If I were asked to name the sort of bird most suitable for the beginner to try his hand in the sport of bird photography, I should unhesitatingly say a lark or a pipit. Birds of these species are quite ideal for the sport, and I myself have spent a great many happy hours hiding up at their nests.

They have every feature to encourage the novice at the art. Their nests are reasonably easy to find; during incubation they sit fairly close; and when with chicks, they are confiding if proper precautions have been taken, without being ridiculously tame. They visit their nests repeatedly at frequent intervals to feed the chicks, usually walking up to the nest, and they then give the photographer plenty of time to be prepared; their movements at the nest are deliberate and unhurried, and the generally open nature of the cup nest and surrounding ground give plenty of scope to portray the bird in serial pictures. The chicks themselves are active and attractive, and lighting, except for direct sunshine which is a great nuisance, is always adequate. But to all this I would add two warnings. Firstly, their nests are nearly always situated in pastures frequented by cows and the amount of damage these stupid inquisitive beasts can do in a short time to a hide is incredible.

Secondly, always choose a position where the bird approaches sideways to the nest from where the hide is, otherwise you will get unpleasant back-on, out of focus, pictures of a headless, tailless or beakless bird. And too, watch that blade of grass which *will* swing in front of the nest after you have hidden up.

On the whole, paragons of a subject; but I confess I have still to obtain a picture of either which really satisfies me. I have taken dozens and dozens; some have been spoilt through stupid faults of my own, others for reasons beyond my control; but I do not mind, and I could go on trying for these sort of birds well into my dotage without being bored.

The whydah grasslands are of course full of larks and pipits as a rule. Perhaps the three most common are Richard's pipit, a somewhat undistinguished bird of streaky appearance; the redwing lark, whose wings are not really red, but chestnut in colour and show only as the bird flicks over the grass; and the yellow-throated longclaw lark, a bird perhaps of the wetter parts of the grasslands. (Plate 25B). The long hind claw is of course seldom noticeable, but the brilliant yellow throat hung with a necklace of black flecks makes a striking contrast with the tawny streaking on the rest of its body.

The latter was one of the first birds I ever photographed in Kenya, and their pretty mewing call and fluttering 'butterfly' flight low over the grass whenever I see them again takes me straight back in memory to that first hide in the land of sunshine. It is a bird which is a good bit larger at close quarters than one at first thinks, and some of these first pictures I took 'decapitated' the bird in a most unfortunate manner. They have a habit of suddenly standing very upright at the nest – a pose which makes for a very good picture – but one which I did not allow for in the field of view focused around the nest. As with most ground nesting birds, it usually pays to get a viewpoint rather too high than too low. The former allows for such unexpected positions and gives an adequate depth of focus; with too low a viewpoint a lot of unpleasant out of focus grass often intrudes.

Next to larks and pipits, I would choose the plover family as delightful subjects to watch and photograph at the nest. They require a more cautious approach than the smaller birds, and are more easily scared by bad technique; but their behaviour at the nest is exemplary, and they are slow and unhurried in their movements. To be under the watchful eye of a plover at the nest, which is yet unalarmed by the proceedings, and confident of no disturbance to its peace is an exciting experience.

Furthermore, with most plovers, both sexes share in incubation, and one very often has the chance of watching the sequence of a change-over at the nest; a charming performance which varies in ritual from species to species. With these kinds of birds however, there is usually little chance of obtaining pictures of the parents with their chicks. The latter leave the nest within a few hours of hatching and run off; they can seldom be persuaded to stay in the one place, and should certainly never be made to do so artificially. The parents brood them frequently of course after hatching, but they have an uncanny trick of calling them to a point just too far away from the hide, or out of focus. There is however a period of just a few hours, when the first eggs start chipping and the chicks start emerging, when the parents will brood them at the nest. The new-hatched chicks are still wet and weak-kneed, and in that short time one is often rewarded with the most intimate glimpse of parental care, when the brooding hen will talk to its unborn chick in the egg; and later when it hatches, will cuddle and dry it, and then remove the empty half eggshells one by one, before leading the chicks away from the nest. Such moments are rare and precious, but require close daily observation of the nest, since it is seldom possible to judge the exact stage of incubation when the eggs are first found.

In the shorter cropped pastures of Kenya, there are two plovers which occur commonly, the crowned lapwing and the black-winged plover; other species are of course locally common such as the more water-loving blacksmith and spur-winged plovers, and others are mentioned elsewhere in this book.

The first two species are easily disturbed, and the former in particular tends to be a noisy bird and will mob any intruder on its nesting grounds. I suspect that many of them remain paired for life, as solitary birds are the exception and pairs the rule; but quite often family parties of four or more birds will stay in the same area for months at a time.

In one very close-grazed area near a former home in the Nyeri district, several pairs of crowned lapwings used to nest each year. This was always in the rains, when the first green flush of new grass covered the hard-baked red earth and when the ground became starred with myriad clusters of ephemerally flowering plain lilies; the moister depressions became thickly carpeted with pinkish and purple flowers of the dainty Kikuyu violet, and the drier ground patched with a seemingly wind-blown drift of pink and white *Rhamphicarpa*, these flowers which always look to me so like a wilder edition of the common garden *Petunia*. This is a wild flower name which my wife always remembers most triumphantly!

Their nests were easy to find; the birds mobbed one when walking anywhere near their eggs, and by lying down some distance away with field glasses, they are easily watched returning to their eggs as quiet was restored and the intruder disappeared. Just a bare scrape in the ground, their nests were nostalgically familiar to the lapwing of home, though the three or four eggs are not quite so pointed. I never succeeded in getting any pictures at their nests; this grazing ground was heavily stocked with native cattle, and Kikuyu huts surrounded it on all sides. A hide erected in the open would have had little chance of surviving the inquisitive attentions of both cattle and Kikuyu *totos*, and in fact all the nests we did find were short-lived in the extreme, being trampled by cattle or robbed by children within a few days of laying.

On the quieter grazing of a neighbouring European farm however, I once found a nest of the less striking black-winged plover, and here a hide was relatively safe. The birds mobbed me severely as I was erecting it, but on the following day I was able to get all the pictures I wanted from this hide, though I had no chance of change-over pictures, nor was I able to watch the nest till hatching time.

Amongst the smaller fry which inhabit the whydah grasslands are some of the confusing and difficult group of grass warblers. The cloud-scraper types such as the brown grass warblers are easy enough, and their high circling flight and wing-snapping descent to the ground are a common sight. They are very difficult birds to get good pictures of. At the nest, their movements are sudden and quick, and their restless behaviour can be most tiresome. Since all their nests are small domed balls of grass, one cannot really see what happens when they return to feed the chicks, since only the tail sticks out of the entrance as they attend to their young. Similar too are the ground-nesting waxbills, which are difficult indeed to study at the nest.

The Kenya quail-finch, related to the weavers, is also a breeder in the wide grasslands of the drier areas, and I once had the chance to study a pair of these at close quarters near Karen. Although again I could see little of what went on in the small domed nest, the two little birds were most confiding and spent a good deal of time sitting side by side in front of the nest, a curious sort of habit.

Part III. Oxpeckers

No doubt a chapter on grassland birds is a queer place to discuss a bird which neither feeds in the grass, nests in the grass, and seldom indeed lands on the ground. Nevertheless, the red-billed oxpecker or tick bird is a bird most definitely associated with grasslands, since it spends most of its time perching and feeding upon the cattle and game to whom pastures such as these are their home. (Plate 26).

Some years ago, I had the pleasant task of assessing officially as much information as I could about the bird, whose role in damaging livestock and spreading disease was by no means above suspicion. While it was known that certainly a large part of its diet was composed of more or less harmful species of ticks picked off the animals, yet it nevertheless has the unpleasant habit of keeping open, and perhaps even enlarging, skin abrasions till they were raw; thus damaging hides and perhaps spreading disease from animal to animal.

Against this was the other suspicion that actually the bird had decreased greatly in number as its natural food – ticks – were being destroyed by the widespread adoption of stock dipping to destroy these dangerous disease carriers in cattle; but the position was further complicated by another belief that perhaps the decrease in ticks due to dipping was in fact causing the birds to turn more and more to wound feeding as ticks became scarce.

In Kenya, opinions, particularly amongst farmers (and anglers), are pronounced and unshakable. Everybody *knows*, without question, but to a scientific mind, it seemed that some fairer assessment of the position was required first, by sampling as many of such opinions as possible. Accordingly, an enquiry was conducted by means of carefully thought-out questionnaire circulars, widely distributed to stockowners and others interested, in the Colony. In particular it seemed necessary to determine on balance whether the bird was really beneficial or harmful, what its present status in the major stock-rearing areas was and what control measures, if any were required, would be effective.

Apart from stockowners – those most directly concerned – the bird has earned a bad reputation too amongst professional hunters. It perches frequently on the larger game animals, and its hissing alarm call clearly gives warning to the duller sighted beasts on the approach of danger. Conversely however, a flock flying in alarm off the back of a grazing or sleeping buffalo or rhino has often given timely warning of the unsuspected presence of these uncertain-tempered beasts to persons travelling through thick bush. Jackson, in his *Birds of Kenya Colony*, cannot give the birds too bad a name, and denounces them on all grounds, as being an unmitigated curse.

And so all the circulars – several hundred of them – went out. The reaction to any such Government sponsored questionnaire in Kenya is similar to that with which the yearly Income Tax registered envelope is greeted; the difference in the result however is due to the fact that the latter is backed by the law, whereas the former can be thrown into the nearest wastepaper basket without further thought. But the relatively small percentage of returns which I did receive came from those genuinely interested in the matter, and those most strongly opinionated; and were therefore of greater value than a law-enforced return might have been. I do not propose here to discuss in detail what the actual analysis of these results showed, since these have been fully described in a scientific publication elsewhere; but the general picture is I think of sufficient interest.

It was clear on the whole that the widespread extension of dipping had led to a general decrease in the number of birds in such 'clean' areas; not perhaps due to a diminution in actual numbers, but due to a movement elsewhere of the birds, who now found the dipped, tick-free animals unprofitable feeding grounds, and sometimes actually repellant. At the same time, there had however been no increase in the unnatural practice of feeding on raw sores, except in 'out of condition' animals. There was therefore general agreement amongst most stock-owners that control measures were not necessary in most instances. When sores are attacked by the birds, the first essential was clearly to keep the stock in good healthy condition, and all horses well-groomed; there was general agreement that healthy livestock were less prone to attack. Sores so caused however, are easily treated, and heal up readily if birds are kept off them by application of thick grease or Stockholm tar.

With the almost universal extension of dipping to all native areas as well, the birds will probably withdraw in time entirely from the stock areas and return to their indigenous game hosts. This has indeed already happened in South Africa, and ox-peckers are now rare outside the National Game Parks.

The staple food of oxpeckers is undoubtedly ticks and flies, which is really a curious diet when considered carefully. Undoubtedly it must be rich and nutritious, but one wonders how such a feeding habit originated in the first place. Their stomachs also contain a great deal of hair, which must be cast up as pellets from time to time, since hair is never present in the intestines.

There is a good deal of information still to be collected about these curious birds. For example, why do they frequently show a predilection for a particular animal in a herd (usually a reddish one), to the exclusion of others nearby equally available and tick-ridden? Also too – and this is perhaps the most interesting query – what do they feed their chicks on, and how and when do chicks take to live-perch feeding? They nest by preference in holes in trees, or similar places, but the diet of the chicks has never been recorded. Jackson has noted a pair bringing discrete food items, resembling caterpillars and grubs, to their chicks; but if such is the staple diet of the chick, and not whole or regurgitated ticks, it implies a complete change of food collecting behaviour on the part of the adult birds at hatching time, and also a change of feeding behaviour by the chicks when they start feeding themselves.

Oxpeckers are really rather unpleasant birds to watch feeding; they have the persistence of a swarm of blue bottles round a piece of meat. They slip and slide all over an animal's hide, often keeping to the side away from the observer, and cling closely to the hair with their long sharp claws. The beak is held parallel to the skin, and they wield it in a scissoring motion from side to side through the hair, two or three sweeps being made in one area before moving jerkily off to try elsewhere. It is rather extraordinary to watch the way these birds seem to slide all over the back, flank and belly of an animal, but they keep a pretty sharp look out for any approaching danger in spite of all their apparent absorption in feeding. Several birds will 'work' one animal together, and all fly off simultaneously with a hissing rattle if disturbed.

Examination of stomachs of shot birds shows that they will swallow any small hard object stuck in the hair, such as grass seeds, and they clearly feed by feel, not by sight. Their touch must be sensitive too, because some of the larval ticks they pick up and swallow are quite microscopic in size. Feeding is quite indiscriminate, and I have seen no evidence of their looking for individual ticks; but their eyesight is sharp for all that, for flies are usually caught on the wing – usually the blood sucking kinds which pester livestock in this country.

I cannot however entirely exonerate them from picking open sores on the skin, for I have watched them doing so myself, with a pick-axe like motion of the beak quite different from the usual scissoring, and I have cine films of them doing this; but even at that, I consider it more likely that they enlarge an existing tick-bite or scratch, rather than start a completely new wound. They squeeze and nibble at a raw sore to get blood or serum (which incidentally they will also take from a flayed dead carcase). It is always curious to note how insensitive cattle seem to be to their attentions, and also how clean the wound keeps. The birds obviously eat out any maggots or fly eggs they find in the raw flesh, though indeed such sores seldom go deeper than the skin layers. They will however also swallow any free-dripping blood.

Like many other birds they will not foul their feeding grounds, but lift the tail and shoot their excrement well clear of their living perch. They take frequent dust baths and will also use an animal as a toilet perch for preening on. Another most curious habit they have is to spread themselves close to an animal's skin with wings expanded as if to get the maximum surface of the body in contact with the hide.

Although they are not colonial nesters, like their distant relations the starlings, tick-birds are social creatures and roost in big flocks at night in bushes and trees, and they feed in flocks on grazing herds. They have therefore certain social recognition signals amongst themselves, such as an odd penguin-like attitude – looking down their noses as it were – which they adopt on alighting amongst other birds of their kind. It is a comical sight to watch two birds 'penguinning' at each other on an animal's back. They also have a hunched threat attitude often seen at nesting time, and though they will squabble over a sore, one bird at a time retains the right to feed thereon.

They do not seem to have particular feeding times, but they certainly have a daily routine round from herd to herd in the neighbourhood; they clearly prefer relatively short-haired beasts, and do not frequent woolly sheep for example to the same extent as cattle.

Like their relations, the European starlings of home and the red-winged starlings in Kenya, they have a predilection for chimney pots, and the dark hole in the centre intrigues them enormously. So much so in fact, that one farmer in Kenya traps them by setting up a stove-pipe in his paddock. On this a bird soon perches, peering down the hole. When another arrives, the first bird will take a header down the hole and cannot get out again. The fuss soon attracts others, and down goes the second bird as a third arrives, and so it goes on! Most effective.

CHAPTER 9

FEATHERHILL AND THE THORN-TREE PLAINS

IF YOU travel along the Nairobi-Magadi road, part of which now lies in the Nairobi National Park, you will see, just before you start climbing up to the windy shoulders of the Ngong Hills, an ill-marked track going to the left. This runs alongside the pipe which takes the cool clear water from the Ngongs down to the fiery desert of Magadi.

Take this road; for it will lead you on and across the thorn-tree plains bounding the Park to one of the most exciting bird areas in the whole of Kenya – the place we know as Featherhill. As you bounce along the awful track, you pass through a dense stand of the glossy green-leaved poison arrow tree, and beyond this the ridge spreads out like the fingers of an outstretched hand – each separate ridge a sea of yellow waving grass, dotted here and there with green acacia trees; those which have the odd-shaped twisted seeds which give them the Latin name of *Acacia spirocarpa*; the flowers are white and honey scented.

It is remarkable country, for on these ridges you can travel where you like by car; the ground is smooth beneath the long grass with only an occasional pig-hole to jar the springs. We know where you can cross from ridge to ridge through the valleys which lie between, but such crossing places bear no mark, so unless you know the country well go back along each ridge to cross to the next in line. To us, each one of these finger ridges bears a name – Vulture Hill leads on to Tawny Ridge and Tawny Ridge to Raptor Crest and Secretarial Hill. All these fingers point to the north where the ground flattens to a monotonous plain of whistling thorn, broken only by the dip of Kongoni Valley.

You will not find these names on any map, for they are our own; and each calls to mind those great raptorial birds who make this wild and open country theirs alone. Year after year the vultures, hawks and eagles choose this lonely spot to breed, and the sturdy *spirocarpa* trees form their nesting place. It is one of the few places where one can bird-nest in a car, and indeed it is essential to do so, for the area is so vast and miles separate each tree-topped ridge. It is exciting to drive from tree to tree and peer up through the branches to see if any nests are at the top. The great bulky nests of eagles and vultures are easy to see, but the smaller collections of thinner twigs which mark the nests of the lesser hawks are nothing like so easy to find.

If a great bird rises from the tree with flapping wings, you can tell at once what kind is owner of the nest; but more often it is a question of climbing up and finding some way round the great platform of twigs to see what it contains. This is luckily an easy game, because although thorny too, these *spirocarpa* trees are not so viciously equipped as other kinds of acacia, and although a few pricks may result the going is quite good. They are handy trees too, for the lower branches are fairly near the ground, and offer a good start up the tree.

As I turn the pages of my notebooks, I realise with something of a shock that it is nearly fourteen years since I last went there; the intervening years have been spent elsewhere in Kenya and abroad. At the same time too, each page brings back the memory of days spent on Featherhill as if they were but yesterday. There is a tremendous fascination about birds of prey at the nest; to get really good sets of pictures calls for all the skill one has – and alas, for almost unlimited time too, which has never been in very plentiful supply. The rewards are rich, and as you watch an eagle swoop up to its nest, and see at close quarters its regal mien and piercing stare, unmindful of the hide as it gently feeds its chicks, then life indeed is good and the sight worth all the hours of waiting in a hot and stuffy hide.

PLATE 27A. Tawny eagle dropping to nest, Featherhill, 1941
PLATE 27B. Red-tailed buzzard at nest with green branch, Ngong 1941

TE 27A

PLATE 27B

Plate 28a

Plate 28b

Unlike most of the smaller birds in East Africa which breed in the rains, these hawks and eagles usually choose the long cool dry season of July to September in which to rear their chicks, and probably for an important reason too. Their rodent and small buck prey have fattened well in the lush growth of the preceding rains, and now in the fall, the long waving grass which hid them from eagle eyes dies back and starts to sere and wither on the plains. Then indeed, they run the hazards of plain-dwelling folk, and as they move about form ready prey for the raptors soaring and wheeling above them. The birds must find their prey far more easily obtainable just at the time when it is needed to feed the extra mouths.

Thus it was, on the last day of August, some fourteen years ago on one of our trips beneath the trees on Featherhill, we flushed a tawny eagle from its nest. At the top of a tree, the nest was a large platform of dry twigs, lined with finer twigs and seed-pods of acacia. There were two eggs, long and oval, and like those of so many birds of prey, the two were quite unlike. One was almost white, the other blotched and streaked near the thick end with rusty marks. They were heavy in the hand, indicating a fairly early stage of incubation.

These tawny eagles of eastern Africa are very similar in appearance and size to the golden eagle of my native Scotland, and have the same wonderfully effortless soaring flight. This pair promised an exciting chance of photographing them at fairly close quarters, because from the top of another acacia some fifty feet away we could just get level with the nest. So in the following weeks we gradually built up a hide in the nearby tree – a rickety structure of planks and roofing felt, with a plank seat over which we dangled our legs; but it was withal sufficiently concealing.

Some eight weeks later, I returned to the hide prepared for an all-day wait, and settled in about quarter past ten in the morning. The hen bird was on the nest when we arrived, which was unfortunate, as she then had a good view of all that

PLATE 28A. White-backed vultures, Featherhill 1941
PLATE 28B. Gabar goshawk, female at nest, Featherhill 1941

was going on as she sprang into the air and wheeled above us.

The chick appeared to be about three weeks old, clad in fluffy white down, and lay passive in the nest. There seemed to be only one, as is often the way with eagles, the other I suppose having been pushed over or killed in a juvenile fight.

The day was gloriously fine and sunny, with the little flat bottomed cumulus clouds so typical of Kenya skies hanging lightly against the blue, each marking the upward draught of warm air from each rising crest on the great sweep of open plains. I could see for miles across the rolling grasslands from my high up perch. During the next two hours, I could see the cock and hen eagle occasionally, soaring high up in the long valley below me. Exactly two hours after I had settled in, the hen bird suddenly appeared winging her way up the valley towards the nest and in sudden excitement I watched her swoop up to the nest, only to sheer away without landing. A few seconds later however she again came sailing up wind, and this time pitched on the right side of the nest, dropping to it from above. (Plate 27A).

She had brought some small item of food in her talons, but I could not make out clearly what it was. This she tossed forward on the nest, and started deliberately tearing it up with her hooked beak, feeding the chick most gently with small portions held at the tip of her beak as she leaned forward to the excited little chick. This lasted about ten minutes, and she only occasionally glanced at the hide without taking any great interest in it. As soon as the hen had pitched down, the chick had started calling with a soft double peeping note, and it kept this up continuously as the hen slowly tore the prey to bits before it.

I took a few photographs, and then by unfortunate mischance the film jammed in the camera. I swore softly and fluently as I wrestled with the wretched thing for it seemed minutes on end. The chick's meal completed, the hen remained several minutes more, preening herself and glancing round at the hide as she listened to my muttered cursing. Before I could finish the job, she took a short run to the edge of the nest, spread her great wings and circled up wind again.

I finished changing the accursed film in the ever-handy

changing bag which I always carry for such misadventures, refixed the camera again and waited for another one and a half hours with no sign of the bird returning to the nest. The weather meanwhile changed, and the wind started blowing strong, gusty and cold; the hide tree and nest tree started swaying to and fro with a distinctly unpleasant motion.

At 2 p.m. I had enough of this reminder of the open seas and climbed down again. Some distance away I saw the two birds sitting together in another acacia tree, and the difference between the two showed distinctively. The hen was a dark bird with a paler rump and back patch, grey-blue bill and whitish eyebrows, the cock being altogether paler and lighter in colour. Both birds showed the typical pale patch on the upper wings in flight.

Seven days later I again tried the bird, settling in the hide about the same time. Settled is hardly the word; for a very high east wind was blowing across the plains, and the hide swayed about violently again, recalling those unpleasant feelings of plunging, lifting and cork-screwing about in a cold green sea, I had often felt before. I prayed hard for an early return of the bird to shorten the wait and give me an excuse for an early return to *terra firma* – and the more *firma* the less *terra* as the bishop said.

Three quarters of an hour later the chick stood up in the nest and *peep-peeped* excitedly, looking out across the valley, and in a few minutes, marvelling at the astonishing eyesight of the chick, I too saw the cock this time sailing across the valley in the teeth of the wind. He lifted as he neared the tree and dropped at the back of the nest with a rat in his talons. He bored the hide for a few seconds then went off downwind somewhat nervously, leaving the rat in the nest. The frustrated chick called for a minute or two more, but the parent did not return; so the chick seized the rat itself, tore it to pieces and swallowed whole chunks of it at a time, throwing back its head as it did so. By now I noted it had a few wing quills showing amongst the fluffy white down, and that it was much steadier on its feet.

I stuck it out till half past noon, and although the chick sat up twice and called as the hen sailed close overhead, neither parent pitched to the nest. By now my organs of balance were urging a strategic retreat, and the wind being just as strong, I could no longer keep my nausea down so I gave up the uneasy struggle and climbed thankfully down to the ground.

Again a week later found me back at the nest once more, settling in again at ten in the morning. There was no sign of the old birds, and the chick was supine in the nest. In a short while it stood up and stretched, and I could see that by now it was well feathered on the wings and scapular regions. In half an hour, I heard the whistling and mewing calls of the old birds far down Kongoni Valley, and the chick immediately stood up in the nest, and began calling excitedly *wee-chik – wee-chik* looking out across the valley. I had a tremendous thrill when a few seconds later both cock and hen swept grandly up to the back of the nest, both pitching on the edge simultaneously. The cock walked slowly to the front edge and stood for a minute or two gazing regally at the hide, and then took off again, leaving the hen at the nest with the chick. She had brought food, apparently a large *Arvicanthus* rat, and the chick staggered up to her still calling excitedly; she stood on the rat and started tearing it up with her beak, offering small portions of the meat in the tip of her bill to the chick. After a short while, the hen took a firmer grip on the prey, and the tastiest pieces having been torn off already, started plucking at the fur, tearing out great beakfuls with a ripping sound and scattering fur all over the nest with shakes of her head. The chick called constantly and occasionally grabbed mouthfuls of fur sticking to the old bird's beak and swallowed them. As the meat was torn off the carcase I could hear the tendons snapping, till nothing but a twisted shred of skin was left. Occasionally the hen looked up and glanced superciliously at the hide where I was very busy with the camera, and then went on feeding the chick.

Then the old bird started a wonderful intimate game with her baby, picking the skin up and dangling it in front of the little chap, swinging it about as he called even more excitedly than before. Occasionally the chick grabbed it successfully, and leaning back on his tarsi heaved away in a tug o' war with his mother, who was so gentle in her play the while. The chick tried to swallow it, but the whole was too big and up it came again each time.

This delightful play held me entranced for nearly half an hour, and then the hen moved to the back of the nest. Overhead, I could see the cock soaring several hundred feet above the nest, obviously watching the goings-on. Finally, when the skin was torn to ribbons, the hen swallowed it herself, much to the obvious disgust of her son who had been far more excited at the dangling skin than at the pieces of red meat he had been offered before. This feeding and play had lasted nearly an hour and a half, and as I climbed down the tree again, I knew I had had an experience whose memories would last a lifetime. On the last day of November that year I went to the nest again, and, as I had expected, the chick had flown. As I watched the tree for the last time, the two old birds and their chick sailed slowly overhead, circled in farewell then soared out over the plains again to my whispered God Speed and Good Luck.

This is the only one of the East African eagles I have had opportunity to watch at the nest on successive occasions. I once had hopes of being able to photograph that much rarer one, Verreaux's eagle, a magnificent black bird with a white patch on its back. A pair of these nested occasionally on a cliff face not far from Nairobi, usually in the roots of a wild fig which had rooted precariously in a crack in a sheer face. One year however, they moved to a more accessible ledge further along the cliff, and I climbed up one day roped to an experienced rock climber who was a friend of mine. I am no good at dizzy heights and the sort of eyebrow clinging which thrills so many people at this sport, though I admire enormously the apparently effortless technique which it involves. My terror of sheer walls and terrific drops was not mitigated by the sarcastic comments my friend made about not sticking my behind out, and that the use of one's knees was not really good form in this sport; so that it was with a gasp of relief I finally crawled on to the nest ledge and saw the one egg lying on its trampled platform of twigs. The site was just possible photographically, but alas, the egg was stone cold, and the bird had clearly deserted sometime previously. I believe the nest had been disturbed before.

Going down I found worse than climbing up, but the steady rope and cool voice of my friend were reassuring as I slipped and scrambled down with relief to the base of the cliff some one hundred feet below. I landed somewhat weak in the knees and thankful really that I would not have to do it again. My friend methodically coiled the rope again and remarked that some pitches on Mount Kenya were really much more difficult – remarks I found hard to believe at the time! Superb fighter pilot, survivor of the Battle of Britain – one of the 'FEW' – expert rock climber with many peaks to his credit, two months later this close friend of my schoolboy days met a tragic and useless death on a wild and lonely lochan in Scotland when the ice treacherously broke beneath his skates; this within a few weeks of his return to Kenya in a civil capacity after years of fighter flying. The eagle's nest was our last encounter.

Most of these big birds of prey are supreme in their effortless use of the thermal currents which rise up from these undulating plains, and none more so than the commonest of them all – the red-tailed or augur buzzard of the Kenya highlands. Many times have I watched them hanging in the up-draught of hot air rising from a hillside, almost motionless, as they scan the grass below for the slight movements which reveal their prey. It is almost as if they are suspended by an invisible thread from the sky, until they suddenly raise their wings and plummet down with outstretched talons ready to drop on a rat or lizard below. They are one of the commonest birds of prey in the highland areas, and the advance of civilisation has been much to their liking; for the rows of telephone poles and power cables provide the ideal perch from which to survey the grass-lands round. They are beautiful creatures too, with their gleaming white bellies, black backs, chequered wings and striking russet tail. All-black melanistic forms are not un-common either.

They too, are tree nesters as a rule, and the acacias of Featherhill provide many a suitable site; we know of at least five nests there. But the pair I came to know best built their nest in the outer branches of a wild fig tree growing out of a small rocky scarp not far from Featherhill. This was a site which I could easily overlook from a hide some fifteen feet away built in a stout fork near the trunk. In the middle of June, the flat twig nest lined with green leaves contained two typical eagle-like eggs, large, regularly oval, the chalky white ground streaked and blotched with red, and as usual one paler than the other.

Two weeks later we camped near the tree, and built the hide in the evening, the birds flying past and calling *kaar* as they watched us in the tree. By now the eggs were darker in colour with nest stains, and the nest was re-lined with fresh green leaves. Early next morning, the bird was sitting, so I had a short session in the hide. Within ten minutes of hiding up, the bird suddenly swept up from the valley below and pitched on the nest. She stood for a few seconds gazing suspiciously at the hide from under lowered brows, then launched herself off again, sailing far out across the valley.

Five minutes later she was back again, landing on the other side of the nest, and without hesitation walked forward and sank breast first on to the eggs, lowering her wings and spreading her tail out fanwise, so that I could see the lovely chestnut and black barring of the quills. She sat for a long time facing the camera, and seemed somewhat suspicious of what was going on behind the screen each time I reset the shutter. Once I made too hasty a movement and she sprang off the nest. Back she came again not ten minutes later, this time holding a freshly picked twig of croton with green leaves still on it. (Plate 27B). She stood looking at the hide for a few seconds, and let the twig fall from her beak. As it fell, she glanced down, but made no attempt to pick it up or arrange it in any way; finally sinking forward and brooding the eggs again – but not for long. She left again and returned with another green leafy twig which she dropped in the nest. This bringing of green material to the nest is a habit common to most of the large raptorial birds, and is possibly a displacement activity.

By this time, I could see that she had a regular route to the nest; on leaving she sailed right across the valley, and then circled back to a tall euphorbia tree further along the cliffs where she perched for a bit. From here she launched herself down and circled round again up to the nest, always approaching the nest from below, and not pitching on to it from above as did the Featherhill tawnies. Once or twice her mate accompanied her back, but made no attempt to land himself.

I could tell whenever the old bird was coming near, although I could not see clearly through the leaves, because a little male Falkenstein's sunbird kicked up a terrific chattering row whenever she approached. Twice indeed, the sunbird came right up to the nest when she was brooding and sat on a leaf immediately behind her scolding agitatedly, but such little fry were beneath her dignity to notice. A pair of paradise flycatchers in the same tree also scolded when she came near with their *chee-choo* alarm note, but they too she ignored.

A week later there was only one egg in the nest, and the untidy and unforgivable litter of a picnic party below the tree told its own tale. But to our surprise the remaining egg hatched, and towards the end of July the chick appeared to be about three weeks old. It was clad in grey down, with a white diamond mark at the back of its head, followed by a white cranial and dorsal streak. The eye was jet-black, and the gape a brilliant yellow, contrasting with its blackish grey beak. The belly and chest was white, and the vent naked, its future broad russet tail represented only by a comical greyish tuft of down. The feet were dull ochre in colour, and the black wing quills were already sprouting.

During the morning, the hen came back rather suddenly from the euphorbia tree on the left, pitched up, then left as suddenly as she had arrived. Five minutes later the cock turned up dangling a rat from his beak, but also took off again still carrying the food. They seemed alarmed, and called loudly across the valley, so I came down and gave them a rest.

In the afternoon, the sun came out blindingly strong, and the chick became most uncomfortable, walking about the nest, and calling *chuk-chuk* constantly, occasionally sitting on his heels and gasping with the heat. Through his wide open panting bill, I could see his tongue cleaving to the roof of his mouth. Twice he walked to the edge of the nest, and defaecated with an explosive *phut*, shooting the excrement a good six feet clear of the nest. He was most properly house-trained.

After about half an hour of this, the hen returned to the nest with another green branch – poor substitute for good red meat;

but the chick gratefully crouched in the shade of her breast. Twice more she repeated this, dropping the twig each time in the nest. Once afterwards the cock returned with a young cut-throat whydah fledging in his beak. He stood for a minute or two, then dropped the bird in the nest, put his claws on it as if to tear it up, but changed his mind and dropped forward crouching over the chick for a while. He then left, and all activity ceased as the hot drowsy afternoon wore on. Inspection of the nest later showed two legs remaining of a francolin, which must have been the big early morning meal. Other food brought later would have been tit-bits only, which the chick made no attempt to eat himself.

I was unable to spare the time later for another day with the birds, but as I passed by a week later, I saw the chick was feathering well. As the parent bird launched itself off the nest, it picked up in its beak a lizard which it had dropped, and circled off with it; and as I watched, it transferred the lizard from its beak to its feet with a dexterous jerk forward of its claws in mid-air, and then casually dropped it elsewhere.

A year later I found another accessible nest on the same hillside, a little further along, also in June, and here a hide could be built on the steep bank overlooking the tree. This nest had two chicks, one a good bit bigger than the other. Some other large birds, like herons and most birds of prey and owls, start sitting as soon as the first egg is laid. The result is that hatching is asynchronous, and the chicks are all different sizes. This is a rather odd state of affairs, but as has been pointed out quite recently it is an efficient if somewhat ruthless method of ensuring adequate survival of the species, for the parents do not discriminate between which chick is fed first, nor do they ensure necessarily that all get a fair share. The oldest, and therefore largest, gets his food first by dint of shoving and bullying the others. If food is plentiful, then all in time get a sufficient share to live and grow; but if in a bad year, when these large food items such as fish or rats, become scarce, then only the largest chicks survive and the others die of starvation or are pushed overboard in the struggle. A cruel but efficient means of ensuring that at least one bird will survive to carry on the species in a lean year.

In this nest, there was one disembowelled rock hyrax, two decapitated agamid lizards about nine inches long, one small complete *Arvicanthus* rat, and the decapitated body of a Klaas's cuckoo; so that food seemed to be plentiful this year, and both chicks probably had an adequate share.

I spent the whole of the following day in hiding by the nest. The chicks were very sluggish, crawling about the nest, sitting on their heels and contemplating their toes; but from time to time, the eldest pecked viciously at the smallest when it moved, pulling out beakfuls of down. Then he toyed with a rat in the nest, but made no real attempt to feed himself. As with the previous year's chick, they defaecated with an explosive *phut* over the side of the nest. The youngest chick called constantly, a weak imitation of the parents' full-throated scream, but the oldest remained silent all the time.

The hen bird returned five times to the nest during the day; twice with a rat in her talons which she flew away with again each time; twice with a green branch which she dropped in the nest, and once with a dry twig. But at no time did she stay longer than a minute or two, nor did she make any attempt to feed the chicks at all.

Again I was unable to visit the nest again, so that I could not see the feeding procedure. I think one should be in the hide before dawn with these raptorial birds in order to watch the main meal of the day.

While the taller *spirocarpa* acacia trees of Featherhill are the nesting sites of the larger scavengers and birds of prey, the smaller flatter topped whistling thorns of the valleys, with their curious galled twin thorns are the nesting site of one of the most beautiful of the smaller hawks – the black-shouldered kite. These are small dove-grey hawks, with a deep crimson eye, whose powers of hovering rival those of the kestrel at home. They too are most appreciative of the man-made perches provided by the Posts and Telegraph Department, and any wide space of grassland traversed by a line of poles or wires is a frequent haunt of these dainty kites, which perch on the poles, or quarter the ground on beating wings poised for a stoop.

We found many nests of such. One I remember was about eight feet up, an untidy flat cup of tugs, built over an old sparrow's nest; it was lined with dry grass and long straggling bits of asparagus ferns, and contained four chicks clad in greyish brown down. Two had well-sprouted wing quills, one was intermediate in size, and one very much smaller with no wing quills showing at all; again an example of the asynchronous hatching I have mentioned before. Their beaks were bloody and wet, and congealed blood spattered the side of the nest.

For all their fierce glare, they were weak little things and had no grip in their talons yet at all, and only a feeble grip with their hooked beaks.

Using a step ladder as a foundation, we built a hide some twelve feet away – a rather rickety sort of structure with a very uncomfortable seat on top, but the birds seemed bold, and we hoped the wait would not be too long. This was not to be so; for on the first occasion I hid up, the bird took nearly two and a half hours to return, but when she did it was reward enough. She alighted gently from above carrying a single medium sized rat, which she dropped on the nest, then immediately flew off again. But in about ten minutes she was back, and started methodically tearing up the rat and offering small pieces to the chicks in her bill, in that gentle coaxing way of a raptor, holding the rest of the rat down with her foot the while.

The next day, she repeated the curious performance of dropping the food first in the nest, leaving, then returning a short while later to tear it up. The weather was dull and cold, and clearly she had difficulty in finding her rodent prey, for I could see her quartering the plains almost incessantly with no luck at all. Again the next day was dull and misty, and there was the same prolonged searching for food, resulting in long waits by the nest until she did return. She finally came back with a very small rat or shrew, which the biggest chick immediately grabbed and swallowed whole.

The long waits were relieved by the antics of the chicks. Their colouring was very different to the smooth pearly grey of their parents, being brownish with paler tips to the feathers. The belly and vent was white, but there was a marked russet band across the chest. The beak was greyish-blue, but the throat and mouth purplish in colour; legs yellow, but already feathering white on the tarsus like the parents.

While inactive much of the time, they nevertheless had periods of activity when they staggered comically round the nest, flapping their wing stubs, yawning and pulling at the downy tips of their quill shafts. Once, one swallowed the hind legs and skin of an *Arvicanthus* rat which had been left in the nest, throwing its head back and jerking it down his throat. On another occasion the hen bird dumped a whole rat in the nest and flew off to a nearby thorn where her mate was sitting. Then I was interested to hear the cock definitely encouraging the chicks to pull it to bits with his wheezy cry. They played about, tearing it up, holding it down with their feet like their parents and eating small portions as they tore them off. As with the adults, the tail and hind end was left till the last. Then each chick in turn tried to throw these down their throat, until the biggest finally managed at the twelfth attempt. He then sat down for a while, looking very full and uncomfortable. After this feed from the self-help service, there was much wing flapping and walking exercise round the nest.

I was interested too, to see that these chicks had not the cleanly habits of other raptor chicks I had watched. There was no particular effort to squat over the side of the nest, and the very liquid faeces were merely dribbled over the side, till the branches and ground below were literally whitewashed with guano.

They could see their parents dropping from the sky to the nest, and all heads turned together. But they made no particular response to their parents' call, though they uttered a low squeaky call when being fed.

I could watch the parent birds hunting over the plains about half a mile north of the nest, and the final return was very silent, preceded by a slight hover over the tree before the final pitch down. Unfortunately, they usually pitched back on to the hide, which was very trying from the photographic point of view. If the prey was large, the bird spent quite a time cutting up the joint; but if it was only small prey like a shrew it was dumped in the nest for the chicks to sharpen their beaks on. Usually the food was *Arvicanthus* the commonest rodent on these plains, and fair game for all the raptors, but once a quail was brought. There was no discrimination in feeding the chicks, the biggest often grabbing the food first, thus ensuring at least survival for himself by virtue of his early birth.

Raptorial birds usually have high-pitched whistling or mewing calls, curiously out of keeping with their size and mien, and I was interested to note the variety of calls which these small kites possessed. The male had a rather high-pitched *peeo* or *peee-oo*, used as a warning whistle when he was alarmed, as when a car passed along the nearby road, or cattle wandered too near. The female called with a low-pitched *pu-e* when returning with food to the nest. A human intruder standing by the nest would be attacked with swooping flight and a sharp, screaming, *keee-err* just like an angry tern at home. The male again had a raucous wheeze *rrr-ah* which he uttered as a definite encouragement to the hen when near the nest, and this was repeated till the latter actually landed, when she too called with the same note. These were several long and short and tone variations of this wheeze when both birds were close to the nest, calling to each other, and encouraging the chicks to tear up the food. Another curiously tern-like note was a combined whistle and wheeze *peee-rah*, uttered by both birds when apparently in a state of low anxiety by the nest, but not actually alarmed. The usual system of call notes was very distinctive, each variation becoming more urgent in pitch and intensity as the situation demanded.

Altogether they were a noisy pair, and also distinctly territorial. The cock, who has the same colouring as the hen, can be distinguished by his smaller size, and this one usually sat on the top twig of a thorn tree about twenty feet behind the hide, especially if the hen was near – an embarrassing position from my point of view. He took little part in the actual nest duties. Curiously enough, he would drive the numerous rufous-backed sparrows away from the nest, but did not interfere with shrikes, doves, or sunbirds, all of which came near the nest on various occasions.

A few days later saw a repetition of the same nest behaviour, but the birds were much bolder, and indeed the male attacked me twice most savagely when I was standing by the nest. The hen on the nest by now had become completely indifferent to the hide, and she once remained for about twenty minutes at the nest methodically pulling a rat to pieces and feeding the chicks while I whistled loudly to her to be a bit more lady-like and turn round and face the camera – which, however, she refused to do. She also spent quite a time too on an outer branch of the next tree about two feet away, watching the chicks and calling to them with a low piping whistle, uttered with her beak closed. At close quarters her striking crimson eye was most impressive.

The young had feathered well by now, and were most lively, walking about, wing stretching, leg stretching and wing flapping, and two of them actually walked right out of the nest on to a side branch. When handled, they leaned back with their enormous gapes wide open and wings outstretched, looking very fierce; but it was all bluff, for they made no attempt to bite, and the grip of their talons was still very feeble. When they were gaping thus, I noted that the root of their tongue had a curiously curved appearance, forming an apparent hole right through it. Even more than in other raptors, the prominent eyes seemed to be directed forward to a marked extent.

In one nest of which we kept note, the egg tooth of the chicks was not shed till the ninth day after hatching; but all the nests we found showed the same marked asynchronous hatching of the chicks, and curiously enough this first nest had the only really aggressive pair of parents.

The courting flight of these small kites is a marvel of acrobatics, the birds twisting and tumbling in the air. Copulation occurs on trees or on telephone wires, the hen soliciting the cock by elevating and depressing the fanned out tail, displaying the buffy under-tail coverts.

If these beautiful grey hawks are the patient hovering kestrels of the plains, the long legged gabar goshawk is the swift-striking terror of the thorn-tree clumps of Featherhill – the counterpart of the sparrowhawk of English woodlands. Though indeed the goshawks take their prey in the open, they are still essentially birds of the scattered trees, and are one of the most elegant of the smaller hawks in Kenya – this land of so many hunters of red-blooded prey.

Their nests in these Featherhill thorns take a good deal of finding, for they are small insignificant clusters of twigs in a high fork and are invariably woven over with grey spiders' webs so that they appear old and disused. So a good deal of patient investigation of all such clusters of apparent débris is necessary, unless perchance the bird is flushed off and gives its nest away; but they are keen sighted and shy, and usually slip quietly away long before the tree is approached. It was therefore with especial pleasure that we found one with chipping eggs late one October, in a *spirocarpa* tree in a situation which could be easily overlooked from another tree a few feet away. Here the usual planking and roof felt hide was built, giving screening from the front and sides.

As usual, the eggs were hatching at daily intervals, and the bird was anxious for their welfare. As in most raptors, the cock was much the smaller of the two, and the hen alone did the incubation chores.

On the first occasion I tried her, the eggs were just hatching. I was taken completely unawares by her utterly silent approach; one moment I was watching the vacant nest, the next she had suddenly appeared from below and was standing by the eggs, leaving me no time to grab the shutter release. Always, on subsequent occasions, this curious silent approach from below was quite characteristic, and I never did have any warning of her coming. Seldom could I anticipate her departure either, for she would quite suddenly drop downwards from the nest and glide silently away on scimitar wings through the trees. At close quarters the hen was a striking bird, with the clear cut lines of a swift pursuer, and her long legs and prominent eyebrows were particularly noticeable.

Although the last two eggs had still not hatched, the first two chicks out had already had a meal of a plucked pipit; but the hen was still brooding, and it was unusual to note that she did not sit facing the wind as do most birds, but tail on, so that the wind caught her long tail from time to time and cocked it over her head. The fact that there were two live chicks and two apparently inanimate eggs in the nest seemed to puzzle her somewhat, and she kept coming and going at short intervals, often standing by the nest doing nothing for minutes on end; at other times raking the eggs under her and brooding them, ignoring the chicks who struggled into the warmth of her fluffed-out breast. There was no sign of the cock bird at all.

I could not return to the nest for nearly a month. In the interval, two of the chicks had disappeared, and when I arrived one well feathered chick was standing on a branch at the side of the nest, the other was not at first visible. I later discovered him sitting on a branch near the top of the tree, also well feathered and just in the pre-nest-leaving stage.

The chicks were most active, calling constantly with a whistle in rising crescendo, with beaks wide open. There was much wing flapping, leg stretching and flying hops from nest to branches and back again. After about one and a half hours of waiting, the hen suddenly appeared, as was her wont, at the side of the nest, apparently materialising from nowhere. (Plate 28B). She dropped a small piece of meat, apparently the thorax of some small bird, with a sideways flick into the nest, and then slipped off to a branch behind the nest. The chicks immediately descended on the meat, the eldest grabbing it in his foot, the younger trying to pull it away in his beak. In a few seconds, the old bird slipped back into the nest and stopped the tug o' war stalemate by ripping up the meat, and then disappearing as silently and swiftly as she had come.

Meanwhile the chicks still squabbled violently over the meat, the eldest still holding down the large portion in his talons, and tearing at it with his beak. He dropped his wings outspread, and 'guarded' it from the smaller chick, who got severely buffeted each time he tried to get near; it was a most unseemly family squabble.

Two minutes later, the hen most unusually called just before pitching on the nest again with another large piece of meat in her left foot. Standing back on to me, she held the prey down and ripped small portions away, holding them out to the chicks indiscriminately who grabbed them from her bill. Twice she called again with the same crescendo whistle as the chicks, and she took about five minutes to feed them both in that quick decisive way these raptors have; then slipped off the front of the nest and twisted away through the trees again.

This whole episode was rather interesting, for it appeared as if on the first occasion she was deliberately trying out the chicks feeding themselves, and intervened only when it appeared that an unbrotherly situation was developing. Though I cannot be sure, the interval between her first and second visit with plucked prey was so short, that I cannot help feeling that the second portion had been passed to her by the cock, somewhere not far away, since the interval was far too short for her to have made another kill herself, *and* plucked it; but again the cock never appeared.

In the afternoon, the larger chick was again above the nest, and the smaller to one side. Then both started calling, and were answered constantly by the hen bird sitting in a tree behind the hide; she appeared to be encouraging them to leave the nest altogether. The chicks became more and more active, hop-flying from branch to branch, but this effort was too much for the smallest, who crawled back to the nest and dozed off for nearly an hour. When he woke, the calling and answering were repeated again, and the acrobatic hops and leaps of the oldest chick in the top of the tree were watched the whole time by the younger with a wistful 'wish I could do that too!' look. After a time, the youngster in the nest started amusing himself by wing and leg stretching, pecking at the branches and débris in the nest, and practising pouncing and grasping in a most comical fashion. I noted that both the chicks were greatly interested in large insects flying about the nest, following them round with a piercing gaze, and first spotting them from about a yard away. Like the buzzard chicks, but unlike the kites, they defaecated most explosively, lifting the tail and bending forward, shooting out the liquid excrement at least a yard clear of the nest. After about three hours further wait, there was still no sign of the old birds again, and I climbed down. I have little doubt the chicks finally left the nest a day or two later.

Those supreme scavengers of the great game plains of East Africa – the vultures – are of course common on Featherhill, and five species are to be found there. Certain trees we knew well as vulture perches, where the great birds sat and dozed with paunches bulging with carrion, almost too lethargic to move as one got near; and of course, the flocks of vultures round a kill gorging on the fast-rotting meat are a sight never to be forgotten.

The commonest are, I suppose, the white-backed (Plate 28A), which occur in flocks of a score or more. The smaller, more domesticated forest vultures accompany them in twos and threes, and the pale buffy backs of the solitary griffons are distinctive. Solitary too, are the white-headed – whose name is descriptive – and the gigantic lappet-eared vultures who stand a good head and shoulders above the fighting flapping mob at a kill, with their curious Elizabethan ruffle round the bare neck extending almost up to the ear-holes.

Some of these nest too, in the Featherhill thorns, and though we found two or three nests of the white-headed vulture, none were readily accessible from the photographic point of view. But the hunched, ill-omened shapes on the bare branches of Vulture Tree were easy to approach after a full meal.

No chapter on these great birds of prey of the open plains is complete without mention of that most elegant and characteristically African bird – the secretary bird – so well-named as he stalks long-legged through the grass, with his hands clasped beneath the tails of his smart morning coat and his bunch of secretarial quills stuck professionally behind his ear.

They are great favourites of mine, but I have wasted on them more feet of film than I care to recall, for they are uncannily difficult to photograph well on the open plains. It is easy to approach them within reasonable photographic range in a car, but astonishingly difficult to get them to look at you, or even appear at least sideways on. Like the flamingos I have mentioned elsewhere, they are good judges of 'escape distance' as it is called, and when approaching just those few feet extra to get a really satisfactory image, the bird will slightly turn away and start walking round in a circle. Nearly all the photographs I have taken of them show the head just turned away so that the beak is not clearly shown. When they take wing too, they will nearly always run at a tangent to get up speed for the take off – practically never sideways, which would give the best picture.

They, too, nest on Featherhill, and we know of several of their huge flat nests, always right on the top of a small tree; but none of them have ever been in a really satisfactory position for photography without building a separate tower hide nearby – which I have never had time to do.

I recall finding one nest near Magadi in May, which had a huge well-feathered chick in it, which was so limp with the blinding heat on the exposed nest that it could scarçely move. They seem to nest earlier in the year than most of the other large raptors, because by July most of the Featherhill nests had been vacated. Below one such vacant nest, in which a chick had been successfully reared, we found several large grey casts, about four inches long by an inch thick, containing *Arvicanthus* fur, leg bones and the legs of locusts. They are however, great snake killers too, killing them by stamping on them first as do crested cranes. This particular nest tree was surrounded by a white ring of droppings, well clear of the tree; like the buzzard and eagles, the secretary chicks do not foul their own nest.

We have however also found nests with very fresh eggs in July. The eggs are large, oval and pointed, with a chalk white ground sparsely and finely speckled with red at the wider end. The clutch of two lies in a very shallow cup, and the nest as a rule is most difficult to photograph without a wide-angle lens; they are so large and flat that it is all one can do to peer over their side at the top of the tree.

Apart from the archaic looking ostriches, which for all their 'domestic' appearance are also exceedingly difficult to approach sufficiently near in a car, and about whose home life I know nothing, the other striders of the plains are the bustards. Like buck and gazelle, these birds have evolved fleetness of foot, rather than wing power, for survival. The largest of them is the great kori bustard. They too, like secretary birds and ostriches, are difficult to photograph really well – the final print usually shows the head turned slightly away. Like the secretary birds too, they are fond of stalking over newly burnt ground, on which many tasty tit-bits seem to occur.

The smaller bustards, like the black-bellied and blue-necked, are common too. Their call is an astonishingly loud and strident honk. All the bustards are ground nesters, but I have had no luck in finding them.

The grotesque, pouch-necked and bald-headed marabout storks join the vultures in their necrophilic orgies on the plains, and at one time were a common sight just outside Nairobi scavenging on the Etcoville rubbish dumps. European storks, and the much smaller Abdim storks with their white rumps and red garters, come and go with the seasons of migration and are magnificent locust control officers; but they alone can never compete with the vast swarms of the fifth plague which darken the Kenya skies from time to time in devastating, life-destroying millions. Even man himself with all the modern resources of science and aircraft can barely hold his own against the rustling swarms of grasshoppers on the move.

The smaller fry of these open plains are too numerous to mention in any detail. Sandgrouse, those curious pigeon-like birds whose flocking habits at desert water holes are so well known to shooters, are found in numbers on these Featherhill plains, and are often easy to approach in the car as they run through the grass. Francolin, spurfowl and guineafowl all frequent the yellowing ridges, but the striking, shimmering blue-hackled vulturine guineafowl is not common on the higher plains; they prefer the hot scrub desert of the lower altitudes, and are birds of the burning hard baked ground.

Button quail (not really a quail at all), the lovely blue quail, and the ubiquitous ventriloquial harlequin quail all nest in the long grass round the swamp in Buzzard Valley. The trapping of the latter with pole decoys hung with baskets in which are imprisoned the decoy birds is a time-old custom still practised by the Jaluo in Nyanza Province.

The technique of the trapping is ingenious. The birds are imprisoned singly for life in a conical pear-shaped basket in which there is just room to move. These are hung with a fibre rope wound on a tall pole, the topmost basket being spaced further up the pole than the others, this usually containing the best decoy caller. The tall pole is then stuck in the centre of an area of suitable short grass, and very often single baskets with a good caller are suspended on shorter forked poles at the periphery of the area in three or four places a few yards away from the centre pole. Sometimes the baskets contain one or two single large empty *Achatina* snail shells, whose clinking noise in the wind resembles the calls of the birds.

As the pole sways in the wind, the birds call with their liquid ventriloquial *twat-wat* note, and thus lure their inquisitive migrant relations to drop into the deadly area; for as the latter run through the runnels made in the grass towards the calling birds, they are caught one after another in deadly little nooses placed across the runs. These are made of fine black hair, and are kept open with thin forked sticks about an inch off the ground. The old established trap sites are a maze of runs all leading to the centre pole, and may cover two or three hundred square yards; often these are planted with criss-cross low hedges of the stiff succulent plant called *manyala* – a plant which always encircles the traditional Luo homestead; and these low hedges have small openings made at intervals in the impenetrable stems, each opening being noosed.

Decoys are set early in the morning and left perhaps till noon; or sometimes they are set overnight to catch night migrants. A good day's bag may bring in perhaps twenty to thirty birds which are sold and eaten, the meat being 'very sweet'. In the older days, the legs and wings of the trapped birds were broken to prevent escape on the way to market, but this cruel practice is now illegal – when it can be enforced! The owners are careful of the decoy birds, and do not leave them hanging in the hot sun for too long; to feed them, the baskets are detached from the poles and placed on a pile of millet. The birds peck this through the open weave of the basket.

Near Magadi too, there is a waterhole where the local Jaluo labour snare the sandgrouse as they drop to drink in the early morning or late evening. The ground all round the edges of the water is snared heavily with fine nooses laid flat, perhaps a dozen or more tied to a pegged out string. In these the feet of the birds become entangled as they scuffle down to drink. For the outwitting of wild animals, be they game, bird or fish, some of these Kenya tribes such as the Jaluo or Wakamba would be hard to equal.

Nor are the Featherhill thorns devoid of interest as regards their smaller feathered inhabitants, for the great raptors are not alone in their choice of the twisted thorny branches for home making. In the outer twigs of these trees are built some of the most exquisitely constructed nests that ever a bird can build – those of the buff-bellied warbler. These build a small globular purse of the finest felted down and fibre, with a little flap-over porch entrance at one side; one of the finest masterpieces of weaving one could ever hope to see.

Here too, on the larger isolated thorn trees, one can find the classical weaver bird colonies, with literally hundreds of nests woven of fine grass clustering like bunches of grapes on the outer branches – the whole tree a living, seething mass of chattering bird life. Each individual bird is busy with its own immediate nest affairs, and yet the whole is an astonishingly coherent organism on its own.

There are several kinds of weavers who nest in these thorn-tree plains, the nests all characteristic of each species, and varying in type from solitary to immensely colonial.

Thus, for example, the pendant gourd shaped nests of the vitelline weaver, without a hanging porch, are built in twos and threes on the very top of acacia tree twigs. Within these nests one often finds the eggs of the little silverbill finch – small white glossy pointed eggs typical of these estrildine finches. It is not parasitic, but hatches its own eggs, and though it may indeed build its own nests, empty weaver nests are often appropriated, even if there are occasional addled weaver eggs in them still. Thus in a small colony of these weaver nests we found respectively clutches of one, five, one and two silverbill eggs, with a single addled weaver egg in two of the nests. The silverbills are smaller birds than their unwitting house-builders, hence a weaver nest occupied by a silverbill often has its downward facing entrance slightly more closed up with finer grass built in later by the silverbill itself.

I have mentioned elsewhere in this book the curious double entrance nests of the grey-headed social weaver which are built on the topmost thin twigs of a certain upright species of acacia. They are very like the nests of the black-billed sparrow weaver, a bird so common in the very dry thorn-bush veldt of the Northern Frontier District round Isiolo for example. The nest is woven of dry grass, with two downwardly facing entrance holes. In the non-breeding season the birds roost on the ridge between the two entrances, but in the breeding season one entrance is closed up, and in the chamber so formed are laid the five to seven rounded white eggs. The sparrow weavers of the N.F.D. build in huge colonies; the social weavers do not really live up to their name, and the nests are in groups of perhaps three or four.

Speke's weavers are the classical colonial nesters, several hundred nests being clustered on one tree, but among them, or separately, are the nests of the Abyssinian masked weaver, characterised by the rather open weave of tough wiry grass with a short dependent spout. Their eggs are longish, white, dull and oval in shape.

The Kenya black-necked weaver nests too singly in these colonies, and their nests are like those of the masked weaver, but built of finer material, and have a very long dependent entrance tube. Speke's weaver nests have no entrance tube at all.

All these vast weaver colonies provide almost free nesting places ready made for the lazier of the smaller finches, such as the silverbill mentioned above: the chestnut sparrow, which can also build its own nest if it really tries; and the cut-throat finch. It is curious however that these lodgers will use only the tubeless nests of the Speke's weavers, and their eggs are never found in the tubed masked or black-necked weaver nests. It is indeed rather instructive to examine all the nests of a large weaver colony, particularly Speke's, and see what the nests contain. A long hooked stick is essential for this, but pull the branches down carefully for the eggs roll out easily. One day we collected the following figures from a large colony of Speke's nests:

Nest 1. 7 incubated, 2 fresh eggs of silverbill.
,, 2. 5 incubated, 4 fresh eggs of silverbill
,, 3. 4 silverbill, 4 addled Speke's eggs
,, 4. 7 silverbill eggs

in addition to numerous 'pure' Speke's nests. Thus, like other estrildine finches, two silverbills may lay in one nest, in spite of the abundant accommodation. The silverbill too add a little extra lining to the Speke's nests for their own use. In a colony of masked weaver nests we found clutches of two, two, four, two and three eggs; all were addled, but actually embryonated, a curious state of affairs. The same high rate of desertion seems to prevail in Speke's colonies, for in one colony we found five clutches of three eggs each, also embryonated, but stone cold. The Speke's eggs are a deep dull blue, and regularly oval. Another nest had four eggs, another six of which three were fresh and three incubated – perhaps the Speke's too may share their nests. A further nest had five Speke's eggs and three cut-throat eggs in it.

The cut-throats again use only the tubeless Speke's nests, and in four Speke's nests we found:

Nest 1. 1 cut-throat egg, 1 addled Speke's
,, 2. 5 cut-throat chicks (well-quilled) and
1 infertile cut-throat egg
,, 3. 1 cut-throat egg
,, 4. 3 cut-throat eggs, 5 addled Speke's.

The cut-throat eggs are also white, but dullish and rather rounded and larger than the silverbill eggs. Although the colonies are full of bustle and noise, amongst all the comings and goings the pairs of cut-throats keep closely together. Only the male has the red cut-throat band, the female none, but both the sexes of this little finch have a most peculiar speckled and scaly appearance, well known in aviaries at zoos. Like the silverbills, the cut-throats add a thicker lining of green grass heads to the Speke's nests they take over, and as in many such small birds building in dark enclosed nests, the chick's mouth is lined with an extraordinary network of white raised ridges. Other species have various arrangements of white spots and dots, and these fanciful patterns are alleged to guide the feeding mother bird to the chicks' mouths in the darkness of the nest. The pattern almost certainly has a 'releaser' function in causing the parent bird to regurgitate its food on return to the nest.

The weavers of eastern Africa are a vast and complex group, which show a wide range of habits from solitary to social, and a full study of their biology and behaviour in relation to courtship, nest-building and general social behaviour would be well worth while. For their very diversity probably has some definite underlying uniform trends, and comparison one with another would be a pleasing intellectual, yet withal practical, study.

Space forbids much further description of the smaller fry of these beloved plains; but a very good illustration of the enormous variety of birds which can frequent such an area was seen one day when we watched a single isolated tree, on the top of which there was a large nest of *Crematogaster* ants, these vicious little creatures with the cocked up tail which infest nearly every tree, particularly the galls of the whistling thorns. From the globular nest plastered round the topmost branch, there was issuing a steady stream of the winged sexual form of this ant on a mating flight, and in the tree, catching these tasty morsels as they emerged, we noted the following birds: one fiscal shrike; one white-winged scrub warbler; one Ukamba rattler; two rock-thrushes; one yellow-vented bulbul; one yellow bishop; one white-eyed slaty flycatcher; one grey flycatcher; one Speke's weaver; four rufous sparrows; one yellow-breasted bunting; one Reichenow's weaver; one blue-eared glossy starling; one garden warbler; one mousebird; one tawny-flanked longtail; and one black-headed oriole. Truly an astonishing list!

From time immemorial the nomadic tribes who graze their cattle on these plains have annually fired the grass just before the rains to provide a flush of new green grass for their cattle. This practice is still hotly debated by the experts; some claim that it destroys the structure of the soil, others that it encourages the growth of the fire-resisting grasses of higher food value, such as the red oat grass. But whatever the experts think or may legislate, the Africans happily start their tremendous fires year after year – sure in their time-hallowed knowledge that it *is* the best for their four-footed bank balances in the end.

Thus it is, when the roar and crackle of the fire sweeps through the long dry grass like a twisting, malevolent being, destroying all in its path and leaving a blackened smoking scar in its wake, palled over with thick billowing clouds of smoke, that death comes to all those living things as are not swift enough of wing or foot to escape the licking flames. But death waits too, hanging in the air for those small fry of the plains like grasshoppers, flies and beetles who leap and fly madly to escape the scorching fury that travels faster than they can do.

For the insect eating birds too, know that these destructive blazes drive thousands of helpless insects into the air and that a cloud of billowing smoke over the grasslands means food in plenty – living food that has leapt to escape a fiery death only to meet death more swiftly, more surely, at beak, talon and claw.

I have often watched the birds round such a blazing area on the plains, and the variety which collect is striking. In the tenuous wisps of dying smoke at the tail end of the cloud in one fire, I once recorded all the following: red-rumped swallows, wire-tailed swallows, European swallows, red-throated rock martins, European house martins, mottled swifts, square-tailed swifts, Abyssinian swifts, two or three goshawks and one African peregrine. Here, at the end of the smoke cloud, all these birds could use to the full their supreme mastery of the air – diving, twisting, turning in an intricate maze of aerial evolutions.

Then, near the centre of the smoke cloud, where the dense brownish smoke rendered visibility poor for both predator and prey, there hung the larger birds – slower of wing, but not so slow that they could not catch the bigger, heavier flying locusts and grasshoppers. There were both the yellow-billed and black billed kites, red-tailed buzzards and several tawny eagles – neglecting their more normal red-blooded prey for these more easy pickings.

The technique of these large birds was interesting in the extreme – for they cannot fly as fast as the swallows and swifts to snap up the flying insects in their beak. Instead, flying in the densest smoke, the grasshoppers were caught with the birds' feet, in mid-air, with a pouncing motion and while still flying the head was bent under the body and the prey torn apart with the beak while held there in the talons – involving a mastery of aerial balance that was a joy to watch.

On the burnt, blackened and still hot and smoking ground in the wake of the flames stalked cattle egrets, a few kites tired of flying, secretary birds and bustards, while an occasional lilac-breasted roller dashed in to snap something up. What these birds in the rear actually eat I do not know – perhaps already roasted insects, or those already crawling in to re-colonise the ground.

When the great raptors such as the eagles and buzzards

gather in numbers thus, it is most interesting to see the almost baffling range of plumage which they wear, depending on age and sex. For it changes thus, and these changes make identification of the numerous species an almost despairing business for the field watcher, and great experience is necessary to be certain of an identification.

Then too, when these great plains fires devastate hundreds of acres of long waving grass, is the time to look for the smaller warblers, pipits and larks who congregate in the smaller remaining patches of still green and unburnt grass in much greater numbers than usual. The blackened stubble has no attraction for these little inhabitants of the plains.

To the east and south-east, the high Featherhill plains slope slowly down across two hundred miles of rolling land down to the sea coast, through the great Game Reserves and the Royal Tsavo National Park. As the land drops, so does the sun burn fiercer in the sky and the rainfall fail, producing a red-baked wilderness of thorn scrub. Here and there the green ribbons of trees mark the course of a trickling stream, or the moister ground of a river bed dry for most of the year.

But too, this is the parched land that breaks overnight into a lush carpet of green, starred with beautiful ephemeral flowers of all colours, when the first refreshing rains of the season fall. Through this dry desert country winds the long, long road which carries now, all the year round, the heavy traffic of weary holidaymakers from the brilliant highlands to the peace and languor of the tropical shore of Kenya.

I have been on this road many times, and never cease to wonder at the wonderful panoramic change from the cool green patchwork of the highlands, down through the dry desert scrub to the lush, green steamy coastal belts of coconut palm and baobab trees.

One September, just before the rains broke, Alex and I drove down this long three hundred and fifty miles in one day, taking turn-about at the wheel. Leaving Nairobi in the cool still darkness before dawn, at about 5 a.m., we were in Mombasa some eleven hours later. To while away the tedium of the journey, we made a count of all the birds we saw as soon as it became light enough some fifty miles out of Nairobi at

Kilima Kiu, right down to Mombasa. The results are shown in the table on pages 261 and 262.

The figures are amusing and yet instructive. While they do not show to any great extent the ecological range of the birds in the different types of country traversed (except perhaps for the palm swifts first encountered near the coconut palms of the coastal belt and the huge numbers of pipits characteristic of the open treeless plains round Emali) they nevertheless give some idea of the variety and number of birds which can in fact be seen in such a traverse from a car travelling in Kenya at some forty to fifty miles per hour.

What is more evident is the diurnal activity of the birds. Right down to perhaps Simba, the birds are more easily seen and active in the comparative cool of the morning hours. Thereafter, although these scrub birds are just as common in the country below, we recorded less and less as the sun climbed in the sky and the heat of the afternoon became oppressive. At this time the birds become much less active and retire to the shade of the trees and bushes where of course they are not so noticeable from a car at speed. Such census counts are liable to all sorts of gross errors, and cannot be really accurate; nevertheless this list of forty-eight species and six hundred and seven individuals is an impressive demonstration of the wealth of bird-life in these scrub desert plains; and at that, is only but a tiny fraction of what may really be seen on more leisurely travel through such country.

To the north-east, north and north-west of Featherhill, the plains again stretch for limitless miles into that exciting and mysterious part of Kenya known as the Northern Frontier District – a land of low scrub, waterless desert, baked earth and fierce heat, which nevertheless forms no less than three fifths of the whole Colony of Kenya. Almost an unknown and closed area until the last World War, its proximity to the Italian held lands of Somaliland and Abyssinia made it an area of major tactical importance. Many thousands of European and African troops came to know these arid wastes as they were poised there for the lightning thrusts on Mussolini's Empire.

I too, at this time, travelled much of this desolate country on war duties, which alas prohibited the use of any photographic work. I have ever since regretted the opportunities I then had for photographing birds. But my notebooks became filled with details of the many scores of birds so typical of this type of country; and in spite of its dreary, scorching wastes, this N.F.D. is one of the finest bird watching areas in eastern Africa and has a richness of bird life which can seldom be equalled.

As I turn the pages of my notebooks, the magic and mysterious names call to mind many half-forgotten scenes, once so familiar. Isiolo – with its rows of trim white Indian shops, weaver-laden thorn-trees and whirling dust devils; Garbatulla – pools of stagnant tepid water and the smell of goats; Habaswein – deep, fine grey dust, and cool shade of great fever trees lining the Uaso Nyiro river, that curious waterway which loses itself there in the muddy greenness of the Lorian Swamp, long before it can ever reach the sea; Wajir – its myriad brackish wells, blistering heat and little Beau Geste fort. And so on, through Dif and Afmadu and the blinding whiteness of the Somaliland coast at Kismayu north to Mogadiscio.

Northwards too from Isiolo, through Laisamis with its hundreds of groaning camels to the unexpected cool heights of Marsabit – land of Paradise Lake, elephants and strawberries in the D.C.'s garden; down again to the rolling desert of Gamra, Kalacha, North Horr and the burning lava plain of Dukana; and so across the border to the ancient land of Ethiopia.

West to Turkana – the ferocious heat of Lodwar, one of the most desolate spots on earth, with its little graveyard of white crosses, grim reminders of the toll of blackwater fever in this tiny outpost of Empire; on to the heat and black lava belt of Lokitaung, down through the impressive red cliffs of Todenyang Gorge to Namaraputh – a cluster of mud huts on the snake infested shores of remote Lake Rudolf; here the brown waters are cloven with the great Nile perch as they leap up to the delta of the Omo river. Then onwards, up the Omo river, swollen brown and muddy, past Kibish Wells and the ancient fossil beds of Kalam – and thus up again to the cool heights of Addis.

Such places are indeed a far country from the heights of

Featherhill, but their magic lingers still. Now, as I finish the chapter, I can call to mind the huge flocks of birds which used to cluster round the drinking-pan I placed beside my outspread fly; for water in these desert places is the Key of Life indeed. Birds will flock from miles away to drink and bathe in a basin of cool refreshing water, placed upon the ground. Here in addition to the hundreds of starlings, weavers, whydahs, hornbills and others who will come to such attraction, you will see two of the most gorgeously coloured birds in the world – the golden pipit, and the royal starling, two birds which have never been photographed in the wild.

The N.F.D. and thorn-tree plains, indeed, offer the most exciting challenge to the bird watcher in Kenya, a challenge which I know one day will be answered as it ought!

CHAPTER 10

PHOTOGRAPHING BIRDS

The Birds themselves

In the British Isles there are numerous books, popular and otherwise, from which even the beginner can identify any bird which he may see. The best and most authoritative is undoubtedly Witherby's *Handbook of British Birds*, without which any serious work is almost impossible. This is however in five volumes with addenda and corrections and is hardly of pocket size, though an abridged version in one volume by Hollom is a most useful adjunct. In the true pocket size, it would be hard to equal Richardson and Fitters' *Pocket Guide to British Birds*, with its recently published companion volume on nests and eggs; while Peterson, Mountfort and Hollom's *Guide to Birds of Europe*, in a similar edition and size is most useful in covering the wider field of the continental traveller. James Fisher's at present incomplete *Bird Recognition* in the Pelican series is useful, while there are too, numerous smaller and more 'popular' books of varying usefulness; but armed with the first few named, no one should have any serious difficulty with any British birds. It is most useful too to have the more general volumes, such as *Bird Watching* by Fisher, and *How to Study Birds* by Stuart Smith, to get a wider view of various aspects of bird study possible for an amateur; and the photographer is well served by the various books published by Hosking, Yeates and Higham.

On the other hand, East Africa itself is singularly ill-served with suitable bird identification books, and here the beginner may find himself in very great difficulties over simple identification of birds. One of the greatest of these difficulties is of course the multiplicity of species and geographical races, such as one seldom has to contend with in Great Britain. Thus for example, while there is only one swallow and one kingfisher in the British Isles, in East Africa there are at least half a dozen species of each, some with local races as well. The bird-life is embarrassingly rich.

The standard work of reference is Sir Frederick Jackson's *Birds of Kenya Colony and the Uganda Protectorate*, in three volumes, and for the serious worker this is indispensable. It is now however, unfortunately both largely out of date, and completely out of print; secondhand copies, when obtainable, fetch enormously high prices, about £30 being the usual figure. Jackson's discursive style, followed by the editor Sclater, is both old-fashioned and quaint, though irritating at times, and it adds much to the literal if not intellectual weight of the volumes. There is a tremendous amount of useful information still required, such as nesting data, length of incubation periods, behaviour, call notes, etc., which was not known at the time the book was published; and furthermore 'Jackson' is on many occasions of little use to the bird watcher in the field, since most of the keys are based on skin specimens, and may include such obscure points as the number of tail feathers or the degree of emargination of the primaries – points which can seldom be settled by watching the living wild bird.

Since World War II, the sale of the late Austin Robert's *Birds of South Africa* and Gill's similar but smaller volume *A First Guide to South African Birds* has been extensive in Kenya, Uganda and Tanganyika. These two books have the supreme advantage of very numerous and reasonably good colour plates – almost a *sine qua non* for any beginner's book, and from which it is fairly easy to identify species seen. While indeed many of the South African birds are similar to, or identical with, the East African species, and these two books can be of great help, nevertheless they should be used with considerable caution in the East African territories, because of the differences which do occur. Sometimes they may even lead one badly astray, particularly with regard to subspecies. In addition, a great deal of Robert's nomenclature is unacceptable to the more serious worker on East African birds.

The English names given in Robert's have mostly a South African bias, with indeed a good deal of Afrikaans included. Popular names simply do not exist for many East African birds; Jackson endeavoured to remedy this in his three volumes, and perhaps his English names should be followed whenever possible though many are inappropriate and some not even descriptive. For the more serious worker, it is better to know the Latin names, such as are used internationally, but only a few of these are ever likely to become popular in usage for the non-scholastically minded, however exact these names may be.

To the less scientifically minded bird watchers, some of the serious workers can be most annoying, when they insist on referring to a bird by its racial or sub-specific name only. Thus for example, when they talk about '*fayi*', other scientific workers know at once they mean *Pycnonotus tricolor fayi*, the east of Rift highland race of the common yellow-vented bulbul or toppie – but to many, yellow-vented bulbul is good enough. I sympathise with the latter, who include the majority of bird watchers in Kenya, although as a scientist myself I appreciate better the exactitude of the Latin nomenclature.

A good many years ago my uncle, Dr V. G. L. van Someren, started a series of papers on the 'Birds of Kenya and Uganda', in the *Journal of the East Africa and Uganda Natural History Society*, illustrated in black and white from his own paintings and photographs. This project has unfortunately never been completed, and the parts published cover only the game birds, plovers, waders and doves. For these groups which are covered, the papers are indispensable even for the amateur, since for accuracy of information they have few equals; a few bound copies are still available on application to the East Africa Natural History Society at the Coryndon Museum in Nairobi.

Even in East Africa, the possession of a 'Witherby' will be found a tremendous help, as many of the rarer migrants in Great Britain, all of which are figured and described, are common migrants to East Africa, as also of course are many British summer residents such as the nightingale, willowren and so on.

Until recently however, there was little else at all suitable, and indeed the want is a long-felt one even among the relatively small European population in Kenya. There are few ornithologists in East Africa who know the whole range of species in a sufficiently popular and exact way, though the Ornithologist and the collections of the Coryndon Museum are invaluable for reference for those able to consult them. The cost of publication of popular bird works for a limited demand is enormous, since colour plates are almost essential for such a work to be of use to the majority.

This want has been filled recently in fact by the publication of Volumes I and II of Mackworth-Praed and Grant's *Birds of Eastern and North-eastern Africa*. Volume I deals with nearly all the larger non-passerine birds; and the remaining far larger groups of the many commoner birds such as the weavers, warblers, buntings, shrikes and so on are dealt with in Volume II.

Volume II also contains necessary corrections to Volume I, and it would be most useful if from time to time later the authors and publishers would issue sheets of additions and corrections as has been done for Witherby's volumes.

Though hardly 'field' books as the authors claim, they are now nevertheless indispensable for all bird watchers in Kenya. It is well however to remember that only a proportion of the birds described therein occur within the boundaries of the Colony, and when identifying an unknown bird with their aid, the geographical distribution should be most carefully checked, though stragglers will of course occur since bird life is forever in a state of flux. However, the text is of the concise 'Witherby' form, and as with 'Witherby' their main usefulness perhaps lies in the way they indicate what is *not* yet known about the bird in question. A great many of the species are covered by adequate colour plates, others by marginal black and white drawings; and most of the species and sub-species by distributional maps, many of which are unfortunately on too small a scale to be really accurate enough. All the groups are covered by keys of the usual dichotomous form, but here also some are hardly of use for field purposes, such as that for the various birds of prey. But one cannot expect perfection at the first attempt to cover the whole vast field of East African ornithology; the book is a most valuable start however, and no doubt in future years it will form the basis for other handbooks similar to the now numerous British bird books which cater for the watcher armed with field glasses only and not a shot-gun.

Captain C. D. Priest's *Eggs of Birds breeding in Southern Africa* is a most useful first attempt to deal with the identification of nests and eggs only, and while some of the colour plates could be criticised, nevertheless the basis is again there, and as a supplementary volume it should be on the African bird watcher's bookshelf. The warning about the use of Robert's book in East Africa applies here also, with an additional warning too that the equatorial breeding seasons are not similar to those further south on this continent.

There is no doubt that the ideal way to know Kenya birds is to accompany some other competent ornithologist in the field. I myself have been very lucky in this respect, and owe most of what I now know to my own relations, who have been studying birds in East Africa since 1905; and I most gratefully acknowledge my debt to them, not only for the identifications which they have made possible for me, but also for what field-craft knowledge I now possess.

Nowadays, the beginner in Kenya would do well to join the East Africa Natural History Society, based on the Coryndon Museum in Nairobi, and learn all he can from the facilities now offered in the way of field rambles, and the use of the study collections in the Museum; but this is of limited use for those stationed 'up-country'.

Quite a number of bird watchers in Kenya find the whole field almost too vast to cope with, and specialise in watching and collecting notes on only certain groups, such as the raptorials, sunbirds or some other group, or specialise in certain aspects of bird behaviour such as bird song, call notes, etc. This is a very good idea, since so little is known about nearly all East African birds that specialised knowledge of one group or one aspect of bird biology can be of the greatest value. A valuable practice also is to concentrate on the birds of a certain defined area or habitat type; it is surprising how little information there really is of the detailed ecology of areas, and even in the British Isles, now a country where amateur bird watching is almost a national pastime, the amount of information published each year on purely local distribution and habits of the most familiar birds in small areas is quite amazing and of immense value.

Birds are universal in Kenya, and there is literally no part of the country where they cannot be studied. There is no doubt that the lower thorn-tree and scrub bush country below the five thousand foot level is by far the best in its abundance and diversity of species, and it is for me, personally, the most exciting country for bird watching; but even the cold highland grasslands and forests have their quota of fascinating species.

Since the nest itself acts as a focal attraction point for any bird, I suppose more bird photography is done at the nest than at any other time in a bird's life; and ability to find nests is therefore of the greatest advantage to the photographer. On this part of the Equator, there is not the alternation of spring, summer, autumn and winter, nor the clear-cut seasonal changes of temperate climes. There are instead wet and dry seasons, which impose their own rhythm on the breeding of birds, but even then many kinds show no really clear-cut season. As a rule however, most of the smaller birds nest either during the long rains of March to May, or in the short rains of October to December, at the seasons when it is supposed their insect or fruiting food supplies are more abundant; on the other hand many large birds such as the raptorial birds of prey tend to nest in the long cool dry season of June to September, when the grasslands are drying up and it has been suggested that their rodent and small animal prey can be more easily seen and caught, and also when the more cloudy weather does not cause so much distress to chicks in an open nest. Others, such as the red-eyed dove and fiscal shrike may nest all the year round; I do not suppose anybody knows the real reason for these diverse breeding seasons. On the whole, remarkably little is really known about breeding of many Kenya birds, and all breeding is liable to be upset by a failure of the rain – an all too frequent occurrence. It is indeed impossible to make categorical statements about the breeding of any bird, and the possibility of finding nests of one sort or another all throughout the year offers delightful opportunities to the bird photographer.

When I first came to Kenya in 1939, I was vastly puzzled by

the nesting habits of the birds. Being used to British birds, I expected to find nests in all those typically English places one sees in Kenya – all the wayside banks; those knotted tree trunks full of holes; those hanging creepers, those open grass fields and hedgerows – all places so beloved by familiar birds at home. It was soon obvious however that Kenya birds do not use these apparently tempting places to anything like the same extent as birds at home. They will indeed nest in creepers, pastures and all those other places, but somehow their nests are not easy to find; in some almost indefinable way the birds choose and build so differently I cannot easily place my finger on the exact difference, although they are certainly there, and I would state quite definitely that bird nesting in Kenya, in spite of the abundance of species, is not so easy as in the British Isles.

This very fact develops in one an even better sense of field craft and patient observation; I am sure that the vast majority of nests I have found in Kenya have been discovered by just sitting still and watching what the birds around were doing. A rather suspicious sort of behaviour, difficult to define, but being perhaps a preference for a certain area; the carrying of bits of grass or food in the beak; the obvious alarm or anxiety note of a bird – all these may indicate the presence of a nest, and nest finding then becomes an exciting business, dependent on close watching of behaviour rather than on a sharp pair of eyes. A nesting walk thus becomes a mere saunter, with frequent pauses to watch what the birds round about are doing. Deliberate searching for nests – what Bruce Campbell in his book *Finding Nests* delightfully calls 'cold searching' – will for some reason produce far more old nests than new ones; there is no doubt that, obvious though a new nest may be once it is found, its presence is usually well-concealed and the behaviour of the birds more cryptic than normal. Time and again, I have thought what a fool I had been not to have seen that nest before – now that it is old and empty! Finding nests requires much more training and observation in Kenya than at home, and if the greenshank's nest is the Blue Riband at home, how many more there are in Kenya. Some people I know, like my friend Bill, are however quite uncanny at the game; I will even swear that Bill can smell them, or possesses some seventh sense denied to ordinary mortals for I have frequently been quite staggered at his astonishing powers of nest finding in Kenya. A greenshank's nest in a Scottish glen would be mere child's play to him.

Of all the types of African country to work in, I think forest easily the most difficult, and forest nests the most hard to find. Merely looking for nests in either the undergrowth or trees is a sheer waste of time; moreover the range of view is always limited, and following the suspicious behaviour of a bird is always a difficult job in the tangle of leaves and twigs, while the light is frequently poor. There is nothing like the open beech and bracken woods of the Old Country in Kenya; all is thick with tropical luxuriance, and getting from place to place amongst the trees often impossible without a *panga* – that useful heavy cutting knife with which Birmingham so kindly supplied the Mau Mau gangs for their deadly work; but without which an African is seldom happy, and no garden can be kept tidy.

There is no doubt the best way to tackle a forest is to find a good 'birdy' place – often an open clearing – and just sit and watch what the birds are doing, with field glasses in constant use. Walking will reveal little, but forest birds usually become most confiding if one sits still. The edges of forests are usually more productive than the dark quiet interior, and a forest clearing best of all.

Most birds slacken the pace of nesting duties towards, during, and after the heat of the day, say noon to 3 p.m. For bird watching and nesting in all areas of eastern Africa, the early morning up to 10 a.m., and again just before the brief twilight are the best hours. Of these, the very early morning just as the sun begins to pale the east at about 5.30 a.m. is by far the best time, and those who say the birds in Kenya never sing, have never been out at this glorious hour. In the low thorn-tree country, the tumult of bird song in this cool freshness before the dawn is one of the pleasantest memories I have of numerous camps in such country; at that time, Africa is a different world to an hour or two later when the sun has risen and blasted the country with its withering heat, stilling all bird song.

One final word about bird-watching equipment for the tropics. Good field glasses, the very best you can afford, are absolutely essential. It is far more important that these be light, easily handled, and have a wide field of view, than that they be powerful. Except for static watching in places such as estuaries, where long range work is required, a telescope is almost useless in Africa. It is almost impossible to hold sufficiently still without a tripod, or a knee rest position such as used by stalkers. The field of view is far too narrow to follow a quick moving bird, and the dancing heat haze after 10 a.m. will ruin definition. A pair of ×8 binoculars is quite powerful enough; and the angle of view should be at least thirty degrees or more – fifty degrees is better. Light glasses are easier to hold steady, and it is also essential that focusing should be by a central screw; avoid individual focusing eyepieces as the plague, for with such it is impossible to keep continually focused on a quick moving bird, though of course one of the eyepieces should have a small adjustment for individual variation in eyesight between the two eyes. Hardcoated, or bloomed lenses and prisms are now almost universal on any reputable make, and a godsend in poor light at dusk or in the forest.

There are numerous types of binoculars of such specifications on the market these days, but I would repeat – get the very best you can afford: their robust precision construction will pay hands down in the end. I used to have a beautiful pair of Zeiss Deltrintem glasses, which were ideal, until a moment's carelessness mislaid them forever in a field; but these were replaced by a pair of Raylite 8×30, made by Wray – an English make every bit as good as their German counterpart.

One word of warning too; the damp heat of the coastal belts of the tropics can spell ruination to the best of optical equipment in a month or less if not safeguarded, as I know only too well. Fungus starts on all the outer and inner lens surfaces, finding the dark warmth and damp in a leather case ideal for growth; coating is no protection, and the cement of the glass loosens and slips, the fungus creeps in and etches the glass surface with evil starred patterns; the prisms cloud over, fine sand from the beach creeps into all the screws, rust into the paint-scratched metal parts, and before you have realised what is happening, the insidious damage will cost £10 or more to repair. The same will happen to camera lenses, shutters, bellows, cable releases and all such precision equipment. In such a climate carelessness is simply not worth it where valuable equipment is concerned. The best safeguard is to keep all such equipment in a sealed biscuit tin when not in use, and fit the tin all round the apparatus with small bags of silica gel – baked frequently in the oven to renew its moisture absorbing powers. About once a fortnight, paint all external glass surfaces with a very soft camel hair brush soaked in forty per cent formaldehyde to kill fungal spores. Such troubles do not arise in the dry heat of the low country or highlands of Kenya, but the rate of deterioration and rot in the coastal regions is both alarming and costly. But too, wherever you are in the tropics, remember that no apparatus or films are ever improved by being left in the sun, uncovered. Temperatures well over one hundred degrees Fahrenheit in full sun are not uncommon anywhere in East Africa.

The Camera and its Accessories

Bird photography cannot be done with cheap apparatus; some may disagree with this categorical statement, but I am quite convinced on this point. You must have the very best you can afford, and the lens in particular – the only part of the camera which really matters – must be of the finest quality. Bird photographs depend for their value and aesthetic appeal on a crispness of definition and sharpness of outline that no cheap lens can ever give. Admittedly, the man behind the camera matters most – but no matter how good he is, no worthwhile results can be achieved with cheap apparatus. It is true also however, that expensive apparatus is equally worthless without the necessary skill to use it, and the latter is certainly the more important.

My own earliest efforts at bird photography were made, I remember, when still a very young schoolboy, with an old folding roll-film Kodak, fitted with an old-fashioned R.R. lens. I cannot remember having produced anything worthwhile with this, though I must have wasted some dozen of films on blue tits hanging on coconuts, and sparrows on the bird table in our garden in Edinburgh. However, the germ was there, and had infected me badly. Within a very short time, and with the ever generous help and encouragement of my parents, I had acquired a folding Sanderson quarter-plate field camera, fitted with a Compur shutter and a Ross Homocentric F 6·3 lens. This camera had all manner of rising and tilting fronts, revolving backs and so on; a superb instrument, and though I little realised it then, the type which is now almost universally used by the masters of bird photography today. The old Compur shutter was excellent, as the bulb setting was quite silent in operation, and excellent for sitting bird portraits, and the Ross, even then, was a magnificent lens.

I had six wooden double dark slide holders, and used the old Imperial Eclipse Special Rapid plates, of the then staggering speed of 600 H. & D.; they used to be twelve in a box for 2/6, and came wrapped in lovely red paper. I shudder now to think how many I must have wasted on useless photographs. Under-exposure always used to bother me, in spite of using Caustic H.Q. developer, which gave appallingly contrasty negatives, and grain like a beach at low tide. Being somewhat gadget minded, I remember fitting this old camera with all manner of extra things – special tightening screws, distant release gadgets and what not – none of which I now recollect as being particularly useful. The climax gadget was a further box and bellows, fitted on sliding shoes with special clamps on top of the camera; this was fitted with a focusing screen, and a cheap lens of only approximately, I think, the same focal length as the Ross. The whole thing was used as a focusing camera only, and was I suppose, an early forerunner of the twin reflex so popular nowadays. There was however great difficulty in getting the front really rigid, and both lenses parallel and moving together, and the whole thing was extremely cumbersome and awkward to use in a hide. It still reposes in my workshop junk box.

The best thing I ever made in our private workshop (another wise provision of my father's) was a turn and tilt head, made out of wood and brass screws, to fit the old wooden tripod I had. I personally considered this of unique design and was most proud of it, for it really did work, and was remarkably stable. I noticed just the other day in a photographic magazine, an entirely similar item which has just been put on the market commercially, and visions of lost patent rights and enormous profits occurred to me.

Meanwhile, my father had acquired in the past a superb library of bird books, which I devoured eagerly – notably a whole series of the works of the late Richard Kearton. He was perhaps one of the most delightful nature writers there has ever been, and certainly, with his brother Cherry, one of the best bird photographers. Some of their photographs, made with apparatus and materials which are today comically antique, have hardly ever been bettered. In some of the sumptuous volumes he wrote for Cassells, it was a pity that so many of the photographs were retouched so crudely by modern standards. Then there was Witherby's excellent series of 'Home Life' books – the Home Life of the golden eagle, the osprey, tern or sea-swallows, and finally the Home Life of the spoonbill, the stork and some herons – all these illustrated with magnificent photographs which I strove in vain to emulate. One of the earliest bird-photography books – *Photography for Bird Lovers*, by Bently Beetham, was my bible, and many were the useful tips I learnt from this.

In time, I found the old Sanderson lacking in some essential features, notably mobility and ease of operation when stalking birds, or photographing flying birds – both favourite occupations of mine; and the wastage of plates seemed to increase. My bird images always seemed too small, and I began to feel that a telephoto lens would be the thing.

I suppose a small percentage of successes, and the winning of some Nature Photograph Competitions in the *Boys' Own Paper* must have created some impression, for before much longer my ever-generous and encouraging parents purchased for me that joy of joys – a Thornton-Pickard quarter-plate Reflex – a really magnificent instrument with which I really could take photographs now.

The well-tried Ross Homocentric lens was transferred to this new camera, and the old Sanderson relegated to my work-box, where it still remains as an apparently inexhaustible source of useful little bits of brass, screws and wood. Looking back now on these boyhood days, I realise now how much I really could have done with that old camera. A type still favoured by many of today's leading bird photographers, its many advantages were not then realised by a callow youth in his early 'teens such as I then was. Now, with many more years of experience behind me, I can realise too what all my faults had been in using it; but in spite of that, and in spite of modern experience, I would still not go back to this field camera type.

This new T.P. Reflex was also fitted with an F 4·5 Dallmeyer Telephoto lens; in those days a first class lens, but it had to my mind the disadvantage of an enormously large front component, which I did not, and still do not, think a good thing, because of the shimmers and reflections it catches when poking out of a hide even with a deep lens hood. It seems altogether too conspicuous, and birds do not like it, for I fancy that at close quarters it almost mirrors all their movements. The last most useful thing with which this Reflex was fitted was a Mackenzie-Wishart slide holder with eighteen plate envelopes. This I consider one of the most useful things ever invented, being remarkably foolproof, the envelopes easy to load in the dark (the metal back ones were more reliable than the celluloid type, which tended to crack), and the whole occupied a small space compared with D.D. holders.

Film-packs I could not manage; I found they jammed at awkward moments, and the negatives were difficult to handle in the darkroom. I did not like them, so kept to the old Eclipse plates which were well tried. I knew their little tricks by now, and could produce consistently reasonably exposed plates; the age of modern photoelectric exposure meters had not yet come, and exposure was a chancy business with birds, regulated as best I could with a Watkins Beemeter, which used small strips of sensitive paper darkening in light to standard tints in a measured time.

Apart from a certain heaviness in the shutter release, and a rather noisy focal plane shutter (which did not in fact disturb birds half as much as the books said it would), this equipment was perfection for me, and I produced with it many photographs which I have not bettered to this day – now all, alas, blown sky-high by a Nazi bomb.

Under the sure guidance of my father, I used to do all my own processing and printing – much to the dismay I think, of my mother at the messes I used to make in the little downstairs washroom which I converted into a darkroom. From some negatives I made gaslight contact prints, or daylight P.O.P. prints, and occasionally carbon bichromate prints – one of the most pleasing processes ever invented, though now much out of fashion. Enlarging I seldom tried, owing to the cumbersome size of the plate and the lack of a proper enlarger; I did try a few, using the camera as an enlarger, but in those days bromide and its attendant techniques were not attractive to me.

Nearly all my best pictures were made into $3\frac{1}{4}$ inch square lantern slides – a technique which appealed enormously to me, as the results are so beautiful. With these slides (a collection which steadily grew, and was lovingly indexed and boxed) I enjoyed giving bird talks at school or to various societies. Up to 1939 these were a source of great satisfaction to me. Hitler's bomb blew all these up as well, and the loss is irreplaceable now.

The old T.P. Reflex served me well for many years, and in later years at university it was in frequent use for photomicrography and other scientific work, a photomicro objective having been added to the outfit. There was no doubt it was cumbersome, but grain, shake, and processing finesse never worried me as they do now! At times the vast black leather box seemed to weigh a ton or more after a long day on the moors or at the seashore after birds; the tripod too was correspondingly heavy and large, not to mention all the accessories which I inevitably added.

About this time, in 1939, I read a book by Dr Fraser Darling, illustrated with some superb photographs all taken by him with a Leica. I was much impressed with these, and also by the vast range of possibilities for all sorts of work from photomicroscopy to landscape which these small versatile miniatures possessed. After much deliberation and trial, I took the plunge and finally sold my Reflex with all its lenses in exchange for a Contax outfit.

The Contax seemed a better camera in many ways than the Leica; lens interchange was easy, it had a greater range of gadgets available, only one knob on the top to twiddle when setting the shutter in a hide and – still its supreme advantage I think – a completely detachable back for ease of film loading and cleaning. It is significant that the latest Leica M 3 has all these points now incorporated. The only disadvantage I could find was the harsher shutter wind compared with the Leica; this however has now been altered in the new post-war Contax III, which has a very sweet action.

By dint of saving and exchange I have gradually been able to add all the other useful accessories such as the Contameter, reproduction outfit, extension tubes and photomicrographic outfit which have all since found much use in my other photographic work. I was lucky too in being able to get all such before World War II broke out, skyrocketed the prices of such German accessories, rendered them unobtainable for a while and nearly strangled them later by terrific import duty and purchase tax.

My standard outfit now consists of the Contax (my 1939 Model II at last replaced with a new III A), an F 2 Sonnar lens of 5 cm. focal length, and 13.5 cm. F 4 Sonnar lens; the latter is used extensively for birds, the former for nests, general views, etc. A recently added Wide Angle 3·5 cm. F 3·5 adapted Old Delft I have found very useful too.

All the pictures in this book have been taken with this equipment, and I have used it all now for the last fifteen years with little trouble. What do I think of it now?

There are times perhaps when a larger negative image would be better, but these are not many. Then there is no doubt that the specialised processing technique for 35 mm. work is an exacting taskmaster; everything from taking to final enlargement must be carried out with laboratory scrupulousness, and intensive care taken at all stages to get the best result. Without such, miniature photography of nature subjects can only be a disappointment. Remember that all mistakes – in shake, in grain, in focusing adjustment – all are enlarged at least twelve times in the final result. I personally enjoy the challenge the technique possesses, but nature photography demands its complete mastery and no less; it is not for the novice, otherwise disappointment and abandonment will follow.

Nearly all modern bird photographers such as Hosking and Yeates use the quarter-plate field camera technique described in their books, and their results are masterly beyond question. For my own part, I like the handiness and portability of the miniature, in spite of its critics, and above all, in these days of costly living, the relative cheapness of the miniature (if all processing and enlarging is done by oneself) is a weighty point in its favour for an amateur like myself.

Even with everything going like clockwork in the hide and the bird behaving well at the nest, no bird photographer could ever guarantee one hundred per cent results from all the photos he takes. Birds will not pose to order, and particularly with the smaller, quick moving birds, an otherwise perfect photo will be spoilt by a bad attitude, or some slight movement of the bird will ruin definition. With the larger quarter-plate size such imperfect pictures are costly, but with the miniature one has ample, relatively inexpensive film available at one loading, and one can afford to take many more pictures in a hide session than with larger sizes – some of which will at least produce the perfect picture, even perhaps a whole perfect behaviour sequence.

The late Bernard Shaw once described the Leica as being like a cod which spawned a million eggs in order to produce only one perfect adult fish; though with careful work the comparison is not quite as bad as this notorious prodigality of nature, nevertheless this ability to spawn, if not a million, at least a good many 'eggs' at one sitting is a great advantage of the miniature, and failures to 'mature' are relatively inexpensive. Though one always tries to produce the perfect picture every time the shutter is clicked, this ideal is simply just not obtainable with birds at the nest.

Moreover, no matter how good one's technique is in the hide, I suspect that the wastage of plates, especially when using Luc shutters in the larger cameras, as recommended by professional bird photographers, must be fairly high! Unsuspicious birds at the nest seldom pose for the perfect portrait, and chances must be taken on the slightest opportunity if the bird is small and lively.

I have read criticisms relegating the miniature to use only for flying bird pictures, and other situations where the stand camera cannot be brought into action quick enough, but as I hope the pictures in this book will show, the miniature is far more adaptable than that. A further criticism has been the relative proportions of bird size to surroundings in the negative.

Using the 13·5 cm. lens however, these proportions are almost the same as when using an eight-inch lens on quarter-plate – the standard professional equipment. It is necessary – indeed I think essential – to enlarge the whole of a 35 mm. negative, and not just the portion of the bird only. I suspect that such criticisms have been levelled mainly at the grossly over-enlarged pictures of the birds only which characterise some Continental and American work with miniatures; and if this is so, I could not agree more, as the results are abominable. A good bird picture must contain a good deal of the nest surroundings to be pleasant, and the bird itself should not occupy the major portion of the picture.

In this connection, there is one piece of Contax equipment which is quite invaluable. This is the focusing adaptor, with magnifier, which can be clipped on to the 13·5 cm. lens in place of the camera body. It has the same register as the camera body, and the picture area can therefore be composed directly on the focusing screen. Trying to focus the critical plane of a nest through the very small rangefinder-viewfinder combination of the usual miniature camera is very unsatisfactory. Limits of field and critical detail cannot be easily seen, nor can the essential depth of focus, and there is always the chance of parallax error at close quarters. Some of the newer eye-level reflex miniature cameras avoid this, but they themselves cannot always be fitted with a telephoto lens of the necessary focal length. Personally, I *always* use the focusing screen when sitting up at a nest and getting ready for a hide session.

Curious popular misconceptions exist still regarding the use of a telephoto. Many people think that, by using such, it is necessary only to get within several score yards to get a good picture, and therefore the bird is not disturbed being photographed from a great distance away. Quite apart from the fact that it is usually almost impossible to get any distance away from a nest and still see it all clearly, the use of a telephoto is in fact for quite the reverse purpose which is to obtain a sufficiently large image of the bird at close quarters. For birds about the size of a sparrow, the hide and camera are seldom more than about five feet away. For this reason, it is necessary to be somewhat careful when using cameras larger than 35 mm, such as the Agiflex or other 2¼ inches square size; these are admirable instruments, but very often the telephoto lens with which they can be fitted will not focus nearer than perhaps fifteen to twenty feet – often a distance physically impossible to achieve in certain nest situations.

Two other pieces of equipment are an absolute essential. One is a good lens hood of sufficient depth and diameter, with the internal surface well matted dead black. I have had one specially made, similar to a normal lens hood in all respects except that the outer edge is turned outwards at right angles to form a flange or rim about a quarter of an inch wide. This modification is invaluable, for when the lens and hood are poked through the front cloth of the hide, the cloth is prevented from slipping forward again over the lens; this was the cause of some unexpected failures in the past, not having noticed in time that the lens was thus obscured.

The second requirement is a really sturdy tripod, fitted with a heavy ball and socket head, or better still, a rigid pan and tilt head. When I first purchased my Contax, I made the fatal mistake of assuming that, because it was a small camera, only a small tripod would be required. Nothing could be more wrong; these small extensible metal tube tripods have an appalling whip in the legs when extended, and this is greatly magnified through the slender support of a small ball and socket head. At shutter speeds below 1/50 sec., this nearly always results in camera shake when the shutter is released – not noticeable ordinarily, but glaringly obvious in any enlargement as a slight double outline which wrecks the whole picture.

When using slower shutter speeds, numerous photos were spoiled thus, but since possessing a heavier tripod these troubles have gone. I now have a Nebro 'London' tripod, a superb instrument which is light enough to be carried for a long time, but immensely sturdy. It has the great advantage in a hide that the legs can be firmly fixed at any extension desired – a most useful feature. This tripod is now fitted with a very rigid cine pan and tilt head, and camera shake is a bogey of the past.

A good camera carrying case, an old piece of rubber sheeting or mackintosh to drop over the camera if wet, and cable release as long as possible (preferably eighteen inches), and a light yellow $1\frac{1}{2}\times$ optically worked filter are perhaps the only other accessories really required, except for a really reliable and sturdy photoelectric meter of the Weston type. The intelligent use of the latter should be completely mastered, and although it will not always be possible to use the exact exposure indicated because of the nature of the subject, at least the error will be known and due allowance can be made in processing.

Other bits and pieces have a habit of adding themselves to one's equipment as time goes on, but such are a matter of individual preference. It is wise to remember you may have to carry your equipment on occasions for miles at a time.

I would also strongly recommend the use of the special self-opening cassettes supplied for such miniatures and, coupled with this the use of bulk film, which can be loaded by oneself in any convenient length (I find twenty-four frames ample for one loading). The reloadable velvet trapped cassette, and bought loaded cassettes are a perfect pest for scratching the film, and many good pictures have been ruined thus, the enlargements having great 'tramlines' all over them. Bulk film is much cheaper than cut lengths and will keep many months if stored in cool dark conditions.

The After Technique

Before passing on to the application of the camera and hide to the actual work, it might be convenient here to write something about the actual photographic technique required.

The perfect delineation of a bird's feathering, and its natural ways at the nest demand that the final picture be of the highest standard of definition and print quality. Although I confess that many of my pictures even now still fall far below exhibition standard, nevertheless only the best should be tried for. A bad bird photograph, fuzzy, lacking in definition, with no shadow detail and burnt out highlights or poor print quality is almost worse than no photograph at all.

Miniature 35 mm. technique also demands a complete mastery of the process involved, and any bird photographer using this medium should make himself completely at home with the best methods. These are best learnt by experience, with the help of the numerous excellent books on the subject, and there is no need to deal with them in great detail here.

Above all, however, the most complete laboratory cleanliness and scrupulousness should be observed at all stages of film handling, developing and enlarging, and it is my opinion that any serious worker must inevitably do everything himself from start to finish if disappointments are to be avoided. Most commercial D. & P. firms have little time to devote to individual films; most are developed in batches in some fast-working coarse-grain developer, which results in a bold negative full of contrast, and also grain; the type which looks 'good' to the uninitiated, but is an anathema to the miniaturist. Moreover, the films tend to be roughly handled, dust-speckled and scratched in enlarging, and sent back in this condition – useless and unfit for any further prints larger than post-card size. Sooner or later, the photographer who does not do his own will get tired of such results, and give up miniature work in disgust, without ever having realised all the advantages of the small-scale technique.

In all bird work, where perfect definition is essential, the inevitable question of grain in large-scale enlargements crops up, and this is frequently the strongest criticism of bird photographs taken with the miniature technique. Graininess is a function of several factors, all of which the competent photographer should be able to minimise or avoid altogether. It depends primarily on the type of film used, the exposure given, the developer used, the development time and the degree of agitation during development.

Firstly avoid the high speed miniature films like H.P.S., H.P.3 or Super XX; their additional speed is practically never required, and a graininess with them is unavoidable. I use only the medium speed pan films of which Ilford FP 2 and later FP 3 used to be my favourites. I confess however I have never had results as good as I used to get with the pre-war Agfa Isopan F and FF types, until the recent introduction of the remarkable grain-free Adox film KB 14, which is like an answer to the miniaturist's prayer. Using this film, with correct development, the limit of enlargement is controlled mainly by the resolution of the lens; in fairness however to British products, with care Ilford Pan F can be as good.

Exposures must be minimal, and controlled by a good exposure meter; development must be exactly controlled as regards temperature, degree of agitation constant and 'γ' should not be greater than 0·7; the film must be acetic stop-bathed before fixing, fixed in an acid-hardening solution, and rinsed in a wetting agent before drying.

I used exclusively to use Meritol-Metol or sometimes Meritol-Caustic development, and obtained excellent results; but the loss of speed with the former, and sometimes increase of grain with the latter was a disadvantage with slow films where exposure had been critical with a fast moving bird. With the advent of the M. & B. Promicrol, and latterly the German developer Neofyn Blue, this problem seems to have been solved. The increase in speed allowed, and the grain-free negatives obtainable with these and KB 14 are of the greatest advantage in bird work. With Promicrol moreover, electronic flash pictures appear to require only normal development time instead of the fifty per cent increase usually advised; thus flash and normal pictures can be taken on the same length of film and given the same normal development. Temperatures, particularly with Promicrol, must be closely watched; in this respect the Kenya highlands are almost ideal for processing, since indoor shade temperatures are almost always about the 68°F mark. In the lower parts however, near Lake Victoria and the coast, the water nearly always has to be cooled. Agitation must be quite definite and correct; I find that five seconds every minute is just about right, except for Neofyn, which I find best to agitate continuously for the specified time. It is well worth while also taking the little extra care required to allow for the time taken to fill and empty the developing tank.

For loading the tank, there is nothing better than a changing bag, of which there are several kinds on the market these days. The knack of working with hands by feel only is quickly acquired; these bags are light, take up little space, and one is invariably carried in the field for adjusting film jams in the camera – which happen at awkward moments with the best behaved of cameras. Such changing bags save suffocating exertions under blankets or fearful ordeals in air-tight cupboards; indeed they eliminate the need for a darkroom for all purposes except enlarging, since development is always carried out in one of the numerous good makes of tanks now on the market.

For enlarging, it is well worth while using an enlarger of reputable make, and one that is really steady in all its movements. The lens should be a proper enlarger lens such as a Ross Resolux or Wray Supar, and not the camera lens. In particular, avoid negative carriers with a glass plate; the glassless ones will save endless worry with dust trouble and scratches. Films should be handled with care by the edges only, and stored in cut strips in a negative album – not rolled up in a tin, a method which is one of the most fertile sources of scratches; in particular they should be carefully dusted before insertion in the enlarger.

Enlarging exposure is calculated with care, using a test square or strip; the former I find more convenient, since it is the same area of the negative being tested for each exposure time. An enlarger time switch is a very great help. Choice of the correct grade of bromide is essential; usually negatives requiring paper of other than normal grade will not give prints of the finest quality. Choice of paper is a matter for individual taste. Personally I find both the Agfa and Kodak ranges excellent, also the chloro-bromides such as Ilford Plastika. 'Fancy' surfaces for bird photographs should be avoided, and only glossy surfaces used for pictures for reproduction, and perhaps semi-matt for exhibition prints. Whatever paper is used, it is the last few seconds in the developer which gives the full richness of black in the shadows, and delicacy in the half-tones; remember however that with the normal bromide safelight, blacks always look blacker than they really are, and that any print looks better when it is wet than when dry. Nowadays control of contrast can be varied quite appreciably by varying the dilution of the developer if makes such as D 163 or M. & B. Contrast 300 are used.

The final enlargement should require nothing further than perhaps occasional 'spotting' with some neutral dye or pencil, and unostentatious mounting on a pale cream or white mount if for exhibition purposes. There is no place in competent honest bird photography for any form of trick-printing, doping or other fancy treatment, and the simplest methods with the best materials are all that should ever be used.

The choice of films, developers, papers and the technique used is largely a personal one. I have mentioned my own preferences above, not because I have any commercial interest in the materials, but because I have found by experience these serve my purpose best. Others will prefer otherwise; but whichever is used, the technique must be exact and completely standardised. There is little chance for experimenting with subjects which often cannot be repeated. Furthermore, the same attention should be paid to each step every time so that there is no possibility of a stupid slip-up. This is a counsel of perfection, but I write feelingly, for on some occasions I have been guilty of carelessness in technique, such as using exhausted film developer or not checking temperatures – faults which have spoilt irreplaceable negatives.

If away for an extended period, there is no doubt it pays to take the necessary small paraphernalia, and develop the film as soon after taking as possible. Deterioration of quality, particularly in hot and humid places, is very noticeable with exposed films, and for this reason many of my Madagascar photos were spoilt. Moreover, even at home, it pays to develop as soon after taking as possible in order that a series can be repeated if necessary before moving the hide. With self-opening cassettes and a changing bag, there is never any need to expose the full length of film first, since exposed short lengths can easily be cut off for separate developments.

All these may seem tiresome technicalities for those keen to get on with the bird side, but there will be only disappointment and disgust with the results if processing is not carried out by the photographer himself; and at the risk of being tiresome, I would repeat again the advice to master the purely photographic side thoroughly if the best results are wanted. There are plenty of good books on the subject, and you cannot be too careful with 35 mm. work.

For those who cannot be bothered with all this technical side, and who cannot afford the expense of the quarter-plate size, the most useful compromise is perhaps a camera of the 2¼ inch square size, which can be fitted with a telephoto lens. These take the 120 or 620 size film, a popular size readily obtainable and not expensive. The final picture is not so dependent on initial grain size since the negative image of the bird is larger than with 35 mm., hence the final degree of enlargement not so great. The mass production developing methods of commercial D. & P. firms will not spoil the results so much.

The Hide and its Technique

For photographing birds at the nest, some sort of hide is the basic necessity, to conceal the photographer and his essential movements from the bird; for movement is much more alarming to a bird than noise.

In my early days, I designed and made several weird and wonderful hides, being influenced by the ideas of Richard Kearton and his hollow cow, stuffed sheep, artificial tree-trunk and artificial rock – all of which the brothers Kearton used with great success. But cost was always a problem to an impecunious schoolboy or student as I was then. Perhaps my best effort was made out of an old umbrella of my mother's, the covering of which was still fairly intact. This had a lengthening pole lashed to the handle to stick in the ground when opened, and a length of brown cloth, sewn all over with little tapes to tie on camouflage, was hooked on all the way round on the points of the ribs.

This design at least had the merit of portability and collapsibility – the latter often too much so. For it was most unstable in a wind, and the centre pole proved to be a perfect nuisance, getting in the way of myself, the tripod, camera and everything else.

Nowadays, like all modern bird photographers, I have given up all these queer ideas, and I use a perfectly simple square hide, whose framework consists of four broomsticks, about five feet long and sharpened at one end. These are driven into the ground (not always possible however) in a square about three feet apart. The tops are joined by four three-foot lengths of heavy galvanised wire, whose ends are bent down at right angles for about two inches. These ends are inserted into eyelet screws, screwed into the sides of each pole near the top. In a windy or sloping site, the four corner poles are guyed to the ground with stout cord and skewer pegs. Very often it is necessary to hold the poles upright by placing stones round the foot of each one.

Over this framework are then slung two lengths crosswise of thick quality cotton cloth of the type usually known as 'Merikani' in Kenya; it must be of thick quality, as the thin is too transparent and flaps about in a wind – a usually fatal fault. These lengths of cloth are secured to the four upright poles by tapes sewn at six inch intervals down the side; or, as in a later model of mine, by lacing them through eyeholes along the edges. One corner is left partly open to form a door which can be fastened from the inside. The two long lengths can of course be sewn together and shaped; but this is not as convenient if the four poles have to be stuck in at different levels as is so often necessary. The poles can of course be replaced by lengths of half-inch gas piping, flattened at one end. These are easier to drive into the ground, and the cross wires just inserted into the open tops of the tubes; but such poles are heavy.

The usual colour of Merikani is white. Avoid green, for it seldom tones with any natural green either in the British Isles, nor in the sunlit Kenya landscape. I have splashed my own cloths liberally and erratically with cream and brown distemper; and better still, in Kenya, when it rains, bundle the cloths up and roll them in a patch of the famous red Kenya mud which will soon produce the required nondescript colour, which improves further on being rained upon.

At the front of the hide, at an appropriate height, I have cut out a circle of cloth about six inches in diameter, not in the centre, but more to one side. To this circle is stitched a short 'funnel' of cloth, the smaller end of which is the diameter of my lens hood, and is taped. When erected in the hide, the camera does not then poke through the front, but is pulled back, so that the cloth funnel acts as an extension of the lens hood. This is a great convenience, for it does not so easily become obstructed with grass, the shading is better, and when it rains, the lens is well protected. I find also that birds do not seem so upset; but you must be very careful that the funnel is made of a diameter sufficiently large not to cut off any part of the picture at any angle of the camera.

The reason for the lens hole being to one side of the centre line is to allow me to sit beside the camera, and not behind it. The latter is a most awkward position from which to peep out.

Below the lens opening is a small slit, through which the front leg of the tripod is pushed (this does not seem to distract a bird); the other two are splayed sideways in the hide to give the maximum space inside.

Most books on bird photography recommend one to cut slit peepholes in the cloth at appropriate places, but I find that peering out with one eye which this entails is an unpleasant business. The eye gets strained after a long wait, and one tends to lose all sense of stereoscopic depth, making it fatally easy to misjudge the position of the bird when it does return. Besides I do not like my hides to look as if they had been riddled with bullets.

Therefore, at the sides of the lens opening, and on a level with it, I have cut a rectangular hole about five inches by two inches, and sewn into this a square of fine mesh mosquito netting stained an appropriate colour. Other similar windows are fitted at the same level in the other three walls, and these large openings enable me to look out from the darkness of the hide with both eyes in comfort. No bird I have yet tried appears to be able to see through this netting into the hide, and very rarely comes level enough to get two windows in a line. With these four windows one can see what is happening all round – an enormous advantage, particularly when waiting with electronic flash as explained later. Ventilation – always a difficult point in a hot climate – is greatly improved, and incidentally the double thickness of cloth on the roof of the hide is good protection against the sun in the tropics.

There are of course numerous variations of this square tent principle, some most elaborate; but really, the simpler it is the better. Wherever the cloth tends to flap in the wind, a tuck is made and pinned with safety pins, an ample supply of which in the hide is useful. With most sorts of birds, further camouflage of the cloth by branches or leaves is rarely necessary. (Plate 29A). Odd though such a square tent may look to us in wild surroundings, most birds accept it in a very short time and later ignore it altogether. (Plate 29B). If grass or twigs are used to cover the hide, particular care should be taken that these cannot fall across the lens opening thus necessitating perhaps a complete disturbance of the bird to put it to rights.

This is indeed one reason why I like the sides to be taped up, and not sewn, as one can often make adjustments to the outside of the hide by sticking a hand through one corner instead of getting out completely. I find too, that a very useful item to have in the hide is a stick about four or five feet long with a forked end. By pushing this out of the hide, it is easy to adjust a recalcitrant twig or blade of grass blown across the field of view without unduly disturbing the bird.

Unfortunately, owing to the predatory habits of the ubiquitous African *toto*, or child, to whom any such cloth is fair and valuable loot, this sort of hide can seldom be used where these pests abound. Indeed, at the coast, I have had a whole square cut out of one side of an erected hide, by an African fisherman, who wished merely to patch the sail of his canoe.

In such cases, recourse must be had to building hides of branches and vegetation, and I have used many such; but they are never really satisfactory as the African sun and wind soon shrivels up cut green vegetation, and the hides are soon full of tell-tale chinks. However, when available, the ubiquitous and much cursed weed known as Mexican marigold is most useful in stopping up such chinks. Its rank smell when bruised always brings back memories of many such makeshift hides.

In the hide, a supply of some di-methyl pthallate insect repellent such as Dimp or Mylol should always be at hand, as biting *Stomoxys* flies and mosquitoes can be a curse; but I have yet to find a bird who objects to smoke, and I often smoke like a chimney in a hide to keep the flies away, and this leaves the birds quite undisturbed. A collapsible folding stool, or better still a folding chair with a back, is not a luxury at all, and will save many a weary cramp; but see that it is not too collapsible such as some I have had. A wooden box will often serve as a chair, but being able to lean back in comfort is not pampering yourself in a lengthy wait.

For nests which are about shoulder height, the four poles of the hide can be lengthened by a simple socket joint, or splicing on an extra pole. The side cloths should be made long enough so that the hide can be erected at full height if required. It is surprising how long one can stand in a hide without getting tired; but a shooting stick is an advantage on these occasions.

A surprising number of birds in Kenya nest at the most awkward height of ten to twenty feet in low trees and bushes, and for such I have made a simple wooden platform, supported on four well splayed and cross-braced legs of three inches by two inches timber, about ten feet high, with a ladder up one side. The hide is erected on the platform, the four poles being inserted into four holes bored at the appropriate places, and the cloths tied over as usual. Such a structure is somewhat wobbly on uneven ground, and should be guyed down with strong quarter-inch rope at each corner. This sort of thing is really somewhat of a fixture however, and is hardly portable. In the field step ladders can be used, or ingenuity expended in other ways with natural materials to hand.

I have found recently that 'Dexion' is excellent material from which to construct a portable platform of this type. It is strong, easily erected and dismantled, and can be carried in short lengths. The platform can be fixed at any height required, but if platforms higher than, say, eight feet are constructed, the weight of material necessary is a disadvantage.

For nests at greater heights in trees, the usual practice is to build a hide in a neighbouring tree at a convenient distance, the shape and structure of the hide depending on how it can be fitted among the branches; and a lot depends on personal ingenuity in this respect. The separate cloths are useful for tying among the branches, as also thin quality Rok-Roofing or rubberoid material. Such hides often do not need a roof, but it is a comfort to have one all the same.

In thinner trees, it is often a good plan to brace the nest tree and the hide tree together with a stout cross pole, as in a high wind the trees may sway apart, enough to throw the nest out of the field of view or at least out of focus. Above twenty feet, swaying in a wind can be most unpleasant, and for those who might need such, a preliminary dose of some motion-sickness pills is well advised.

Nests on their own in a single tree are always a problem, often indeed unsuitable unless, like one of our best known bird photographers, you can persuade a local builder to erect a tubular scaffolding nearby; but builders and scaffolding are rare objects in the Kenya bush. Often the only way is to erect some sort of tripod with long poles, and build the hide somehow on top of this. I have used such on several occasions, but remember that rigidity is essential, and every means to ensure this must be tried. Movement is often fatal – perhaps in more ways than one! Slight movements in the hide are often magnified enormously by the height and are most alarming. If you use a rope ladder to get up, peg the end firmly down. To swarm up a dangling rope ladder may be romantic and in the best traditions of the Saint – but astonishingly difficult to do.

When a nest is first discovered which may prove suitable, it is well worth while to conceal oneself at a little distance away with field glasses and watch the behaviour of the bird on return. Most birds follow a definite route back to their nest, using certain perches or tracks in the grass, and finally pitching or walking on to one particular side of the nest. Note these points carefully, and plan the siting of the hide accordingly; very often a better picture of a bird may be taken on a perch *en route* to the nest, rather than at the nest itself.

The best time to photograph birds during the nesting cycle is during the first few days after the chicks are hatched. With plovers and waders, or game birds, however, the chicks are mobile within a few hours of hatching, and leave the nest. Hence for these, the only time is when they have eggs, unless one can catch these golden moments at the nest when the eggs are chipping and the new-hatched chicks drying off. With mobile chicks, the parent birds will sometimes return to brood them where they crouch, but more often will call them out of range of the hide. On no account whatever should any chicks ever be tethered in the hope that the parents will return; this is unnecessary cruelty of the first order and has in the past been the reason for justifiable criticisms of certain persons claiming to be bird photographers.

With most other birds, while there are eggs only in the nest, pictures of the bird returning or sitting are the only usual possibilities, but pictures of birds sitting in deep cup nests are rarely satisfactory. With chicks in the nest, there is usually much feeding activity, often providing chances of getting both parents at the nest together. With small chicks, the hen will frequently brood the chicks for short periods before food collecting again, and the cock may return with food while the hen sits, thus offering chances of these perfect doublet pictures. Even with plovers and waders, there is often a change-over of incubation duties at the nest, moments of rare excitement for the watcher.

When the chicks are older and fledging fast, the feeding rate, contrary to expectation, often becomes much less and the parents leave the chicks for long periods at a time. This is particularly the case with raptorial birds, whose decrease of parental attention at the nest is most marked as the chicks grow; and at a nest with fledging chicks of such, tiresome waits of several hours between each visit are not infrequent; but with downy chicks they spend more time on the nest.

The other very trying types of birds are those which feed their chicks by regurgitation, as do the serins, whydahs, pigeons and so on. The parents have to collect the food first, and then digest it before returning to the nest. With these, waits of an hour or more between visits, even with small chicks, are not unusual.

Normally, however, with the smaller insect-eating birds, if the parents do not return to the nest within ten minutes or so of settling in the hide, there is something wrong, and it will cause unnecessary anxiety to the bird to wait longer. With proper precautions, the behaviour of the bird should be entirely natural and unsuspicious, and this should be aimed at every time. This is a counsel of perfection, and often no matter what care is taken the bird will not return; I have mentioned frequent instances in this book, and as a rule nothing can be done. As I have mentioned too, it is often the case that one sex will be bolder than the other, but their behaviour often changes as time goes on.

Next, the position of the hide in relation to the nest must be most carefully chosen, so as to give the best view of the bird. With birds which nest in holes, or with birds which build domed nests like sunbirds, a position facing the entrance to the nest is seldom satisfactory. A hide placed to one or other side will give a much more pleasant side-on view of the bird. Face-on to the nest usually results in a back view only, with the head turned away. This often applies too to other kinds of birds which build open nests, since they usually approach from a particular side; get side-on to the normal route – and hence the value of preliminary observation of the birds from a distance first.

As regards distance from the nest, I find that with the 13·5 cm. Sonnar lens, the hide is usually about five feet away for the smaller finches and warblers and birds of that size, a distance which gives the best image size; about ten to twelve feet suffices for plovers and long birds, and twenty to thirty feet for the bigger raptorials, cranes and so on.

Now watch the position of the sun. The bright sunlight in the tropics is a downright menace, and has ruined more pictures for me than I care to remember! In blazing sun, almost vertically overhead in Kenya all the year, the lighting is flat and almost without modelling; the plumage is rendered harsh and staring, and there is no beauty in the final result. When there are shadows, these are hard and black, and the total contrast range is almost beyond modern emulsions; bright sunlight filtering through leaves and twigs produces a dappled pattern which ruins the final results: it glares on glossy leaves, produces black shadows on the bird, and the negative is like a snowstorm. Flash here is a useful help, where such harsh contrasts are unavoidable. There is no real answer to this problem of sunlight in the tropics. Soft fast emulsions which flatten the lighting all have objectionable grain, while medium speed pan films are contrasty in themselves; perhaps a partial solution may be found by using these slow pan films with a modern developer such as Neofyn which softens them a great deal, giving good gradation with finest possible grain. But Neofyn came on the market too late to save many last chances for me, although I now use it more and more in such conditions. I would ten times rather have a cloudy day with a shadowless white light, since with subjects in the open sufficient modelling is always provided by the differential planes of focus. Deep forests are particularly tricky places in which to work, and I have rarely got good results with nests in such places.

Then too, it is important to work out what time of day you are likely to be in the hide. If in the morning, don't face the hide to the east for example. Birds are usually most active in the morning hours in the tropics, so if the circumstances permit, work with the sun, which often cannot be avoided anyway, partly to one side or behind; but be particularly careful that the shadow of the hide does not fall across the nest, or cut the field of view, though in fact I have often used the shadow of the hide, if big enough, to flatten the lighting at the nest. Remember however that the bird at the nest will often see you in silhouette in the hide against the sun, and all your movements will be as obvious as if you were sitting in the open – a fact often overlooked even by experienced workers. So, for all these reasons, take a glance at the hide, and the probable position of the sun, from the position of the nest itself. This applies even more in temperate regions where the sun is always angled, and this business of sunshine is perhaps the most important point to consider. In the tropics, too much care cannot be taken by whatever means possible to avoid its unfortunate effects.

With birds at home, in the British Isles, the cautious approach – moving the hide up gradually from a distance over a period of days, or gradually erecting it in its final position, is almost a *sine qua non*. Birds at home have been trained by years of sitting as models, and expect no less. But there are few birds, in Kenya at least, for whom this gradual technique is really required, except perhaps amongst the open ground nesting birds and others which are obviously shy, and the best technique I have found so far is to erect the hide in its final position as late in the evening as possible. Twilight is very brief in the tropical regions, and as soon as darkness falls I have never yet found a bird who will not return unhesitatingly to the nest once the hide is almost indistinguishable in the dark. By the next dawning, it has already been accepted as part of the landscape. Certainly never put up a hide in the morning, otherwise the bird may worry about it all day long, and perhaps even desert – the unforgivable crime in bird photography.

It is really rather surprising what alterations of their environment Kenya birds will put up with without any worry at all, and for this reason the sport is perhaps a good bit easier in East Africa. There is another curious thing that happens in East Africa too. The natural mortality of nest eggs and chicks is simply colossal in these regions of fierce natural competition, and whether this is due to the nest actually having been discovered by man or not I do not know; but even if the nest is barely glanced at, the chances of it being destroyed by a predator are enormously high, and I have lost many chances thus in the past. Like all such problems, the effect of the observer is hard to assess, and it is almost impossible to say if a particular nest would have been robbed if it had not been discovered. I suspect the answer is yes. The interesting point however is this; that if a hide is erected as soon as possible after finding a nest (in the evening of course), even if it is not in the right stage for photography, and left in position, it will readily be accepted by the owner of the nest and the chances of the eggs or chicks surviving seem to increase immediately the hide is there; the hide appears to have a much more alarming effect on the casual predator than one would think, and I have often used this knowledge to advantage too.

It is seldom necessary to camouflage the hide in any way, and a bare square tent is as acceptable to the birds as is any carefully concealed object; but pilings of grass and branches will often stop it flapping in a wind. However, keep such well clear of the windows and the lens opening.

The day after the hide has been erected, and fully accepted by the birds, is the best time to start a little preliminary 'gardening' round the nest, and no part of the proceedings calls for more skilful attention. The vegetation must be carefully cleared to give the best view, without making the surroundings appear to be unnatural. It is far better to tie back branches than to cut; but if cutting is necessary, do it most judiciously, and smear the cut stump with earth to cover up the whiteness of the wood. Leave the nest still partly covered with a few easily removable bits of vegetation, which can be taken away at the last minute, and replaced when the session is over. Watch the sun again, for it has an uncanny habit of casting additional shadows where they are not wanted (very often a branch a long way from the nest is responsible, and to expose the chicks to the full glare is inexcusable at any time).

Grass is some of the most dreadful stuff to deal with; if it is bent down out of the way it looks unnatural, and has an extraordinary knack of springing upright again and covering some vital portion of the nest – usually after one is settled in the hide and the bird about to return. It is best, I think, to cut just sufficient right down to the ground so that it cannot interfere again, and I always carry a stout pair of garden scissors for this job. Nothing looks worse than some out of focus blades of grass in the foreground of the picture; so that the field of view should be cleared right up to the hide.

While it is important to clear as natural a field of view as possible in front of, and by the nest, it is perhaps even more important still to study and adjust the background with considerable care. It is best to have this out of focus if possible, but see that there are no leaves left to cause glaring spots in awkward places; but if near at hand, and inevitably in focus, nothing looks worse than a twig or leaf apparently sprouting out of a bird's head in the final picture. The light too, changes all the time, and what was a harmless dark branch half an hour ago, may become an unpleasant white streak as the sun climbs higher. This study of the background, and the changes it may undergo is one of the most important parts of the game, and too much attention cannot be paid to it before starting. Any artificial perches too, should be in keeping with the surroundings of the nest.

Before finally hiding up, it is a good plan to watch from a distance for a while and see that all is well. The final settling in the hide is one of the almost ritualistic parts of the sport. The Kearton brothers discovered long ago that it pays hands down to have two people to take part – one to walk away as soon as the other is installed. Birds can seldom count, and this ruse is ninety-nine per cent successful every time. Like the introduction of the hide to the bird, British birds demand this considerate treatment now as a matter of course, and are liable to be greatly offended if the photographer does not conform to the rules of the game.

Nor, really, could I agree more, and my remarks should not

PLATE 29A. Hide at avocets nest, Magadi 1952
PLATE 29B. Hide at crested cranes nest, Sagana 1952

LATE 29A

PLATE 29B

PLATE 30

be misunderstood. It is indeed the ideal way to start, and when it can be done it always saves a lot of unnecessary trouble in the end. This technique should indeed be carried out as a matter of course with anything at all unusual or rare, and even with the commoner birds who, too, are entitled to every consideration wherever they are.

But it cannot always be so, and companions are not always available. I have myself played a lone hand for many years, and sometimes it simply cannot be otherwise. Very often in the past I have hid myself up without any help at all, without, to my certain knowledge, ever having caused trouble to the bird. Birds have astonishingly short memories, and once the hide is quiet and still again with the watcher safely inside, will return without any hesitation at all, provided they cannot see in or notice any further movement. This is, I suppose, particularly so with birds in Kenya, which are normally most anxious to return to the nest, perhaps in defence of their brood, and though I have admittedly disturbed temporarily some birds by being improperly covered in a brushwood hide, I have never found the least trouble using a proper cloth hide.

I still, however, prefer to have a companion to hide me up and walk away if it can possibly be done, perhaps more for conscience sake; but even in Kenya, I would agree that some birds are impossible without this aid. Africans are of course a help; they are nearly ubiquitous, and will usually willingly assist, though it is clearly just another manifestation of the prevailing madness of the European to require such pointless action. But choose such help with care, for sometimes in the past I have been greatly puzzled by the non-return of a bird to whom I have been introduced with such assistance, only to find my black helper squatting patiently on the ground a few feet away from the hide, dimly trying to puzzle out what this *shauri* is really all about.

There are some tribes, such as the Wakamba, most of whose members take a deep interest in birds – mainly, it must be admitted, from the gastronomic point of view – but some of them are absolutely first class helpers, and take a really intelligent part; as witness the numerous magnificent African trackers and collectors who have been employed in the past, and are

R

still employed. We once had an excellent Mkamba boy who used to bird's nest for us, and he was quite uncanny at the game. His only failing was an inability to resist popping a succulent live chick into his mouth and eating it, on the theory that, like a box of sweets, one would never be missed. This led to his downfall in the end. But a great many of them can be trained as assistants to an astonishingly high degree of efficiency if they have not forgotten their native bushcraft in the unfortunate veneer of civilisation which they now possess. Even with Africans about however, I prefer to work alone, if I am certain I can get away with it, but not otherwise.

The camera should be focused with care, with the nest towards the bottom of the frame – not dead centre – to allow for the height of the bird as it stands; this seems an elementary point, but I have myself been surprised at the number of times I have made this very mistake, and obtained excellent pictures of a decapitated bird. Nothing is more useful than a matchbox placed where the bird is expected to be; they always have printing and usually an intricate design on the label, which is ideal for critical focusing; but allow for the 'thickness' of the bird, for it is better to have the head dead sharp than the tail. At the same time, the lens should be stopped down as far as circumstances will permit, to get the greatest depth of focus, which is always slightly greater behind the critical plane than in front. Superb definition is the whole answer to a good bird picture; look at any of Hosking's and Yeates' bird portraits, with their enormous depth of field, and you will see at once why this is so.

The 13·5 cm. Sonnar has a maximum aperture of F 4·5, but I practically never use any stop larger than F 8 or F 11, both of which allow for a great depth of field at close quarters. It is almost always impossible to give the 'correct' exposure for a bird at the nest. The lighting varies widely throughout the day, and speed of exposure also depends mainly on the type of bird, whether quick or deliberate at the nest; but with 35 mm. work, with ample negative material to hand, it is better to sacrifice shutter speed to depth of focus, and hence use the smallest possible stop with the slowest possible speed. The exposure meter should of course be used; for I defy any photographer, no matter how expert, correctly to judge, for example, exposures in a forest. The shutter and stop should then be set as near as possible to the 'ideal', bearing in mind the need for focal depth and the character of the bird. It is well worth while getting to know by 'feel' how to set the stop ring of the lens and the shutter speed scale, since such changes are almost inevitable during a period of hours in the hide. The camera and tripod must be really rigidly fixed, and even with that, I seldom like to go below 1/50 sec. if at all possible. As I mentioned before, the cable release should be long, as there is nothing more tiring than to have to hold one's hand up at camera height, and if the cable is not immediately to hand, it is often too late. Arrange camera bags and everything else in the hide in an orderly way, with everything available with the least movement or noise, and above all sit as comfortably as you can on a chair preferably with a back to lean upon.

With the Contax, it is worth while checking to see that the camera will not twist on the stand as the shutter is wound, throwing the field of view out. It is a hard wind on this particular camera, and I have had this happen before; but do not bother about the viewfinder if the focusing adapter has been used – it is better to memorise the actual field of view available round the nest, and this is an easy thing to do. Check everything over again and again before finally settling down.

The first return of a bird is a most exciting moment, and it still has not lost its thrill for me, even with the humblest bird. Sometimes they will call first, putting all ones senses on the alert (but see that this tensing up does not release the shutter too soon – I have done this too!); at other times, with other species, the approach is quiet and must be watched carefully through the windows. Whether or not to take pictures this first time back is a very moot point, and temptation is great to 'mak siccar' at least once. Some birds will not object to a slight shutter click, others will fly off right away. It depends a lot on the sort of bird, and this judgment comes only with experience. With those birds which will not return again for hours take the chance, for the next time back they will have forgotten anyway. As a rule however, birds such as these, which pay infrequent visits, do by contrast, spend a long time at any one visit, so give them a few moments to get engrossed in chick feeding before firing away; once feeding has actually started, a bird which a moment before was 'windy' on approach, will become much more bold and almost oblivious to other slight distractions, such is the compulsion exerted by expectant chicks and the first satisfaction of the feeding drive of the parent.

The 'right moment' comes only after practice, and estimation of it is all the difference between a first class bird photographer and an average one. Anticipation of what the bird will do is half the fun, but with the relatively quick setting of the shutter in the miniature, and no plates to change, since film wind is automatic, matters are a good bit easier; but even at that I have often mentally kicked myself in the hide for firing off too soon. There is no golden rule at all except the training of one's reaction to the moment at hand. There are however, one or two harmless tricks that can be tried with an awkward bird to make it hesitate that vital fraction. A very slight noise (I often clink the cable release against the tripod leg), will sometimes make them look up for a second; but do this carefully. After a time, many birds will completely ignore all sorts of noises from a hide, and as I have frequently mentioned in these pages before, I sometimes carry on a long conversation with my subjects. This sounds perhaps a little mad, but it is extraordinary what a bond of confidence one can build up in this way between the bird and yourself, and I often think that birds *like* being spoken to quietly at the nest.

Perhaps some of the most difficult subjects are those which nest in holes or in domed nests. If confident, they fly straight in without hesitation, and give no chance at all of a picture. I detest the practice of blocking up the hole which is sometimes done, and if a slight noise will not make the bird hesitate at the entrance, there are several different ways that can be tried. A perch below the nest is often most effective, as with bee-eaters; or if the bird will not use one immediately by the nest, try putting it a little distance away in the line of flight and focusing on this. Or there is another way which is often very successful, and that is to hang a strand or two of the actual nest material across the entrance – not to block it in any way at all; but its mere presence out of place there will often cause the bird to stop a second before going in. But note that I write 'nest material', as I do not think anything else is quite so natural or has the same effect.

Some years ago, I had been trying to get a picture of a saw-wing swallow entering its nest hole in an earth bank. These birds are constantly on the wing, and will not perch at all, but fly straight into the nesting hole. After some while trying all the tricks I know, I finally tried the expedient I do not like, of placing a large leaf just inside the entrance, not to block the hole but to cause the bird to settle on the entrance ledge before going in. She took one look at this when flying past the hole, and became completely wild, not even coming near the hole at all thereafter. After a few minutes I saw that it was hopeless, and pulled the leaf out; but in so doing I caught sight of a shred of grey old-man's beard lichen, of which their nests are exclusively made. It gave me an idea, and I hung a little across the hole. The bird came circling after I had re-settled in the hide, and pitched at once at the entrance to the hole, for this was stuff she recognised; and she spent quite a while picking it down sitting on the entrance ledge, and gave me all the pictures I wanted while so doing! With birds which nest in tree holes, and use no nest material at all, a few wood chips hung on spider webs across the entrance will do the trick, and often spider webs alone are very effective. The main thing is to use a material which the bird is likely to associate with its nesting hole in the first place, and then no alarm results. Sometimes however, none of these tricks will work at all, so pack up and try elsewhere!

This 'manipulating' of birds at the nest is an interesting art. It does them no harm at all if commonsense is used and will often make all the difference between getting good pictures or none at all. It often leads too, to these exciting moments with both birds at the nest together, since if say the hen can be persuaded to stay by talking to her, the cock will often pitch up alongside while she is still there. In employing all such tricks, consideration of the subject must be of paramount importance, for the only good pictures of a bird are those in which the bird is completely natural and unsuspicious. One learns by experience in what way particular kinds of birds will react to certain situations, and this knowledge is half the battle. Like good horsemen, or good fishkeepers, a good bird photographer should develop a 'feel' for birds at close quarters; but this is an art, which cannot be explained.

Properly practised, bird photography is a great deal less disturbing to the bird than a great many of the modern techniques of experimentation on bird behaviour, which may involve disturbance of nests and eggs, experiments with artificial birds and so on.

I cannot emphasise too strongly the necessity for jotting down rough notes at times in the hide; these can be transcribed later, when memory is often at fault. As Yeates has pointed out, bird photographers are often taken to task for not producing results of first rate importance from close watching of birds at the nest with the opportunities provided from the hide; but I agree fully with him that such criticism is quite unjust. The view from a hide is restricted, and one watches the bird at only one small stage of its total life cycle; the chances of epoch making discoveries are remote, and principles can seldom be deduced. But the taking of careful notes may well help to fit yet one more piece into the final jigsaw picture of the life of a bird and the world in which it lives.

Not all bird photographers want to be considered as scientific observers, nor do I blame them, for bird photography is primarily a sport. May it remain such – an essentially satisfying thing. Not all golfers want to become professionals, nor are they interested in the mathematical equations which can be deduced from the impact of club head and ball; but golfers obtain great satisfaction from the long straight drive or long putt that sinks, in the same way that an honest bird photographer obtains great satisfaction from his trophy too, without worrying about what its scientific implications are. Though as a biologist, I would be the last to deny the scientific values which may be obtained from photography of birds at the nest if one is so inclined, there is no need for the sport to have a scientific excuse.

Leaving the hide is just as important a part of the technique as getting in. It is, as I mentioned above, preferable to have a companion to release you at a preset time or signal, which can be altered if so required, though again on very many occasions

I have crawled out by myself, leaving the birds carrying on quite happily without taking much notice of the disturbance. It depends on the bird; I remember once an occasion with a red-throated diver in the north-west Scottish Highlands, who was wild and shy on all occasions; but who appeared only mildly astonished and continued brooding her eggs when I suddenly appeared behind the hide alone after a session, apparently having risen out of the loch waters.

At each session with a bird at its nest, I personally like to take as many pictures and obtain as full a sequence as I can of the bird, and for this of course the 35 mm. technique, with its abundance of negative material at one loading, and cheapness of operation, is ideal; but unless required for serious purposes in illustrating some behaviour aspect, I rarely print more than two or three of the best of the lot to serve as mementoes of the time, and with twenty to thirty pictures in the bag one can afford to pick and choose.

As regards photography in colour, I have little to write and cannot be a judge. I have taken quite a few colour pictures of birds, but have never been satisfied with them myself. The negative-positive process produces a print which is to my mind still lacking in natural quality, and although theoretically they are ideal, since from the colour negative one can produce as many black and white prints as you like, yet with all the types I have tried the negative image is lacking in that crisp definition so essential when enlarged, and indeed I have often wondered whether they are really sharp at all.

This does not apply to the reversal processes such as Kodachrome, and I cannot deny the great beauty and fine detail obtainable in these tiny transparencies; but somehow I have never been able to bother myself with either peering at a small transparency, nor with the preparation required to project it to see it as it should be seen. Nor do I like having only the one positive of my subject, and I have always preferred doing the whole processing myself from start to finish, which one cannot do with Kodachrome, although with Ferraniacolor and Pakolor one can. The slow speeds of colour materials must also be borne in mind for bird work.

I know, and confess quite frankly, that I am prejudiced in

this respect, and that a great many of my objections have now been swept away by the new facilities which Kodak now offer for colour prints from transparencies, duplicate transparencies, and black and white negatives from transparencies. For amateur use however the cost still remains high, and as I do little bird work for commercial gain, but mainly to please myself (and perhaps the family), one has to watch the pocket too.

Colour work is a much more exacting taskmaster than black and white, and so, paradoxically, I enjoy that technical challenge too. I may yet change to all-colour for birds, if the cost and results finally measure up to my requirements.

Away from the Nest

There has recently been something of an outcry against 'the hackneyed subject' of a bird at its nest, and indeed I suppose that by far the greatest percentage of bird pictures are taken at the nest. And why not – for that is the time when it is easiest to watch the bird at close quarters, and no two photographs, even of the same species, will ever be alike. I for one, will never tire of pictures of birds at the nest, and one might as well complain of many other far more hackneyed themes seen in exhibitions of both painting and photography year after year.

I do admit however that a different viewpoint is occasionally refreshing, and the photography of birds away from the nest is a distinctive challenge to one's skill and sometimes far more difficult too. In Kenya, countless opportunities exist for such work, though I myself have never done a great deal in that country, preferring the fieldcraft that photography at the nest entails.

Birds are readily attracted to bait in Kenya – from large carcases and offal for vultures and crows to millet, crushed maize and fruit for garden birds, with tubular flowers for sunbirds, and all such means can be employed with or without a hide. I dislike intensely pictures of birds at some sort of artificial table spread to attract them, though sprays of flowers such as salvia or leonotis are often the only way to photograph male sunbirds in full plumage as they feed on the flowers, since this sex practically never visit the nest, the females only carrying out nest duties. (Plate 30).

Then too, birds in flight are a speciality of their own, for which the miniature is ideally adapted. John Barlee's *Birds on the Wing* cannot be surpassed for useful hints in this respect. I myself have a great liking for migrant photography, such as one can do at the coast in season, at sewage farms or on the lakes in Kenya. Guy Farrar pioneered that type of work in England, and some very beautiful pictures can be taken this way; but it is a question of getting to know exactly when and where the birds will be, and placing a hide accordingly. The exciting part of this photography is that one never knows what will turn up next, and here again the quick focusing miniature can be used with great advantage.

A great many Kenya birds can be stalked and 'shot', but in this remember camera shake in the excitement of the moment. It has ruined a good many such pictures for me, and now I use nothing slower than a 1/250 sec. in the hand for this; though some form of 'gun' camera rest is useful too.

Perhaps some of the most repaying 'away from the nest' photographs can be taken from a car. Like big game in Kenya, birds seldom associate a bulky moving car with anything really alarming, and driving over the plains after birds can be great fun, as it is with game; but never chase them too much, as a slow and cautious approach is always far more successful. Even with this however it is astonishing how secretary birds and bustards for example will rarely face you, and their heads turn slightly away which spoils many a picture. Plovers, sandgrouse and other birds can all be approached this way without alarm, and eagles and vultures on trees are ridiculously tame.

There are no special technical points to be considered in this sort of photography, except perhaps the use of the fastest shutter speed possible consonant with a reasonably small stop, in order to eliminate that bugbear of miniature work – camera shake, which is intensified by the vibration of the car. The same type of medium or slow-speed fine-grain pan film should be used, since the resultant negatives will often have a small image size necessitating a good degree of enlargement for the final picture in which grain will be intrusive if care is not taken. As always, an efficient lens hood must be used, since the direction of the photograph is not always under control.

It is a good thing too, thoroughly to familiarise oneself with the depth of focus scale on the lens, and the use of hyperfocal distance, since in many cases accurate focusing will not be possible, and more in the nature of a snap shot at a moment's notice will be required. Chances may present themselves at any time in any place, and the camera should be at the ready; I once missed the picture of a lifetime through this lack of readiness, when a doe bongo – the shyest of all forest buck in Kenya, and so often hunted for weeks in vain – suddenly stepped out together with a tiny fawn, into the one and only patch of sunlight on the forest path on which I was walking, not five yards from me. She stood looking at me for it seemed an eternity, while I wrestled with the wretched camera slung at my back; in vain, for she was gone silently like a shadow a second later into the green depths of the forest. I have never seen a bongo since, and how very few Europeans ever have! Then too, by contrast, how very few good pictures, for example, have ever been taken of ostriches – the largest of all wild birds, and so common on all the game plains of Kenya!

Water birds offer particularly good subjects, since most can be approached very close in a boat, and round the shores of Lake Victoria and numerous smaller bodies of water in Kenya there exist abundant opportunities for this sort of work; but don't expect a winner every time.

Nests and Eggs

This is a line which has been largely neglected, even at home, and yet the results can be exquisite pictorial records, in addition to being of scientific value. I suppose that not more than a tenth, if that, of African birds' nests have ever been recorded in this way.

The technique is straightforward, and demands only technical skill, coupled with some artistic appreciation of the site; the photographs should convey a very good idea of the nest surroundings as well as the nest itself.

For this reason, I often take two of each nest; one of the general site and one showing the details of the nest itself. A wide angle lens is useful for the former, and for the latter I often use the telephoto if at all possible to avoid distortion at close quarters work; but nevertheless in most cases, the standard 5 cm. lens will do both jobs.

If taking a picture of the nest and eggs in its surroundings, it is worth while paying a little attention to the so-called rules of composition, since the subject can be studied at leisure and composed at will. It looks far better in the finished print for example to have the nest and eggs placed at one of the intersections of the lower thirds rather than dead centre. (Plate 31). With close up work, avoid unnatural tilting of a nest to show the contents, and choose a higher viewpoint if possible to see in; but it is often far better to show perhaps only one or two of the eggs than the whole clutch in order to produce an aesthetically satisfying print. (Plate 32).

Biting sharpness is essential in all such work to show the utmost detail of the nest, eggs and their surroundings. Therefore use a very rigid tripod, and give a slow bulb or time exposure with the lens stopped to F 16 at least to obtain the maximum depths of focus and crispness of detail. (A good many lenses however, actually show a falling off in definition, or at least no improvement, at a still smaller stop, so test this point with your own particular outfit.) Study the play of light and shade on the subject, and assess the final result in your mind. Exposure should be exact and measured with the meter, using either the high light or incident methods, and not the 'average light' way, since shadows may be dense; make the exposure with a cable release.

Wind can be troublesome, so shelter the camera and the nest either with the body or a coat. As always medium or slow-speed film should be used to stand the final degree of enlargement necessary. With views including a wide part of the surroundings, and perhaps some sky, it is a good plan to correct tones slightly with a good optically flat light yellow filter clipped on the lens, but do not overcorrect with anything darker. Reflections on glossy eggs can be a trial, and a viewpoint should be chosen to minimise this; polaroid filters are rarely useful for this, since they eliminate reflections only at a fairly acute angle, and require up to a 4 × increase in exposure time.

Photography of chicks too is a neglected field which can be almost as difficult as photographing children! Exposure should be short enough to eliminate movement. I have very rarely seen any good pictures of plover and wader chicks standing up and looking lively, though it is of course easy to take them as they crouch.

New-born passerine chicks are unlovely objects, though photographs of such are of at least scientific value. But they are very attractive when they fledge, but never at any time remove a fledgling from the nest and try to make it pose on a twig. It won't stay there, but will flutter off and look thoroughly frightened; and once out of the nest, nothing will ever persuade it to go back, and the parent birds will very frequently desert it, since they are almost incapable of the reasoning necessary to attend to a chick which has left the nest prematurely if there are others still in the nest. Treat them with care and consideration.

Electronic Flash

In addition to the ordinary kind of night or dark situation photography of birds taken with expendable foil-filled bulbs, there has within the last few years been a remarkable interest taken in electronic flash pictures of birds, which arrest them in mid-air with wings outspread, a field so ably pioneered by Hosking. Such pictures, when successful, are a technical *tour de force*; and once the capital expenditure is realised the running cost of such flash outfits is negligible.

But such work is full of snags, which should be clearly realised, and I make no excuse for dealing with these in some detail, since I have tried a good many such pictures and know the disappointments which can result.

In the first place it is most important to realise clearly that with the great modern development of electronic flash outfits there are now on the market many different types; these fall into two main classes – one of which can produce those pictures of birds frozen in flight, and one which cannot do so. There is the original type, whose power pack consists of a relatively low voltage accumulator or battery, which charges, through a vibrator, a set of condensers up to an extremely high and lethal voltage of 2,000 or so, which when discharged causes a spark in a high voltage electronic tube of a duration of about 1/5,000 sec. or less, with a light intensity somewhat less than that of ordinary foil-filled bulbs. These have a power rating of 100-300 joules, and the flash is quite short enough to stop any flight movement. These outfits are pretty heavy as a rule, but are the ones used to produce such flight pictures. These types have certain snags with which I shall deal later.

Then there are the other, somewhat cheaper types now produced for 'home-work' in a variety of models and some quite small sizes. These are powered usually by dry batteries of a relatively high voltage to start with – up to 500 or so – and these charge smaller, more compact condensers directly, without a vibrator unit (and are therefore silent in action) to a much lower voltage than the former type. These discharge through a low voltage spark tube, and the flash duration is longer, from about 1/700 to 1/1,000 sec. This is amply fast enough for all normal photographic use, but – and this is the point – not nearly fast enough to stop a bird in flight.

I shall refer to these two as the high-voltage and low-voltage types, but the terms are relative only, since even in the 'low-voltage' type, the final discharge of the capacitors (and in some cases the battery too) is high enough to be fully lethal if improperly handled.

Now these two types, apart from the wide difference in flash duration, differ also in two very important practical aspects as far as bird work is concerned. Owing to the technical nature of the circuit, the high-voltage types have a relatively long recycling (charging) time of ten seconds or more before the condensers are ready to fire; and once the condensers are fully charged, they cannot, in nearly all models, be kept charged for any length of time, ready to fire, without running the batteries flat in a very short time. A model was produced once which did indeed have a trip-charge device, which cut out the battery current when the capacitors were fully charged, and cut it in again as soon as the stored voltage dropped below a certain level, thus saving the batteries to some extent. But this model is I believe no longer available, and in all the other high voltage types the drain on the battery is very heavy all the time – they cannot be left switched on for very long.

In the low voltage type, again owing to the different circuit involved, the charging time is often very short, as little as three seconds perhaps; and once the capacitors are fully charged, the drain on the battery drops to a fractional amount, thus allowing the set to remain switched on for a long time – perhaps several hours – without undue battery waste. The heavy drain is only when the current is first switched on.

I understand that for technical reasons it is at present impossible to design a set having both the extremely short flash duration of the high-voltage type and the quick recharging time and ability to be left switched on for hours of the low-voltage models; one must therefore weigh the advantage and disadvantage of each for the special demands of bird photography. The differences in power output and intensity of flash are negligible for the moment; one 100-joule set does not necessarily have the same light output as another of the same rating, since this depends on the type of reflector and spark tube used amongst other things. Ignoring these differences for the moment however, 100 joules is as low as is practicable for bird work at the usual distances involved; the more the better of course. Thus Hosking couples two or more lamps or sets together to give 300 joules or more for colour work with these slow-speed films; but this sort of thing becomes very expensive.

However, supposing the high-voltage short duration flash is definitely required for high-speed pictures of birds in flight, consider now the technique required and the disadvantages involved, and in particular the disadvantages peculiar to using electronic flash with the miniature camera. Interchangeable lens miniatures of the type I use, are usually fitted with focal plane shutters which can be synchronised for electronic flash only at shutter speeds of 1/50, 1/25 or less – the only speeds at which the whole of the negative area is exposed at once in the camera with such focal plane shutters. Miniatures with shutters which can be synchronised at any speed cannot usually be fitted with telephoto lenses, and hence are of little use for bird work anyway. With the focal plane type, unless an enormous intensity of light is used, completely to swamp the daylight, or in any well-lit conditions, the relatively low shutter speed required will result in one image due to daylight and one due to the flash; with a quick moving object, this gives a blurred double image which is useless.

This can be largely overcome, as I have done with my outfit, by setting the focal plane shutter open at 'Time', and using in front of the lens a screwed-on bladed shutter of the Compur type to which the flash outfit is synchronised and connected. This gives synchronisation at all speeds, and exposure of the whole negative area at all speeds too. But there is another snag with such a fitting. The front component of the 13·5 cm. Sommar lens is 42 mm. in diameter, and this necessitates a shutter of the Compur type, whose actual opening is almost as wide as this; otherwise a portion of the light will be cut off when the shutter is open. The only shutter of this size, with a sufficiently large diameter, which can at present be obtained, can for technical reasons again be speeded only to 1/200 sec. This speed, though much faster than the 1/25 of the focal plane, is I find still not fast enough to cut out the residual daylight image in an exposed situation. So the situation is really not satisfactory for miniature work, unless electronic flash is used only in places with very subdued light, or the movement of the bird is not sufficiently fast anyway to produce a blurred second image.

This particular snag does not of course apply to any of the larger field cameras fitted with between lens shutters, such as the experts use, since usually such shutters are speeded to at least 1/500 sec., which is as a rule fast enough to cut out any daylight image.

This question of shutter speeds apart, the slow charging time of the high-voltage models and the heavy drain on the batteries when remaining switched on are distinct disadvantages in bird work from a hide. With a great many birds, they do not give sufficient warning of their arrival at the nest to allow the set to be charged up first – ten seconds is a long time to wait before a picture is possible; and if the set is left switched on, so that it can be used the moment the bird arrives, like as not the batteries will be flat just when that moment has come; for too, a great many birds are hesitant in coming to the exact spot required. Though they are seen in time to allow for charging, they may still take several minutes to arrive just where they are wanted, during which time with such sets, the batteries may well run down if they have been switched on at the first sight of the bird.

Using such a set therefore calls for clear thinking and planning ahead, and a very exact anticipation of what the bird will do; coupled with an automatic mastery of the various moves required in switching on, together with a good sense of time. With eyes on the bird, minutes pass extraordinarily quickly.

There is unfortunately still more to the business than this. Supposing it has been planned to photograph a bird alighting on a particular stump, the focusing must be made exactly on some imaginary aerial spot through which it is hoped the bird will pass, and variation slightly out of line will have to be allowed for in the field of view chosen. Here however, the small stop which electronic flash allows, and the consequent increase in depth of focus are most useful. Personally I find it handy to carry a small white card with some bold black design on it; this is stuck on the end of a knitting needle and the card made to occupy the spot in space which the bird should occupy by sticking the needle at an appropriate spot in the stump or bank. Remember however that a bird with outstretched wings and tail will occupy a far larger area on the negative than the same bird at its nest, so allow sufficient field of view all round.

Assuming that the focus can be correct, the set can be charged up in sufficient time and the bird flies up at just the right place to be taken; then come the final two most awkward snags. The first is a purely physiological one, in so far that a human being's reaction time is never fast enough to anticipate exactly the right moment to take the picture. If you take it when the bird is in the air at the spot focused on, your negative will be blank, because by the time your muscles and nerves have reacted to your eyes and caused the shutter to be released, the bird will be well past that spot. Therefore – and it is a matter of training – the shutter must be released before the bird has apparently reached the chosen spot. There is no golden rule or short cut to help with this, except a fine understanding of your own reaction time (it increases with age), and a first class appreciation of distance, speed and direction – plus a pile of wasted films! In this field it is vitally important to be able to use both eyes from the hide to obtain stereoscopic vision; pictures with the tail, head or wing tips cut off are seldom of any use. To obviate this source of wastage, experts like

Nest of stone curlew, Watamu 1953

PLATE 32

Nest of white-browed robin chat, Kiganjo 1948

Hosking use the bird itself to take its own picture, as it interrupts an invisible infra-red beam thrown across the area it will pass, and this form of photoelectric relay is of course practically foolproof in releasing the shutter at exactly the right moment. These are expensive sorts of toys however for the ordinary amateur, and apart from taking a lot of fun out of the game, there is still the snag of keeping the battery up while you wait for the bird to cross the beam – unless you are conveniently near a main-plug and can use an all mains set!

Then comes the final difficulty of all, which no amount of human ingenuity can overcome; it may be that the timing has been perfect and the image of the bird perfectly recorded in the centre of the film – but what sort of position is it in? This you cannot tell until the film is developed, and disappointment may still result if the bird has finally been caught in some sort of impossible position with its wings covering its head and so on! But this is a matter of pure chance and nothing can be done about it. Out of a series of course, several will be perfect at least, for the Goddess of Chance is not quite as fickle as that.

Now, as long as it is realised that pictures of birds in actual flight are virtually impossible with the low voltage type of set, since the flash exposure is nowhere near short enough to stop them, a lot of the snags mentioned above disappear when using this sort of set. The very short recharging time gives one plenty of time to anticipate the bird, and if it delays longer than anticipated in coming to the area in focus, no serious drain on the batteries results if the set is left switched on ready. I have sometimes left my low voltage set switched on for an hour or more, with little loss to the battery, and the set is of course ready for instant use. Providing flight pictures are not attempted, the 1/1,000 sec. or so exposure is amply fast enough to stop all normal movement at the nest, even for such quick little birds as grass warblers, and the percentage of successful pictures is vastly greater than using daylight alone.

The quick stuffing of insects into a chick's beak can be instantaneously recorded, and even the wagging of a wagtail's tail stopped. Exposure is quite constant whatever the daylight is doing – a fact of inestimable advantage in the usual British summer – and if the stop is set according to the power of the equipment, the speed of the film and distance of the lamp from the subject, calculated either by the flash-factor method, or by one of the numerous ingenious calculators on the market, then every single picture will be correctly exposed. This will appeal at least to the economically minded.

Flash makes work possible in previously impossible places such as under bridges, in dark banks, or in deep forest shade – places which have had in the past offered so many opportunities which regretfully have had to be turned down because of poor light. In Kenya, it finds an especial use in reducing the terrific contrast of light and shade on exposed nests in the brilliant sunshine, and this indeed I find one of its most useful attributes. So many pictures of mine in the past have been ruined by a soot and whitewash effect in Kenya taken in the ordinary way; but now one can expose for the sun only, and the dark shadows are brightened by the flash sufficiently since the lamp inevitably illuminates these at a different angle to the almost vertical sun.

There are certain important technical and aesthetic points to be considered when using flash from a hide, and the first of these is the question of background and distance from the subject. It is necessary to get as close to the subject as possible, since the light falling on it from the lamp decreases in intensity as the square of the distance – not in direct proportion. Therefore, objects only a few feet behind the bird will not be lit at all sufficiently by the flash to record in the negative, and a receding background will appear almost jet-black in the print by contrast with the well-lit bird. This is not a pleasant effect. With flash therefore it pays to have the natural background as *near* to the bird as possible – the reverse of daylight practice. Thus the bird stands out against a pleasantly graded series of tones, always bearing in mind what I have written above about intrusive and shiny leaves and twigs. The former particularly may give trouble if the new angle of reflection is not considered. For this reason, a good many American pictures of birds in colour taken by electronic flash show an even background of perhaps blue or green, this being from a cloth hung immediately behind the nest. This is a result which personally I find distinctly unnatural and unpleasant.

The nearer the light is to the subject, the smaller the stop that can be used, and the greater the depth of focus. Within reason therefore the position of the camera does not matter so much as regards distance, and it is therefore not at all necessary to have the lamp or lamps at or even near the hide; they can be placed much nearer the nest in the open and birds seldom seem to take much notice of them. It is however a good plan when erecting the hide to stick a shiny tin disc on a post to resemble the lamp in its final position, to which the bird can become accustomed. The actual flash itself I have never found unduly to worry any bird I have so far tried. I write lamps in the plural deliberately, for far better modelling of the subject will result from two lamps angled to the subject; a single lamp always gives hard unidirectional shadows. If a single lamp is used however, it should never be placed in a line with the camera, otherwise the result will be flat and uninteresting. Placed fairly well to one or other side the modelling is better; if two lamps are used, angle them to the camera, but place one slightly further away than the other on the opposite side so that modelling is still preserved. See that both lamps and the power pack-camera cable are at least ten feet long to allow for this outside positioning. Most modern lamps can be attached to a tripod, and for this a light tubular one is quite good enough – quite a point as the total overall weight of the outfit is considerable and it may have to be carried far.

Camera shake problems disappear with even the low-voltage sets, but still it pays not to be too careless over this. As indicated above, most commercially bought sets have a very short cable between power pack and lamp, so get this lengthened by the makers to ten feet or so. I write 'makers' deliberately, for they are qualified electrical engineers and know what they are doing. A badly made amateur connection could be lethal, especially if it rains. Such an extension enables the lamp to be set up outside the hide near the nest, while the power pack with its switches, etc., remains in the hide with the operator. An odd bit of plastic tied over the lamp, not obscuring the face, will prevent shortage due to rain, and it is worth while choosing a lamp with a front glass, or at least a horizontally fixed spark tube, not a vertical one; also one in which the power cable enters from the underside, not at the back.

Test the batteries well before any hide session, and see that the drill of shutter setting, switching on and so on is automatically at your finger tips.

Although electronic flash produces a soft white light – almost ideally balanced for colour work – and not the hard flash of foil, I have still not quite reconciled myself to the appearance of the final picture. No matter what you do, it still somehow 'looks like a flash picture', with too much dead black in it, and it is not completely natural. While certainly the technique enables a great deal to be done where nothing could be done before, this slightly unnatural result still jars on me, and unless therefore there is real reason for using flash, I still prefer the normal technique where circumstances permit.

Remember however that a very great deal depends on the after treatment of the exposed films, and the type of development can do a lot to make the result more pleasing. With ordinary development, it is always recommended to give fifty per cent more developing time to electronic flash pictures to allow for the phenomenon of 'reciprocity failure'; and in general this is sound advice. Using Promicrol Developer however this is not always required, and often the same development time can be given to such negatives as with normally exposed ones; this is a great advantage in so far that flash and normal pictures can be mixed on one roll without the necessity of cutting or fiddling about before development. It should not however be done as a matter of course with purely flash pictures which should have the over development recommended.

I have written a great deal about the snags and disadvantages of using electronic flash for birds, but I have done so deliberately. I have been through the mill myself and know now what it entails, and if I have been able to make the aspirant only pause and think it will have been a useful service.

This method is not a universal panacea for all the snags of normal bird work, but must be used intelligently, with full appreciation of all its failings as well as advantages.

NAIROBI-MOMBASA ROAD

Bird Census List, September 1951

PORTION OF ROAD

Species	Kiu-Ulu 0630 hrs.	Ulu-Sultan Hamud	Sultan Hamud-Emali	Emali-Simba	Simba-Kibwezi-Mtito. 1000 hrs.	Mtito-Tsavo. 1100 hrs.	Tsavo-Voi. 1200 hrs.	Voi-Mack.-Road.	Mack.-Rd. Mariakani	Mar.-Mombasa. 1400 hrs.	Totals
Superb starling (*Spreo superbus*)	14	1	8	13		2					38
Babbler (*Turdoides* spp.)	4										4
Finch lark (*Eremopteryx leucopareia*)	6										6
Laughing dove (*Stigmatopelia senegalensis*)	10	5	1	80	32	20					148
Ring-necked dove (*Streptopelia capicola*)	32	19	1	4							56
Lilac-breasted roller (*Coracias caudata*)	1			2		1	1				5
Brimstone canary (*Serinus sulphuratus*)	5	10									15
White-bellied go-away bird (*Corythaixoides leucogaster*)	2			5							7
Yellow-necked spurfowl (*Pternistes leucoscepus*)	4	7		6	2						19
Emerald-spotted wood dove (*Turtur chalcospilos*)	7	3		1		7		2	1		21
Plum- or fire-finch (*Lagonosticta* spp.)	2										2
Red-cheeked cordon-bleu (*Uraeginthus bengalus*)	1									2	3
Black-headed bush shrike (*Tchagra senegala*)	1	1		1							3
Blue-naped mousebird (*Colius macrourus*)	2			4					4		10
Little bee-eater (*Melittophagus pusillus*)	1				1			1			3
Grey hornbill (*Tockus nasutus*)		2			4	3		1	1		11
Long-tailed fiscal (*Lanius cabinisi*)		1		2	1		1		1		6
Kite (*Milvus migrans*)			1							1	2
Redwing lark (*Mirafra africana*)			18								18
Long-tailed namaqua dove (*Oena capensis*)			6	3							9
Pipits (*Anthus* spp.)			51								51
African hoopoe (*Upupa africana*)			1								1
Guineafowl (*Numida* spp.)			20	10	1						31
Teita fiscal (*Lanius dorsalis*)				1							1

Species	Kiu-Ulu 0630 hrs.	Ulu-Sultan Hamud	Sultan Hamud-Emali	Emali-Simba	Simba-Kibwezi-Mtito. 1000 hrs.	Mtito-Tsavo. 1100 hrs.	Tsavo-Voi. 1200 hrs.	Voi-Mack.-Road.	Mack.-Rd. Mariakani	Mar.-Mombasa. 1400 hrs.	Totals
Sandgrouse (*Pterocles* and *Eremialector* spp.)				16							16
Black-billed sparrow weaver (*Plocepasser mahali*)				4	1						5
Tawny eagle (*Aquila rapax*)				1							1
Bustard (*Eupodotis* or *Lissotis* sp.)				2		1					3
Bateleur (*Terathopius ecaudatus*)				1		2					3
Drongo (*Dicrurus adsimilis*)					3	3		5	5		16
Vulture (prob. *Pseudogyps* sp.)					2					1	3
Red-billed hornbill (*Tockus erythrorhynchus*)					6	3					9
White-headed buffalo weaver (*Dinemellia dinemelli*)					1	2		10			13
Black-chested harrier eagle (*Circaetus pectoralis*)					2						2
Crowned lapwing (*Stephanibyx coronatus*)						1					1
Red-billed buffalo weaver (*Bubalornis niger*)						3					3
Slate-coloured boubou (*Laniarius funebris*)						1					1
Yellow-vented bulbul (*Pycnonotus tricolor*)							1				1
Yellow-billed hornbill (*Tockus flavirostris*)							1	1			2
White-crowned shrike (*Eurocephalus anguitimens*)							1	6	1		8
Golden-breasted starling (*Cosmopsarus regius*)							1				1
Blue-eared glossy starling (*Lamprocolius chalybaeus*)								6			6
Vulturine guineafowl (*Acryllium vulturinum*)								10			10
White-rumped swift (*Apus* spp.)								6		2	8
Golden pipit (*Tmetothylacus tenellus*)									4		4
Paradise whydah (*Steganura paradisea*)									10		10
Palm swift (*Cypsiurus parvus*)									6	3	9
Pied Crow (*Corvus albus*)										2	2
	92	49	107	156	56	49	6	48	33	11	607

Note: Latin names are after Mackworth-Praed and Grant, Vol. 1 and 2. Racial names are not included.

APPENDIX

Index of Birds mentioned in the Text

Note. I have mentioned elsewhere in this book the difficulties of using common English names for many East African birds. Though an attempt has been made in both Sir Frederick Jackson's *Birds of Kenya Colony and the Uganda Protectorate*, and the more recent Mackworth-Praed and Grant's *Birds of Eastern and North-eastern Africa* to standardise English names, many of these are not yet in general use, nor in fact do Jackson and the other two authorities agree. In addition to this, there are a great many names in common use in Kenya (partly influenced by South Africa) which are not found in either book.

Therefore, for the sake of completeness, and to assist those more scientifically minded readers to be quite clear about the birds to which I have referred, I have appended a list of the Latin names, in addition to the English names, of the birds mentioned in the text. Where appropriate, the racial (subspecific) name is also added, though this is not in conformity with scientific practice, since there are no 'specimens' to produce. This list will include a few English names, which will not be found in either Jackson or Mackworth-Praed and Grant, but there can be no dubiety about the bird from its Latin name.

This list also is in no particular scientific order, but is arranged alphabetically. As the latest authority (since even the experts do not agree), I have used the Latin names given in both volumes of Mackworth-Praed and Grant; for the sake of brevity I have omitted authorities for these names, but these can be obtained from the appropriate volume, together with all other information about the bird in question, since I have bracketed, after the name, the page number of the particular volume on which the bird is described in detail: thus (1, 81) or (2, 102), the first figure being the volume number, the second the page.

For the chapter on Madagascar birds, I have followed the Latin and English nomenclature of Rand, *Bull. Amer. Mus. Nat. Hist.* 72 (5), 143–499.

KENYA BIRDS

The figures in brackets inserted immediately following the latin names refer to the volume and page numbers of Mackworth-Praed and Grant: Birds of Eastern and North-eastern Africa *in which these birds are described in detail.*

MADAGASCAR BIRD LIST